Steam generating and other heavy water reactors

Steam generating and other heavy water reactors

Proceedings of the conference held at the
Institution of Civil Engineers,
14–16 May, 1968

The British Nuclear Energy Society,
1–7 Great George Street, London, S.W.1.

ORGANIZING COMMITTEE

Mr P. H. Wolff, NDC Ltd (Chairman)
Mr H. Cartwright, UKAEA
Dr J. E. R. Holmes, UKAEA
Dr D. J. Millard, CEGB
Mr R. J. Symes, UKAEA
Mr G. Williams, UKAEA

TECHNICAL ADVISERS

P. Cameron, TNPG
C. Carse, N of Scotland H-E Board
T. Currie, APC Ltd
F. G. Greenhalgh, UKAEA
A. Gregory, NDC Ltd

J. R. D. Jones, CEGB
D. W. Lawson, UKAEA
R. McKeague, UKAEA
G. L. Shires, UKAEA
T. Standen, UKAEA

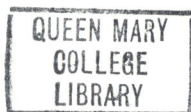
Made and printed by offset in Great Britain by
William Clowes and Sons Limited, London and Beccles

Contents

Opening address

E. S. BOOTH, FRS, FIEE, MIMechE, MInstF

Member for Engineering, CEGB

1. It is now almost a quarter of a century since the first heavy water reactor (the CP 3 reactor at Argonne) went critical in 1944 and the fact that heavy water moderated reactors have not yet established a real foothold in the commercial power field, with the notable exception of the Canadian programme, has certainly not been due to lack of interest on the part of designers over the intervening years. It must rather be ascribed to the recognition of an incentive to concentrate first on systems which could be exploited most rapidly. The graphite moderated and light water moderated systems had a much greater initial boost from military programmes, and this helped these types of reactor to 'get off the ground first' and take the lead in the power generation field.

2. However, now that there are quite a number of heavy water moderated power reactors operating in various countries, some of them having features closely resembling those proposed for large-scale commercial plants, the time is opportune to re-examine the status of this family of reactors, so that no chance is missed of reaping the benefits of work done so far.

3. In principle, the addition or sub-stitution of another reactor type in an existing national programme has the disadvantage of considerably increasing the demand for specialist skills and for research and development monies, all of which are in short supply, and also the disadvantage of foregoing some of the benefits of series production and operating experience of the existing designs. However, it is I think questionable whether these factors will outweigh the advantage of continued competition between reactor systems.

4. Nowadays one hears far less than one used to about the theory of the 'squeeze', according to which there was no economic place for the so-called advanced converters between the thermal reactor types already developed and the fast breeders. Indeed it is now widely accepted that however soon fast reactors reach commercial maturity, further large programmes of thermal reactors will be required in order to prevent a shortage of plutonium from unduly retarding the growth of the nuclear component of electrical energy supply. In this context it is worth noting that the newer reactor types which are now claiming our attention have very attractive fuel utilization characteristics and their relatively modest uranium ore requirements must be counted in their favour, however confident we may be about the ultimate success of fast breeder reactors.

5. In these circumstances there is good reason to consider the emerging thermal reactor systems as serious contenders for a share of what will be a large market. Provisional estimates suggest that the CEGB alone may well add to its existing system another 30-40,000 MW of thermal reactor plant, even allowing for a substantial fast reactor programme. This being so, we in the United Kingdom are continuing to undertake detailed assessment of alternative thermal reactor types, of which one is the steam generating heavy water reactor, which we believe are likely to be competitive with the AGR in which we already have a big stake.

6. Perhaps it is permissible in these opening remarks for me to mention specifically two aspects of reactor design which I know must continue to receive special attention, at least in Britain, and to express the hope that this conference will give them due consideration. I am thinking of flexibility of operation and acceptability for urban siting.

7. Nuclear power is now a strongly competitive source of electrical energy. In Britain it is economic even when evaluated against surprisingly low lifetime load factors. In the UK, nuclear powered generating stations will be added to the system to supply a very large part of the increase in demand for power, providing at the same time a steadily growing proportion of the electrical energy used.

8. Thus it follows that any new reactor type which is to warrant consideration for introduction into the CEGB system must have sufficiently flexible operating characteristics to enable it to play a part in meeting daily changes in electricity demand, either by a two shift operating capability or by an ability to be adjusted to follow load variations. It may be that we do not yet understand clearly what degree of plant flexibility can be achieved most economically, but it is clear that the very success of nuclear power places more emphasis on

this aspect of plant design, as well as adding to the very real incentive to reduce capital costs.

9.   The other aspect which I singled out - the freedom of siting which can only follow thorough and satisfactory safety analyses - is obviously going to be of great importance if we are to gain the full benefit of nuclear power. A continued policy of 'remote siting' would not only lead to increased transmission costs, but in a densely populated country determined to preserve as much unspoiled landscape as possible, such as is the case in the UK, would soon use up all the available sites. The British Government have already relaxed their siting policy in relation to gas-cooled reactors in pre-stressed concrete pressure vessels and the urban siting of the AGRs proposed by the CEGB for recent stations is in line with this new policy. It is vitally important that the safety of new designs of nuclear stations be of the high standard required for such environments. Any system which cannot be agreed to be at least as safe as the concrete vessel gas-cooled reactors we are now building will quite rightly not be looked upon with favour.

10.   The greater part of this conference is to be devoted to the SGHWR. Delegates will hear a much more detailed account of the scale and quality of effort mounted by the UK on this system than has hitherto been published. The prototype at Winfrith is naturally exciting a good deal of interest at the present time.

11.   The concept of devoting the latter part of the conference to the 'broader scene' is a good one, for we can all learn from one another. It will certainly be useful for us in the UK to hear of the latest developments in Canada and continental Europe.

12.   In fact this promises to be a very interesting conference, and one which will help put the various types of heavy water reactors in perspective, at least relative to one another, which will be a useful step towards assessing their viability in countries where they will have to compete against the established water and graphite moderated reactors.

13.   I now take great pleasure in wishing this conference well and in expressing the hope that you all have a controversial and profitable round of discussions in the course of the next few days. I myself believe that the SGHWR will find its own place as a supplier of electric power both in the United Kingdom and around the world.

The SGHWR system

R. V. MOORE, GC, CBE, BSc(Eng), MIMechE, FIEE,

Managing Director, The Reactor Group, UKAEA, Risley

J. E. R. HOLMES, BSc, PhD, UKAEA, Winfrith

SYNOPSIS   This paper constitutes an introduction to those papers being presented at the Conference which relate to the Steam Generating Heavy Water Reactor of the UKAEA. It traces the origins of the concept and the evolution of the reference design for the Winfrith SGHWR and the supporting research and development programmes. It then reviews the construction of the prototype reactor which is now supplying its full-rated output to the national electricity grid. It concludes with a brief section considering possible future steps in achieving the development potential of the system as a commercial power generator.

INTRODUCTION

1.   A very important stage was reached in the development of the Steam Generating Heavy Water Reactor system when the 100 MWe prototype reactor at Winfrith was successfully commissioned at the end of 1967. This reactor is now operating as an effective power producing unit supplying its full rated output. The construction was carried out on a time scale very close to that originally set when financial sanction was given to the project back in 1963. It was then planned that the reactor should be at full power by the end of 1967 and, in the event, electricity was first exported to the National grid on the 24th December, 1967 while sustained operation at full power was achieved on the 25th January, 1968. Since then, up to the 16th April, the reactor has operated at an average load factor of 69%, attaining a value of 93% for the last completed monthly return of March. Two important factors have contributed to this success. Firstly, detailed planning was exercised throughout the whole of the construction and the commissioning stages of the plant, and secondly the Steam Generating Heavy Water Reactor, although a new reactor system, has behaved in close accord with its expected performance.

2.   A project having the size of the Winfrith SGHWR was not, of course, embarked upon lightly. The decision to proceed was the outcome of detailed consideration of a number of alternative reactor systems backed by development work on key feasibility items.

ORIGINS OF THE SGHWR CONCEPT

3.   It is well known that the United Kingdom has undertaken a substantial programme for generating electricity by nuclear installations and that gas cooled reactors now constitute an important fraction of our total generating capacity. In advancing on this programme, we have inevitably amassed a considerable amount of experience which is broadly applicable to any sort of nuclear reactor system.

4.   The origins of the SGHWR system can be traced back to the middle of 1957 when the initial design study of the advanced gas cooled reactor (AGR) was reviewed within the UKAEA. It was decided that, while all promised well, it would only be prudent to have some alternative advanced thermal reactor system under study. Accordingly, the features of a power reactor were broken down into five main headings - fuel, cladding, coolant, moderator and form of construction. The solutions selected for the AGR were considered and possible alternatives put down which could be evaluated for this, so far, unidentified new system.

5.   The first possible system which emerged was one using the pressure tube construction, heavy water as the moderator and steel as the fuel cladding material. At that time we were still thinking of steel pressure vessels which required site fabrication and thereby tended to interfere with the civil construction programme and were raising questions of output limitations. Graphite, too, at that stage was giving rise to some problems associated with Wigner energy release. The alternative reactor system was christened the Gas Cooled, Heavy-Water Reactor - the GCHWR - and a design study was carried out on a reactor for use in the national power programme. One of the important features of a pressure tube reactor is that not only can different materials be used for the moderator and coolant, but the operating conditions of these media can be selected quite independently to suit their functions. An effectively unpressurized moderator was chosen to simplify construction of the moderator tank and to reduce the possibility of leakage of the expensive heavy water

whilst, for the CO_2 coolant, a pressure of 600 lb/in^2 was selected. This, in conjunction with a coolant tube diameter of some 5 in, established a fuel element design which, with 'roughened' cladding, was acceptable both as a practical fuel assembly and a heat transfer system. Zircaloy was selected as the pressure tube material. The design of the reactor, including access for fuel handling, inlet and outlet headers, reflectors and shield tanks, did not give rise to any apparently unsurmountable problems. However, being an indirect system so far as the coolant was concerned, it was necessary to design steam generating towers, generally similar to those produced earlier for the Calder Hall plant. The selection of 600 lb/in^2 for the coolant pressure here began to give rise to undesirable features since the shells for these steam generators were much more expensive than those of the contemporary Calder Hall type reactors or those of the AGR study. Thus, while the study gave valuable insight into a number of physics and engineering aspects of this type of reactor design, it did not lead to a system with particularly favourable capital costs or development potential.

6. The basic description for an alternative reactor was re-examined and it was decided to move along the route towards a direct coolant cycle, thereby substantially reducing heat exchanger equipment. In the next study, steam was adopted as the coolant with a recirculatory coolant circuit in which the steam was alternatively superheated within the core and then desuperheated in a small exchanger, generating thereby part of the initial steam flow from the returned feed water, before being passed to the reactor once more. According to the steam conditions chosen, the number of passes through the reactor varied from three to four in order to evaporate all the feed water and provide the supply of superheated steam which was directed to the turbine. This gave a reactor system in which the reactor coolant did finally become the turbine working fluid, although steam generating plant was incorporated. This coolant circuit was, in our opinion, the most acceptable form of Steam Cooled, Heavy-Water Reactor, and was called the SCHWR. While it still involved steam generators, the circulatory energy was economically imparted to the coolant in the liquid phase by the feed pumps. The overall economics were superior to those of other steam cooled reactors we studied in parallel, using thermo compressors for coolant circulation or spray evaporation of feed water for cooling.

7. This phase of the work included studies on optimizing coolant conditions against investment in pressure tube material and required the investigation of methods of ensuring that the Zircaloy used for these pressure tubes did not have to be subjected to more than the saturated temperature of the coolant. It did not, however, require much extension to methods of estimating the nuclear performance of the system, since the moderation was still predominantly achieved in the low tempera-

ture heavy water contained in the calandria. There were, moreover, major difficulties concerned with establishing reliable fuel cladding for the superheating sections and it was judged better to defer further work on this type of system.

8. A number of the features of pressure tube reactors that had been established by the study of the GCHWR and SCHWR, nevertheless, looked attractive - namely:

(i) the prospects of being able to complete the civil structure of the reactor buildings before the most substantial nuclear component, the calandria and shield tanks, had to be installed;

(ii) the small physical size of the pressure parts which could be wholly shop fabricated and tested;

(iii) the prospects of being able to build any required unit size by merely grouping together the requisite number of pressure tube assemblies;

(iv) the possibility of arranging both the load control and shutdown elements without the need for drive mechanisms in close association with the core area;

(v) it also appeared to be relatively simple to incorporate on-load fuel handling, which was becoming characteristic of our gas cooled graphite moderated reactor designs.

9. All these features were judged to be valuable attributes for the design, construction and operation of a power reactor. It was then decided to make a further study of this generic type of system. This time, light water was selected as the coolant and it was allowed to boil in the core. This is the concept now called the Steam Generating Heavy Water Reactor and is the one which was later selected for construction. The principles are shown schematically in Fig. 1 where it can be seen that the nuclear steam raising plant has close similarity with a fossil-fired, assisted circulation water-tube boiler. It will also be seen that the pressure tubes are arranged vertically. Whilst other arrangements were studied, vertical pressure tubes with access for refuelling from the top were selected as the most convenient design for power reactors.

10. This outline of the conceptual thinking explains why the title SGHWR was chosen. It could equally well have been called the pressure tube boiling water reactor since the heavy water fulfills no other role than providing the neutron moderation. The Canadians have arrived at a very similar system, which has evolved from their CANDU design of pressure tube reactor, (which used pressurized heavy water as coolant and an indirect cycle) and they have called it

4

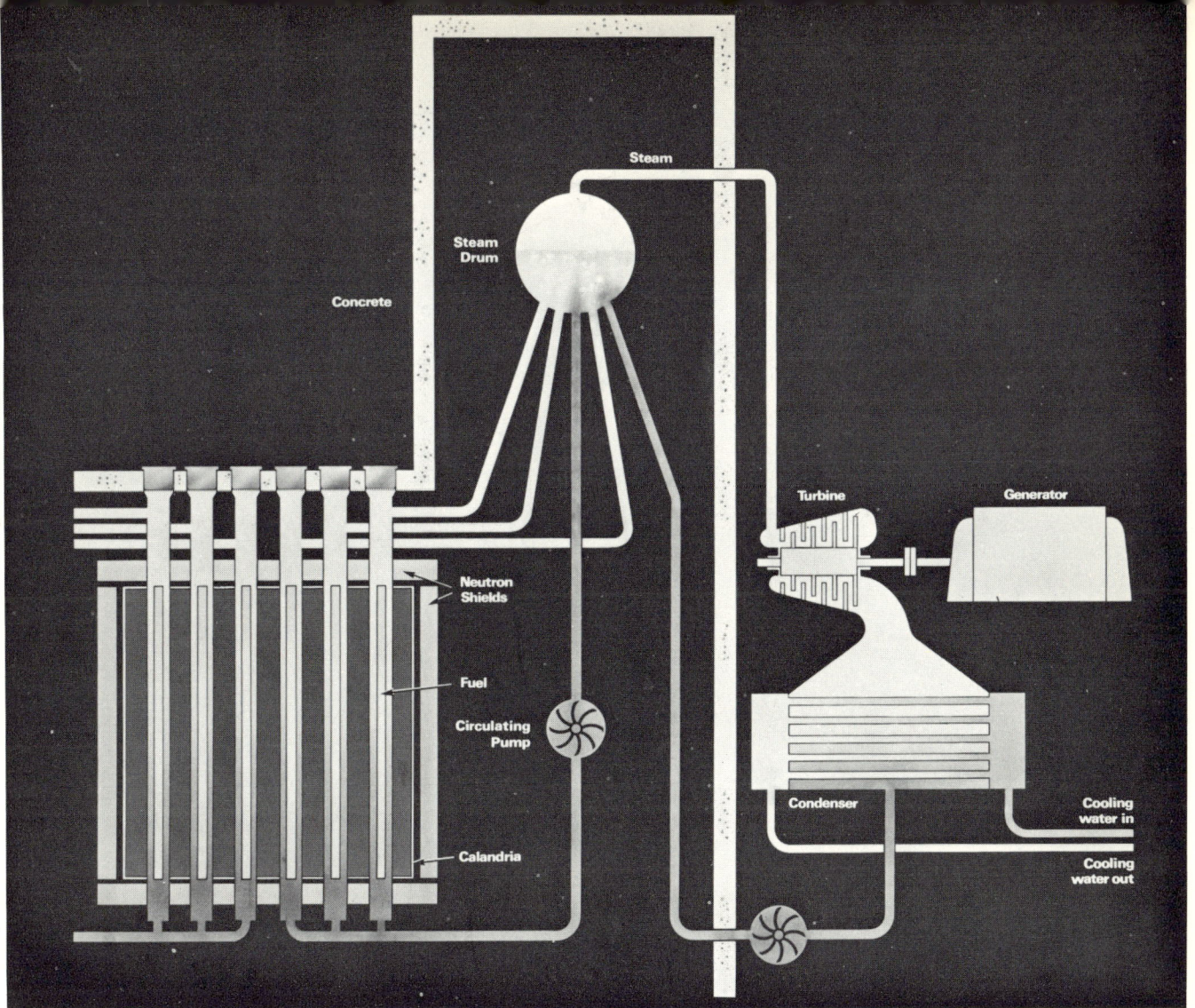

Fig.1. Diagram of the SGHWR core and coolant circuit

Fig.2. General view of the Winfrith SGHWR buildings showing the
Administration offices on the right

Fig.3. The Winfrith SGHWR main hall from the turbo-alternator end showing the reactor area and the refuelling machine in the background

Fig.4. General view of the Winfrith SGHWR with the reactor at power

the Boiling Light Water Reactor. It is perhaps appropriate at this point to record that the Authority has enjoyed close collaboration with our colleagues in Atomic Energy of Canada (Ltd) over many years to the mutual benefit of both countries.

11. The first design study for an SGHWR showed that the system had possibilities for attractively low capital costs combined with low fuel costs. Slight enrichment of the fuel with U-235 was adopted rather than using natural uranium, since the optimization studies showed that any increase in fuel cost by the use of enrichment was more than offset by reductions in capital cost when calculating the generating cost of the system. Before proceeding further, a systematic comparative study was made of the SGHWR with other forms of alternative thermal reactor which were entering the commercial market. This study included an evaluation of the water cooled, pressure vessel reactor systems as well as other pressure tube systems. The outcome of the study gave the UKAEA confidence that the commercial prospects for the SGHWR were good. It was, however, realized that it was important to demonstrate that there were no technical uncertainties of a feasibility nature before proposing the construction of a major project.

12. At the time the SGHWR concept was first formulated, there were a number of new technical issues raised. Some of these resulted from the intention to generate steam by boiling light water in a pressure tube core and pass it directly to the turbine. On the nuclear design side, the light water in the core contributes appreciably to the neutron moderation (about 30%), whilst the light water would be at a substantially different temperature from the heavy water in the calandria. Further, steam voidage would be generated in the core as the coolant boiled which would influence the control characteristics of the core. It was known that there could be thermal performance limitations due to burn-out or dryout phenomena occurring within the fuel element cluster. Boiling in the pressure tubes at the necessary ratings might give rise to hydraulic instabilities and there was also the possibility of coupling effects between the boiling process and kinetic nuclear behaviour giving rise to possible instabilities. On the materials side, there was the question of the use of zirconium for both the pressure tube and the fuel cladding material in a boiling water environment. The water chemistry conditions, too, could influence the selection of the material for the rest of the primary circuit which could be either ferritic or austenitic steel.

EARLY DEVELOPMENT WORK

13. A development programme was mounted, starting in 1958-59, to investigate these and other questions which were matters of concern at that time. There was already within the UKAEA a fund of knowledge and expertise to build upon. At Harwell, the work concentrated on physics, heat transfer and corrosion aspects of zirconium while at RFL, Springfields and RML, Culcheth, work was started on fuel and structural materials both on the irradiation behaviour of such materials and the establishment of manufacturing techniques. At Winfrith, the development of lattice physics calculation methods to deal with this system was begun and an experimental programme was mounted in the DIMPLE zero energy reactor to simulate an SGHWR-type lattice. On the thermal performance side, attention was concentrated on the problem of predicting dryout conditions in complex, multi-rod fuel assemblies following previous work that had been associated with much simpler geometries of single tubes and annuli.

14. The materials development work included investigation of manufacturing routes for producing pressure tubes of 5 in. or more diameter. Attention was given to the development of a suitable joint between the Zircaloy tube and the remainder of the primary circuit, both a bolted and rolled design being satisfactorily produced and proved. At a later date, a rolled joint incorporating a stainless iron hub was selected for use since this was simpler in construction. On the fuel element side, early investigations showed that it was practical to adopt a full length 12 ft fuel pin and some work was carried out on the design of grids to support a cluster of pins. Reactor control and stability were studied to ensure that an effective scheme could be devised. Reactor safety, too, was the subject of investigation so that satisfactory criteria could be met.

15. In parallel with this early development work, the design of power reactors using the SGHWR concept was examined at Risley for a range of sizes, the objective here being to identify the preferred size of key items of construction for a power reactor which could be satisfactorily demonstrated in a prototype. The units which received most attention were of course the design of the pressure tube and the fuel element. This work led to the selection of a 36-rod fuel element cluster, each pin of 0.57 in. ID, 12 ft in length inside a pressure tube with an internal diameter of 5.14 in, a set of dimensions which we still believe to be very satisfactory for reactors in the output range of 100 to 600 or more MWe.

16. As indicated, this work involved the efforts of a number of establishments within the Authority and culminated in a proposal to build a 100 MWe prototype of the SGHWR system at Winfrith. Construction of this reactor started in May, 1963 as already noted, and it successfully achieved full power in January of this year.

THE WINFRITH SGHWR

17. The design of the Winfrith SGHWR and the development work in the various fields which has supported it are the subject of a number of papers presented to this conference.

18. The size of the prototype was selected to make use of the channel unit and fuel element which was regarded as appropriate for large power reactors and also to ensure that the unit was of sufficiently large size to provide meaningful manufacturing and construction experience. In addition, provision was made for a number of experimental facilities to support the further development of the system. These included channels for demonstrating superheat and further channels in which fuel could be run at substantially higher rating than in the remainder of the core. Consideration of all these aspects led to the selection of a 100 MWe as the nominal output for the prototype, an output which is fed into the National electricity grid thereby providing a significant revenue from electricity sales. Further, throughout the design of the prototype the possibility of a general uprating of the reactor output was borne in mind. The main parameters of the Winfrith SGHWR are given in Table 1 while Figs 2-4 provide some general views of the station.

19. Additional features of note in the design include the absence of any form of mechanically operated, solid control rod. Reactivity control is provided in the short-term by variation of moderator height and in the long-term by variation of boron absorber dissolved in the heavy water. Rapid shutdown cannot be achieved by merely dumping the heavy water since this would have required both large outlet ports and either a complicated gas pressure balancing system or large control valves. Fast shutdown is in fact achieved by supplementing the moderator dump with a liquid shutdown system. In this, boric acid solution is 'fired' by gas pressure into closed tubes which are located in interstitial spaces within the lattice of the main channel tubes in the calandria. This arrangement consisting of relatively small dimensioned pipework and valves has permitted substantially greater flexibility in overall reactor layout than would have been the case if some form of movable solid absorber were incorporated.

20. Since there is direct access to individual fuel channels, the fuel cycle and fuel management scheme can be devised to take full advantage of this feature. It is not necessary to restrict fuel handling to an annual event and the interval can be varied from, say once every few months to continuous refuelling with an on-load machine.

21. The calandria which is the tank holding the heavy water, is made of an aluminium alloy and is of all-welded construction to obviate leakage of heavy water from joints. Since the heavy water is at an operating pressure that is effectively atmospheric, it is not a difficult or expensive requirement to provide a heavy water circuit which is leak tight. Here the experience gained in the design and operation of the materials testing reactors of the DIDO class has been valuable, particularly when it is remembered that the first of these reactors was commissioned at Harwell in 1956.

22. It is an inherent feature of any power station that a significant fraction of its capital cost is represented by work which must be carried out on site. In the case of conventional power stations, it may be assumed that the organization and sequencing of this site work has evolved to the point where 'practice' constitutes an acceptably economical process for carrying out such activities as, for example, civil engineering, building construction, plant erection, pipe and cable running. Even with such plant, it is nevertheless still necessary to review the consequences of some new requirement to establish whether a major modification of the construction programme is required. However, in the case of a new class of power producer, among which must certainly be included a new type of nuclear reactor, the ability to incorporate established processes during the construction programme may easily be comparable in capital savings with those produced by some technological advance gained as a result of research and development.

23. In this context, the SGHWR does not constitute a novel plant outside the limits of the reactor core. Admittedly, the configurations and extent of the civil work, piping, steam drums, tank systems, valves, circulating pumps and so on, do not precisely follow conventional plant, but this is of second order significance because of the essential similarity and function of the main circuits. As regards the reactor core of the SGHWR, this may be divided into pressure tubes, calandria and neutron shield tanks. The manufacture of these involves the fabrication of either materials that are not in common use in power systems or more usual materials that require to be formed into structures of above-normal precision for structural components in conventional steam generators. Nevertheless, these can all be completed and tested as individual components in manufacturers' works and delivered to site ready for placing in position and connecting into the associated circuits. Therefore, so far as the site construction programme is concerned, there are few truly 'novel' components in the basic SGHWR system. This applies to a commercial plant of this type as well as the Winfrith SGHWR.

24. At Winfrith, control of construction was exercised by application of critical path planning procedures. Thus, once the detailed overall construction plan has been drawn up, certain key stage points were identified within the length of the nominal critical path established from the information available at the outset. As these points were achieved, the actual situation was compared with the anticipated position and the succeeding period replanned to take account of the practical circumstances then current in order to make sure that the targets at the next review point were met. This turned out to be a very productive arrangement since, by varying the ground rules that had been used to create the original overall plan, for example, extra construction staff or their redeployment

Table 1
Main parameters of the 100 MWe Winfrith SGHWR

Parameter		Winfrith SGHWR 100 MWe
FUEL		
Fuel material		UO_2
Pellet diameter	in (mm)	0.57 (14.5)
Can material		Zircaloy-2
Can thickness (nominal)	in (mm)	0.028 (0.71)
Number of elements in cluster		36
Fuel length	in (mm)	144 (3660)
Weight of U per channel	tU	0.198
PERFORMANCE		
Fuel average rating	MWth/tU	14.3
Coolant pressure at core inlet	lb/in^2 (kg/cm^2)	970 (69.0)
Coolant inlet temperature	^{o}F (^{o}C)	527 (275)
Coolant outlet temperature	^{o}F (^{o}C)	538 (281)
Heat to Coolant (maximum channel)	MWth	3.8
Coolant mass velocity (maximum channel)	lb/ft^2h (kg/cm^2s)	2.18×10^6 (0.296)
Steam exit quality (maximum channel)	%	11.3
Maximum can temperature	^{o}F (^{o}C)	554 (290)
HEAT BALANCE		
Alternator output	MWe	100
Station net electrical output	MWe	92
Station net thermal efficiency	%	31.4
Reactor thermal output	MWth	292
REACTOR DESCRIPTION		
Core diameter	in (mm)	123 (3120)
Core height	in (mm)	144 (3660)
Lattice pitch (square)	in (mm)	$10\frac{1}{4}$ (260)
Calandria diameter	in (mm)	146 (3700)
Calandria height	in (mm)	156 (3960)
Pressure tube internal diameter/thickness	in (mm)	5.14/0.2 (130/5.1)
Calandria tube outside diameter/thickness	in (mm)	7.25/0.13 (184/3.3)
Number of boiling channels		104
Number of circulating pumps		4
POWER PLANT		
Steam pressure-turbine stop valve	lb/in^2 (kg/cm^2)	900 (63.3)
Steam temperature-turbine stop valve	^{o}F (^{o}C)	532 (278)
Steam flow rate to turbine	lb/h (kg/s)	1.19×10^6 (150)
Condenser back pressure	in (mm) Hg abs	1.35 (34.2)
Final feed water temperature	^{o}F (^{o}C)	390 (199)

and repositioning of items within the programme, it was always found possible to drive the situation back to the basic schedule. At peak, the system was controlling the activities of some 700 construction personnel though the average was closer to 300. Some 82 contractors supplied plant and components for the SGHWR Prototype, although not all of these participated directly in site installation.

25. Reverting to the manufacture of the core components, the calandria and neutron shield tanks constituted critical activities on the construction programme. Although their delivery to site was not required until after the main civil and building work had been completed, they were nevertheless the first reactor components to be required on site. The time available for their design and construction was therefore comparatively short and, at the same time, their manufacture required a high standard of dimensional accuracy. Thus, while these tanks are not of themselves among the major cost items, delays in their manufacture could have produced considerable financial loss by delaying the whole reactor construction programme.

26. The care exercised in applying this comprehensive construction 'tool' has been regarded by the achievement of the building targets so that the completed plant was handed over to the operators in accordance with the overall programme.

THE FUTURE

27. The Winfrith SGHWR was designed and built with eight channels specifically arranged for investigating superheating. These channels are located around the edge of the core so that the reactor can be operated without detriment with no fuel in these channels. During the commissioning and early operation, superheat fuel was not loaded and indeed no date has yet been fixed for loading such fuel. In the early stages of the project, superheating was seen as one of the possible lines of development of the SGHWR with the objective of improving steam conditions at the entry to the turbine and enhancing the plant efficiency. However, so far we have not identified either clear economic or operational advantages for the introduction of superheat which would justify the necessary development work, and effort is now concentrated on establishing the SGHWR system as a saturated steam producer.

28. The Winfrith SGHWR was designed for low enrichment fuel since, under the UK conditions, this resulted in the most satisfactory economics. It was appreciated, however, from an early stage that there was a considerable degree of flexibility inherent in the system which was available to vary the design so as to provide a number of interesting alternatives in the fuel cycle such as optimizing for plutonium production or alternatively optimizing for using plutonium enrichment possibly on a fuel recycle basis.

29. Another important possibility, which could be attractive for a number of countries, is the use of natural uranium fuel. However, whilst it is clear that an SGHWR can be designed to operate with natural uranium fuel, a number of detailed changes are required to produce an economically competitive reactor. This is because with unenriched fuel, there is incentive to achieve in the design the maximum possible irradiation for the fuel. As a result, the control and safety problems need re-examination. Nevertheless, it is considered that an attractive design is possible and a detailed study of the natural uranium fuelled SGHWR is in progress. This study is being carried out at Risley by a joint UK, Australian and New Zealand team.

30. The ability of a reactor to operate in a manner other than base load is becoming increasingly significant particularly in the future, when nuclear power will constitute a significant proportion of the installed capacity in this and other countries. It is believed that the SGHWR concept is especially well adapted to part-load operation and load following determined by the grid frequency. This aspect is currently receiving close attention and it is likely that the Winfrith SGHWR will be operated to demonstrate its capability on load following regimes later in 1968.

31. The subsequent papers presented to this symposium describe the development programme the UKAEA has mounted to back the SGHWR system, the design and operating experience of the Winfrith SGHWR and the Authority's proposals for fully commercial stations. We believe this reactor system will prove to be a very attractive one to electricity utilities both at home and abroad.

Engineering design of SGHWRs

N. BRADLEY, BSc, MIMechE, UKAEA, Risley

D. J. DAWSON, UKAEA, Risley

F. G. JOHNSON, MEng, AMICE, UKAEA, Risley

SYNOPSIS   This paper describes the Winfrith SGHWR and its subsequent development for, commercial power stations. Sufficient detail is given to provide an introduction to and overall appreciation of subsequent detailed papers on particular aspects.

The scope of the paper is concerned with designs using low enriched fuel but studies are proceeding on similar reactors burning natural fuel.

THE WINFRITH SGHWR

Outline description

1.   The Steam Generating Heavy Water Reactor (SGHWR) is a pressure tube reactor using light water as the coolant and heavy water as the moderator (ref. 1). The fuel is enriched uranium dioxide, clad in zirconium alloy and arranged in 36-rod clusters. The light water partially boils as it flows upward over the fuel elements, which are contained in vertical pressure tubes. The steam is separated from the recirculating water in the steam drums, and passed directly to the turbine.

2.   The pressure tubes, which are made of zirconium alloy, are located within, but separated from the tubes of the aluminium alloy calandria, which contains the heavy water moderator. A significant part of the moderation in the reactor takes place in the light water coolant, thereby reducing the heavy water inventory appreciably. Also, since the heavy water temperature does not exceed 80°C and the pressures in the moderator circuit are low, leakage losses of heavy water are likely to be very small.

3.   With the 100 MWe reactor built at the Authority's Establishment at Winfrith, Dorset, it was decided to demonstrate on-load refuelling, although this type of reactor can be designed for on-or off-load refuelling.

4.   The Winfrith plant also uses a vented system of containment. The building was therefore designed for low pressure and conventional structural methods have been used, except for a number of special features to limit leakage.

Reactor core

5.   The core of the reactor comprises the calandria and the channel tubes and together they form an integrated structure with the neutron shields (see Fig. 1).

6.   The function of the calandria is to contain the heavy water moderator (ref. 2). The design and the materials of this component were selected to obtain low neutron absorption, a high leak-tightness and a high standard of integrity, and to be compatible with the heavy water and the circuit materials.

7.   Nuclear activity causes heat to be generated both in the moderator and in the calandria material itself. In addition, heat is transferred to the calandria from the channel assemblies by conduction across the gas gaps. The heavy water is therefore circulated through coolers to maintain the temperature in the calandria below 80°C.

8.   The neutron shields which surround the core are water filled tanks, made as pre-fabricated units. The water, which is chemically dosed to inhibit corrosion, is circulated through coolers to remove the heat generated in the tanks. The radial shields are filled with steel pellets and are of sufficient thickness to avoid the necessity of cooling the concrete primary shield which surrounds the core structure. The upper and lower tanks incorporate internal steel plates to provide the necessary shielding properties. These tanks are pierced by through tubes which must be in alignment with the calandria tubes and, during manufacture and construction, common templates were used for the calandria and shield tanks.

9.   The channel tube assembly is shown in more detail in Fig. 2 (ref. 3). The pressure tubes are 5.14 in inside diameter and each channel tube assembly is approximately 35 ft in overall length. The assembly was designed so that it could be

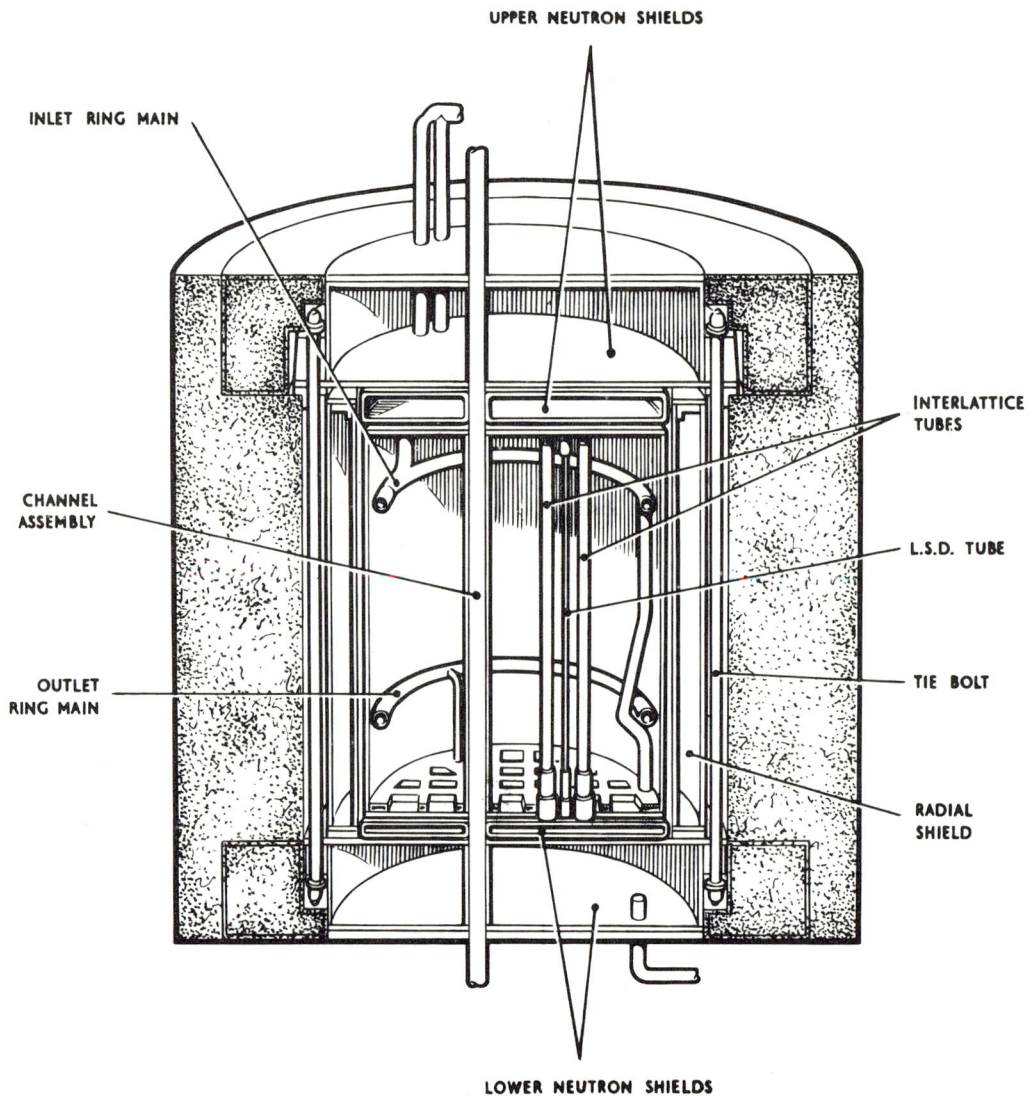

UPPER NEUTRON SHIELDS

INLET RING MAIN

INTERLATTICE TUBES

CHANNEL ASSEMBLY

L.S.D. TUBE

OUTLET RING MAIN

TIE BOLT

RADIAL SHIELD

LOWER NEUTRON SHIELDS

Fig. 1: Calandria and neutron shield tanks

1. CALANDRIA
2. UPPER NEUTRON SHIELDS
3. LOWER NEUTRON SHIELDS
4. SEAL PLUG
5. STEEL STANDPIPE
6. ZIRCONIUM PRESSURE TUBE
7. STEEL TAIL PIPE
8. EXPANDED JOINT
9. CHANNEL SUPPORT FLANGE
   (BOLTED TO NEUTRON SHIELD)
10. THERMAL INSULATION BLOCK
11. SEALING BUSH
12. GAS INSULATION GAP
13. COOLANT OFFTAKE PIPE
14. SEAL PLUG HOUSING
15. FUEL ELEMENT
16. REFUELLING MACHINE
    CONNECTION PIECE

FUEL ELEMENT
STRINGER

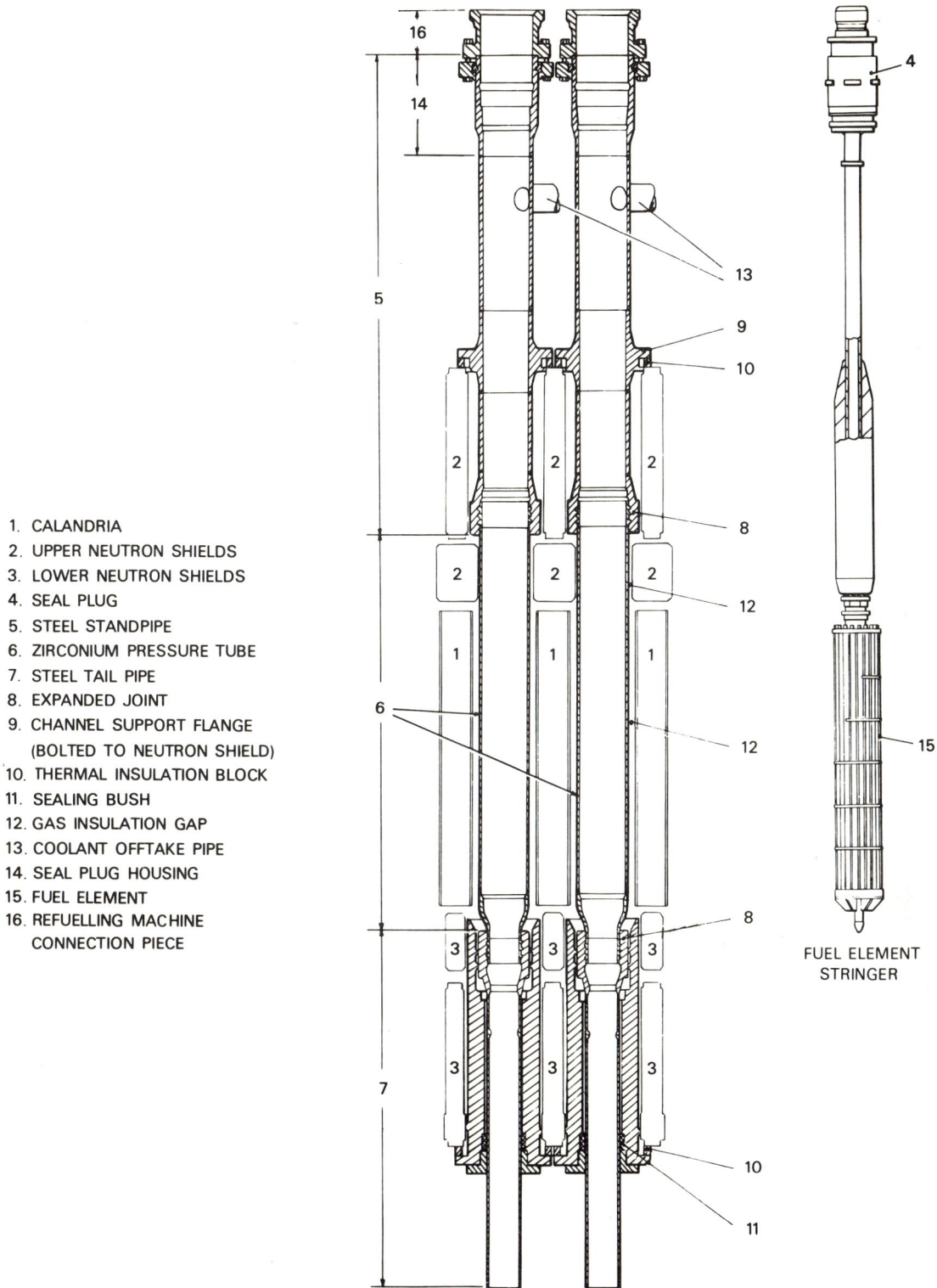

Fig. 2: Channel tube assemblies

13

completely manufactured and tested in the factory, and so simplify site erection.

10. Each channel assembly is made up of three sections: the steel standpipe above the core, the zirconium pressure tube and the steel tailpipe. The standpipe and tailpipe assemblies are joined to the zirconium tube by expanding the latter into steel hubs. The weight of the whole assembly is supported by a flange from the upper neutron shield tank. A thermal insulating block is interposed between the hot channel assembly (280°C) and the shield (80°C). At the tailpipe section, the assembly is guided by a sealing bush which is also thermally insulated from the cold lower neutron shield tank. The gas gap between the hot channel and the cold tanks provides thermal insulation. Above the support flange is the coolant off-take pipe and the top of the standpipe is closed with a seal plug which affords rapid access to the channel for refuelling. The refuelling machine connection piece is bolted to the seal plug housing.

Primary cooling circuit and pumps

11. The primary cooling circuit is divided into two similar forced circulation systems as indicated on the flow diagram, Fig. 3, each circuit having a steam drum and two circulating pumps (ref. 4). After partial evaporation of the light water as it flows up the channels over the fuel elements, the two phase mixture is conveyed to the steam drums where the water and steam are separated. The unevaporated water is returned with incoming feed water to the circulating pumps and the steam after being dried within the drum is passed directly to the turbine.

12. In the Winfrith reactor stainless steel has been used for the boiling circuit with ferritic materials for the feed and steam pipework.

13. The circulating pumps are of the glandless type, each of 550 HP. Reactor transient studies showed that it was necessary to prolong coolant circulation during the first few seconds after a reactor trip in order to prevent dry-out of the fuel. Additional inertia was therefore built into the pump units. Apart from this, the units are conventional and of the wet winding type.

Emergency cooling system

14. An emergency cooling system has been installed to provide cooling to the fuel elements in the unlikely event of a rupture of the primary circuit and with it the loss of normal cooling. This system injects water into each fuel element cluster through rings of small holes located at several levels in the hollow centre tie rod or sparge pipe of the cluster. The water is initially supplied from a high pressure tank containing water at 200 lb/in^2 above circuit pressure

and pressurized by nitrogen gas (see Fig. 4). The capacity of this tank is sufficient to provide adequate cooling of the fuel elements until the circuit has been depressurized: thereafter the cooling water is supplied under gravity from a tank. The system is automatically initiated by detection of a pressure rise or rate of change of pressure in the primary containment and, apart from trip valves, is independent of moving parts or prime movers.

System power control

15. The behaviour of the reactor is determined primarily by the void co-efficient (the fractional change in reactivity divided by the change in steam void fraction). The Winfrith reactor was deliberately designed to have a zero or slightly negative void coefficient with fresh fuel (which will become more negative with fuel irradiation) thereby limiting reactivity excursions. This led to the choice of a decoupled pressure control system in which a change of turbine loading is achieved by first altering the reactor output, the subsequent alteration in system pressure being automatically controlled by movement of the turbine throttle through its speeder motor. In effect, this meets the requirements of a base load station.

16. Due to the absence of large heat exchangers, this type of reactor is however capable of fast load changes and can be easily adapted to give automatic grid load following by feeding back the appropriate signals from the grid to the reactivity control system. The Winfrith SGHWR is designed for 10% per minute load changes over the range of 50% to 100% load but this is capable of extension to 20% per minute, the main limitation being the permissible loading rate of the turbine. The turbine trip which automatically closes the turbine throttle, simultaneously opens a dump line to the condenser. System pressure is automatically maintained using an in-line control valve and the reactor is kept in operation.

Reactivity control

17. Fine reactivity control is achieved by moderator level variation. There can be limitations in the total amount of reactivity which can be controlled in this way since large changes of level at full power reduce the dryout margin and increase the fuel centre temperature. Variations in the level of the moderator are, therefore, confined during full-load power operation to the top 12 inches of the calandria. The moderator filling and emptying valves have been sized so that excessive rates of increase of reactivity are not possible. The maximum rate of change of reactivity is limited to about 2 mN/s with a full calandria.

18. Long-term reactivity changes caused by fuel burn-up, start-up xenon, xenon over-

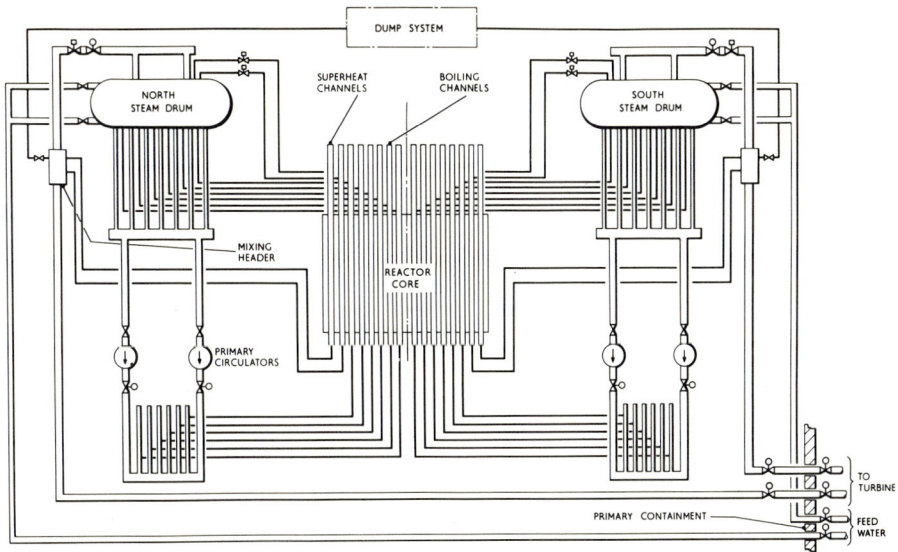

Fig. 3: Primary circuit flow diagram

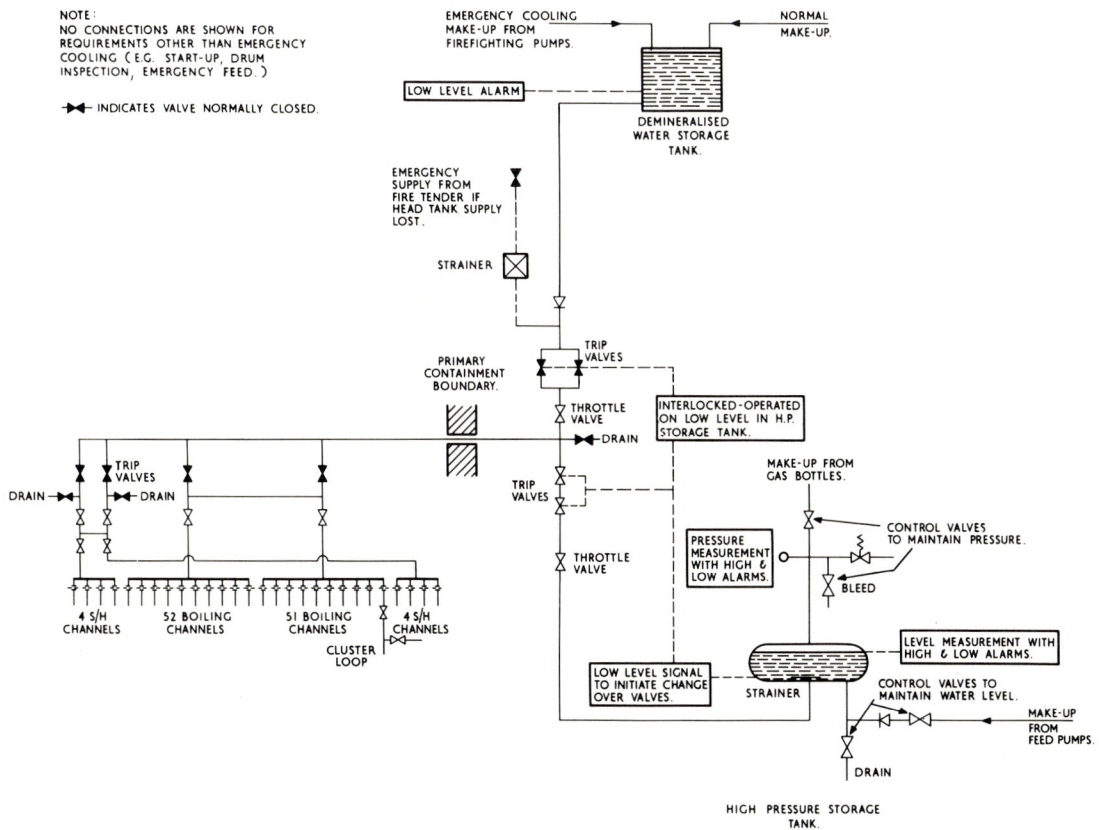

Fig. 4: Flow diagram for channel emergency cooling system

ride and refuelling are compensated by varying the concentration of boric acid in bulk moderator. The boric acid is removed by passing part of the moderator cooling flow through a strong-base ion exchange bed. The maximum rate of removal of boric acid corresponds to a rate of removal of reactivity of 4 mN/s at a maximum boron-10 concentration of 15 ppm by weight. This method has the advantage that the large amounts of excess reactivity which occur with fresh unpoisoned fuel are absorbed in a uniform manner, thus avoiding the localized flux distortions usually associated with solid absorber rods and the attendant safety protection problems arising as a result of possible accidental withdrawal of such rods.

Emergency shutdown

19. There are two shutdown systems, one inserting negative reactivity rapidly by introducing neutron absorbing liquid into tubes located in the calandria, while the second ensures shutdown in the long-term by draining the moderator. Both systems are brought into action simultaneously for every reactor trip. The draining system, while giving the highest possible reliability that shutdown will be maintained, could not be satisfactorily engineered to operate rapidly.

20. Rapid shutdown is affected by injecting lithium borate solution into twelve $2\frac{1}{2}$ in. internal diameter tubes positioned discretely in the core at inter-channel positions (ref. 6). Each tube has its own independent reservoir of absorber solution. The reservoirs are pressurized by helium and are individually connected to the associated core tube through a three-way trip valve. The upper end of each core tube is connected via a vent tube to a buffer tank. Since each loop is thus completely independent, it is considered to be extremely unlikely that a fault on one loop could affect any other. The trip valves have also been located so that they are outside the core area, are physically protected and operate in a cool environment. A diagram of the system is shown in Fig. 5.

21. During normal operation all tubes are purged continuously with helium gas and each trip valve is held closed against the force of powerful springs by electromagnets energized through the protective system. A reactor trip signal de-energizes the electromagnets and the valves, opened by the springs, allow the fluid to be forced into the core by the pressure of gas in the storage tanks. The fluid is eventually brought to rest by the rising pressure of the trapped gas in the buffer tank.

22. Facilities are provided to test the operation of the trip valves with the reactor operational, without absorber entering the core. Even if two valves supplying adjacent tubes fail to operate, there is sufficient negative reactivity to hold the reactor shutdown until the

moderator is drained.

Refuelling system

23. New fuel is received in a store set aside for this purpose and situated in the South Annexe of the building adjacent to the fuel storage pond. After unpacking and inspecting, it is transferred into the secondary containment building through a low pressure air lock and is lowered into the fuel pond. The support tube and seal plug are then attached to form a complete fuel stringer which is stored vertically in a rack until required. The pond handling equipment then transports the new fuel stringer from the storage pond and presents it to the refuelling machine. This machine removes the irradiated stringer and inserts the new stringer in the vacant channel in the reactor core, discharging the irradiated stringer into another section of the pond where the fuel cluster is uncoupled from the stringer and stored in racks. The support tube and seal plug section of the stringer are held for re-use later, see Fig. 6.

24. All these operations may be carried out with the reactor either on-or off-load (ref. 7). The former requirement was embodied to demonstrate on-load fuelling feasibility and, at the same time, permit the maximum flexibility in use of the experimental facilities with the reactor remaining on power.

25. The refuelling machine is positioned over the reactor by a pair of rotating shields one mounted eccentrically inside the other (ref. 8). The machine is fixed to the inner of the two shields and off-set from the inner shield centre line. The centre line of the inner shield is off-set from that of the outer shield by an amount which, by relative rotation of the two shields, allows full cover of the reactor core, storage tubes and charge/discharge facilities. The secondary duties of the rotating shields are to provide a seal for the primary containment and biological shielding for the operators. The use of a hydrostatic bearing gave an elegant and effective solution to the problem of designing the combined bearing and seal.

Experimental facilities

26. To demonstrate and exploit the inherent potential of the system, various experimental reactor facilities are incorporated as listed in Table 1.

Turbine

27. The turbine is supplied with steam from the reactor at saturation temperature so that the expansion of the steam lies wholly in the wet region. Furthermore, since the steam is generated in the high neutron flux of the reactor core, it is radioactive and special account had to be taken of these two features in the design

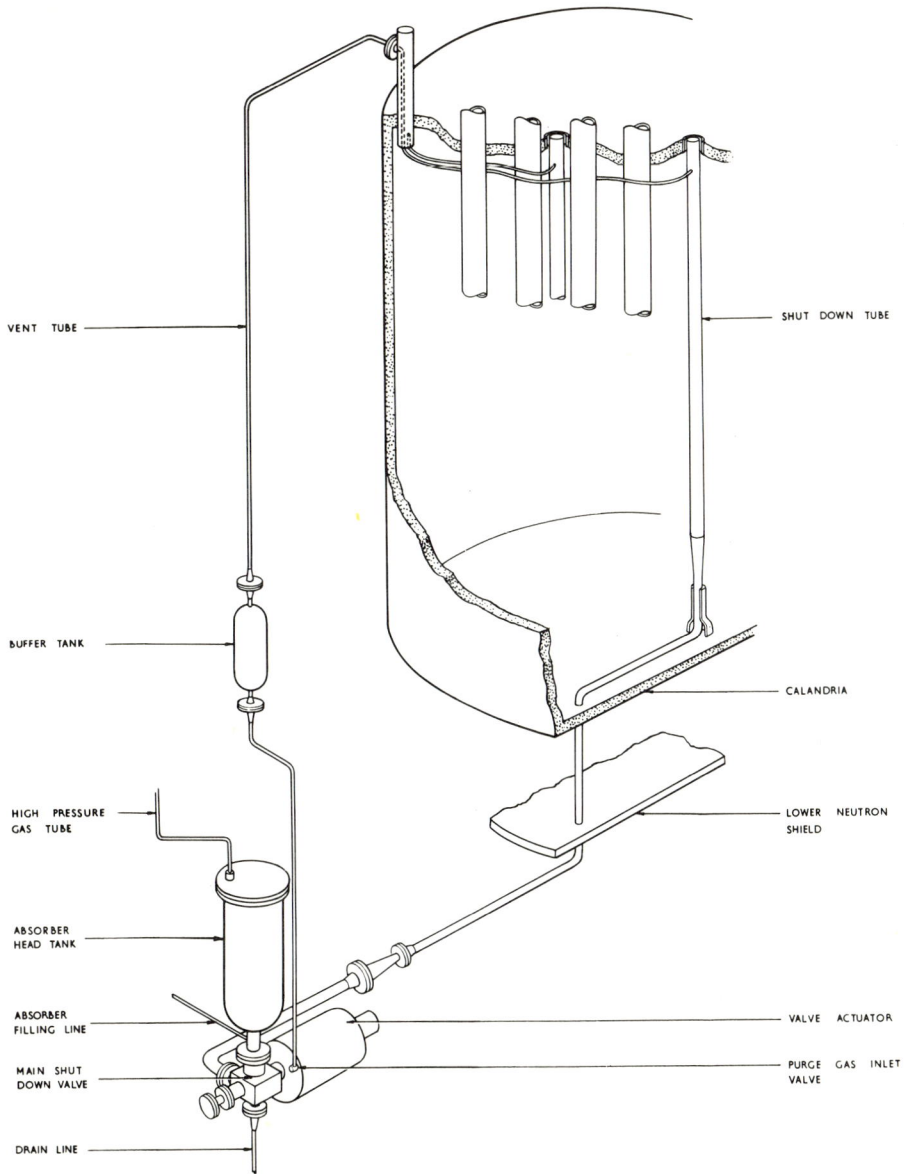

VENT TUBE

SHUT DOWN TUBE

BUFFER TANK

CALANDRIA

HIGH PRESSURE
GAS TUBE

LOWER NEUTRON
SHIELD

ABSORBER
HEAD TANK

ABSORBER
FILLING LINE

VALVE ACTUATOR

MAIN SHUT
DOWN VALVE

PURGE GAS INLET
VALVE

DRAIN LINE

Fig. 5: Typical fluid shutdown loop

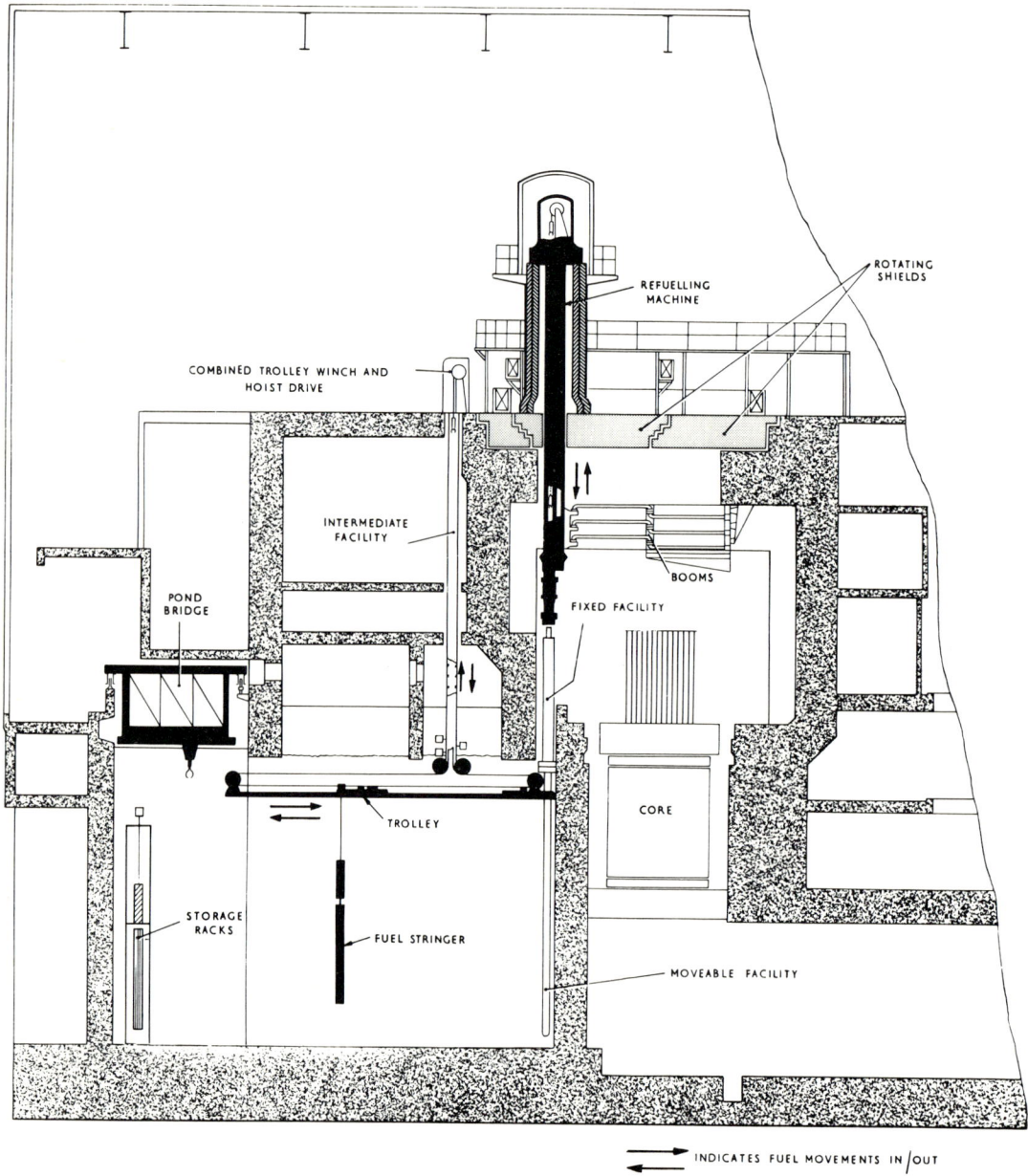

Fig. 6: Fuel handling route

ROTATING
SHIELDS

REFUELLING
MACHINE

COMBINED TROLLEY WINCH AND
HOIST DRIVE

INTERMEDIATE
FACILITY

BOOMS

POND
BRIDGE

FIXED FACILITY

CORE

TROLLEY

STORAGE
RACKS

FUEL STRINGER

MOVEABLE FACILITY

INDICATES FUEL MOVEMENTS IN/OUT

and operation of the set. Other turbines have been built and are operating under these conditions so that these circumstances are not new. Reference 9 gives details of the turbine design.

Containment

28. Vented containment was adopted for the Winfrith SGHWR. It comprises a primary containment situated within a secondary containment and connected to it but sealed from it by water lutes. The concrete biological shield surrounding the core and primary circuit is utilised to form the primary containment but the boundary is extended to envelop that part of the refuelling machine above the rotating shield. The power hall, which houses the reactor, turbo-alternator and fuel pond is utilised to form the secondary containment.

29. Following a breach in the primary circuit, pressure in the primary containment is relieved through two series of water lutes, which condense the steam and automatically reseal the primary containment after blowdown. Any air and uncondensed steam is discharged into the secondary containment and an equivalent volume of clean air is displaced to atmosphere at the end of the building remote from the reactor. The secondary containment is then maintained at a pressure which is slightly subatmospheric by discharging air at a rate equal to the total in-leakage into the building via a clean-up plant to an exhaust stack.

30. The advantages of the system are that only modest pressures and leak-tightness standards have to be accommodated permitting the use of conventional building materials for the two structures and avoiding the close inter-working of mechanical and building trades during construction. Moreover all plant required is either static or running during normal operation, and, during the critical post accident period, double containment is afforded with enhanced safety.

Site and station layout

31. The objectives adopted in laying out the Winfrith SGHWR were compactness leading to economy, operator convenience and the separation of building and civil engineering work from mechanical and electrical work. The layout of the Station is shown in Fig. 7. The reactor, turbo-alternator, feed train and condenser cooling water pumps and the fuel storage ponds are all accommodated in one power hall with a central loading bay and served by one 60 t overhead gantry crane; this crane has been used as the main construction crane. The control room, electrical switchgear, workshops, ventilation and clean-up plant, laboratories, etc., are housed in annexes running down each long side of the power hall. With this layout, feed, steam,

electrical and instrument cabling and services are minimal in length. A separate building accommodates administration facilities and is connected by a short direct link into the centre of the power station.

32. New and spent fuel is loaded into, and discharged directly from, the refuelling machine via the pond which is immediately adjacent to the primary containment of the reactor. With this arrangement, fuel handling and containment transfer is minimal. The pond acts as fuel storage, suppression and dump pond for the reactor. The face of the primary containment opposite to the pond affords ready access for reactor ancillary services such as instrumentation, burst can detection, in-pile loop equipment, etc.

33. The site layout is shown in Fig. 8. Planning requirements limited the height of the cooling towers to 60 ft, with the result that induced draught cooling towers have been provided. These are sited to the east of the Station complex in order to cut down water carry-over onto the main area of the site to a minimum. The switch compound is sited to the South-West affording convenient egress for the power lines.

DESIGN DEVELOPMENTS

34. The design of the Winfrith SGHWR was preceded by a study of a 500 MWe reactor in 1959-1960. One of the major purposes of that 500 MWe study was to identify the key design features and parameters. Wherever possible, these were then incorporated in the design of Winfrith SGHWR to ensure that the system could eventually be developed readily and confidently into larger units. As a result, the techniques and manufacturing methods used for, and proved by, building the Winfrith reactor have direct application to larger commercial stations as outlined in the following part of the paper.

Calandria

35. The height of the reactor core determines the height of the calandria which together with packaging comes within the limitation of 15 ft. Studies have generally shown that the height of core optimises in the range 11 to 15ft regardless of the size of the reactor. Adopting a core height any greater than the 12 ft used at Winfrith would only show small savings but would introduce major transportation difficulties for the calandria and neutron shields, and require a new fuel element design. The top and bottom tube plates of the calandria are designed on a module basis which has already been repeated many times on the Winfrith SGHWR, further multiplication is only required to meet the size requirements for larger reactors. Structural differences only arise in the case of the barrel but, since the thickness for Winfrith was chosen on the grounds of manufacturing

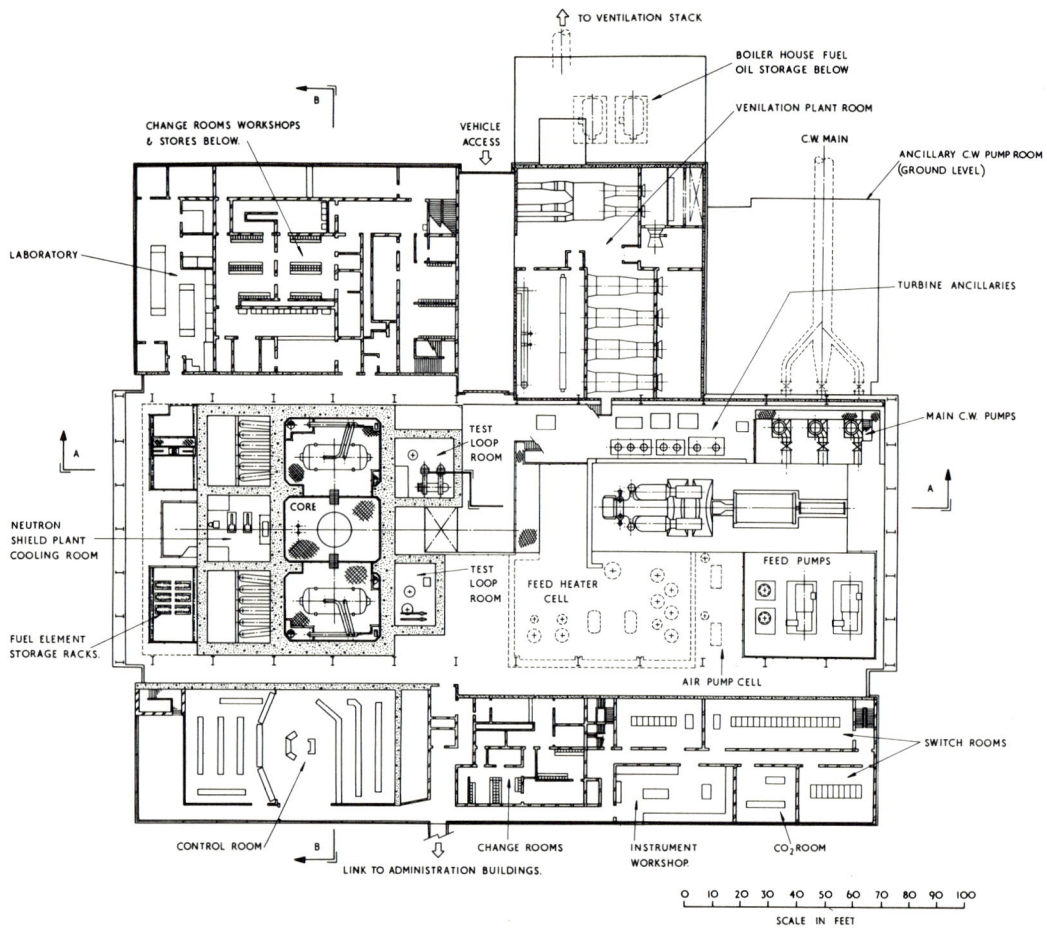

Fig. 7A: Station layout of Winfrith SGHWR (plan)

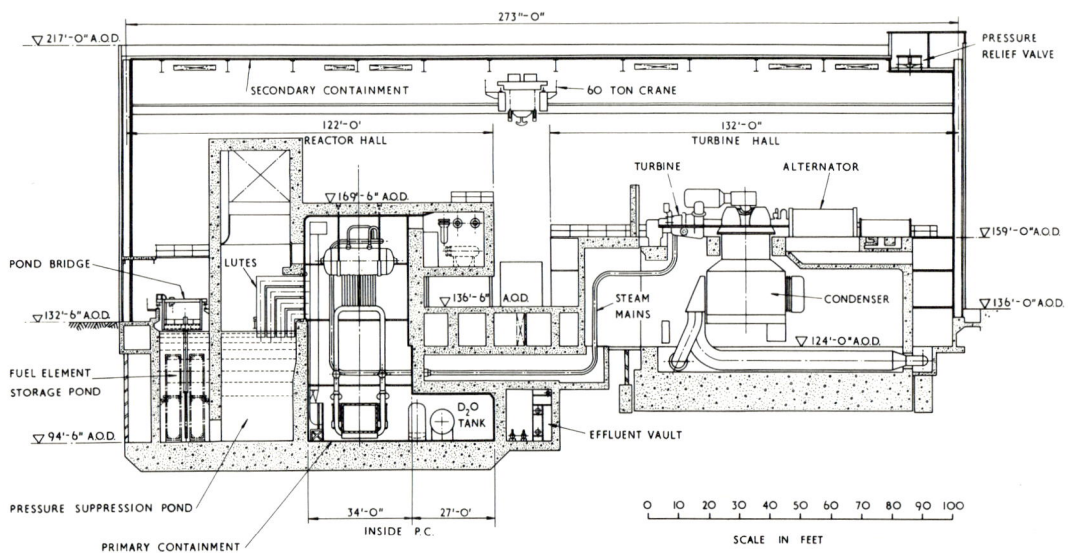

Fig. 7B: Station layout of Winfrith SGHWR (section on AA)

20

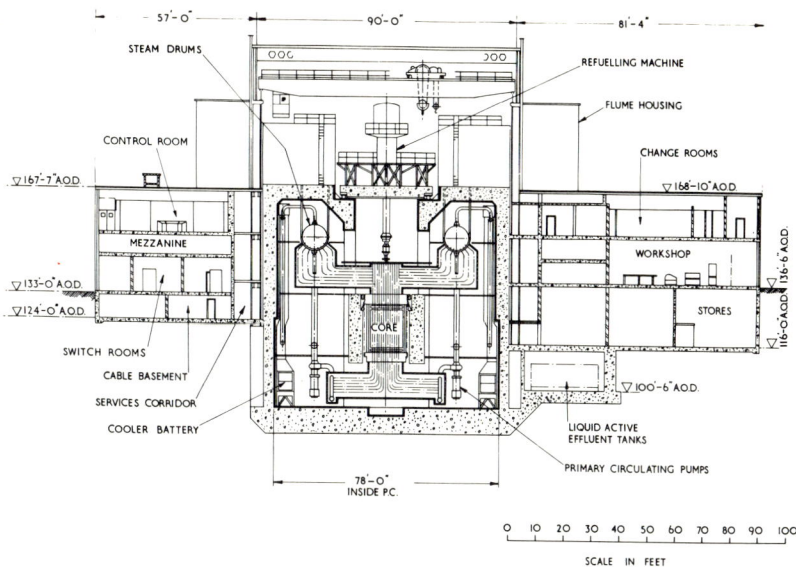

Fig. 7C: Station layout of Winfrith SGHWR (section on BB)

Table 1
Experimental facilities (ref. 5).

Item	Description	Circuit
1	One standard boiling channel	Independent closed loop or main reactor circuit
2	Two small interlattice boiling channels	Two independent closed loops
3	Mk.I boosted loop, Four standard boiling channels	Extra pump in series with main reactor pumps
4	Seven superheat channels	Saturated steam from drum mixed with main turbine steam
5	One superheat channel	As item 4 or can be passed direct to main condenser
6	Water corrosion	Item 1 loop constructed in mild steel
7	Core vault gas corrosion rig	Recirculation of vault gas over in-core zirconium and aluminium samples
8	Moderator corrosion rig	Samples suspended in moderator and helium blanket gas
9	Zirconium sample tests	Special fuel stringer
10	Zirconium pressure tubes	Zircaloy 2, 4 and Heat treated zirconium/niobium alloy

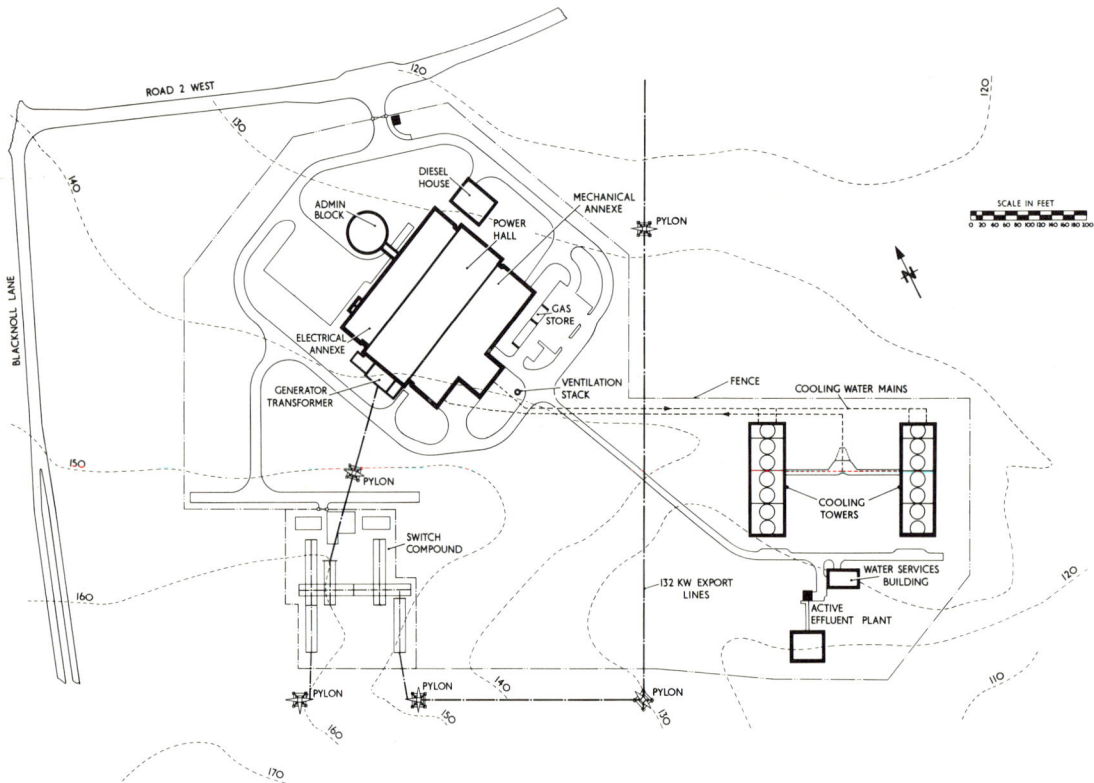

Fig. 8: Site layout of Winfrith SGHWR

rigidity, it is found that up to 500 MWe no increase in thickness is required. Where the transport limit of 15 ft width applies and for outputs greater than about 150 MWe, it is necessary to divide the core into two sections which can be transported to site individually and seal welded together to form an all welded fabrication. Beyond 650 MWe, it is necessary to split the calandria once more, see Fig. 9a. The clearance already allowed between the channel tube assembly and the calandria tube bore on the Winfrith assembly is generous and is sufficient to meet the increased requirements for differential expansion between the calandria and shield tanks with the larger reactor diameters.

36. Spatial instabilities are possible with the large core diameters, and these are catered for by dividing the helium gas space above the moderator into zones using vertical "curtain walls" welded to the top of the tank. Variation of the helium blanket pressure between these zones gives differential moderator levels capable of inhibiting the development of spatial instabilities.

37. In the Winfrith reactor considerable "in line" site work had to be carried out welding extensions to the service pipes from the bottom and top of the calandria where these pass through the neutron shield tanks since if these had been added at the factory, they would have caused a transport limitation. For commercial designs, this problem has been overcome by taking all connections out at the side of the tank near the base, see Fig. 9b. These connections then appear in the lengthways direction for transportation purposes.

38. No radical change from the design and manufacturing procedures used for the Winfrith reactor are envisaged on the commercial designs. The principle of trial erection at the factory and dowelling to minimise setting-up time at site is maintained. With the largest sizes of reactor, the component dimensions and weight become large both for normal manufacturing facilities and site transport, and the assemblies are therefore broken down into convenient unit size. There is no penalty of neutron absorption if division plates are used between the individual units and therefore these can be self-contained.

Channel units

39. Individual channel tube assemblies are of the same general design as for Winfrith and are completely manufactured in the workshops. In the case of Winfrith, each individual riser connection to the steam drum was installed at site and constituted a large 'in-line' activity. For the larger station designs, groups of channel tube assemblies are mounted together with their risers as one sub-unit comprising up to 14 individual

channels, the risers being connected to a smaller number of delivery headers. The small bore channel pipework required for power measurement is also integrated into this assembly, thus avoiding a considerable amount of site erection. Typical sub-assemblies are shown in Fig. 10 from which it will be seen that the dimensions allow transportation to be conveniently provided. The total weight of the largest assembly is approximately 8 tons.

40. For the Winfrith channel assembly, the zirconium pressure tube had a reduced diameter at the lower end (see Fig. 2) so that the completed unit including the tailpiece could be lowered through the calandria tube. Development work on joints has continued and results have shown that a thinner hub can be used, thereby permitting the same method of channel installation without reducing the diameter of the zirconium pressure tube.

Coolant circuit

41. Improved layout of the coolant system and the absence of the experimental facilities provided at Winfrith have enabled a two circuit 350 MWe system to be accommodated in the same sized building. Attention has also been given to pre-fabrication of assemblies. For example, the bottom feeder header can be delivered with the feeder pipes already attached to it together with the channel power measuring pipework.

42. The method of decay heat removal following reactor trip and isolation from the turbine has also advanced. Provision for guaranteed feed water has been made by using steam driven feedpumps and it is therefore no longer necessary to depressurize the reactor, immediately following the loss of electrical supplies. These feedpumps take their water supply from the blowdown pond. The pond is cooled by the ancillary cooling water system on guaranteed supply, thus permitting the shutdown cooling system to continue to operate very prolonged periods with the reactor held at pressure.

43. With the larger commercial reactors, the size of the primary circulating pump units increases considerably, particularly since the core rating has also been increased and the unit size is now beyond that developed for glandless units. Glanded units have therefore been selected which permit the incorporation of large amounts of inertia directly on the rotor shaft.

Reactivity control

44. The fast shutdown of the reactor is achieved with a similar system to Winfrith (ref. 6). Development has revealed that, for the valve size chosen, a capacity several times that required for a single rod is possible. The larger designs of reactor generally use like

SITE SEAL WELD

TREBLE

DOUBLE

SINGLE

0   150 200   400   600 650   800

NET OUTPUT M W(E)

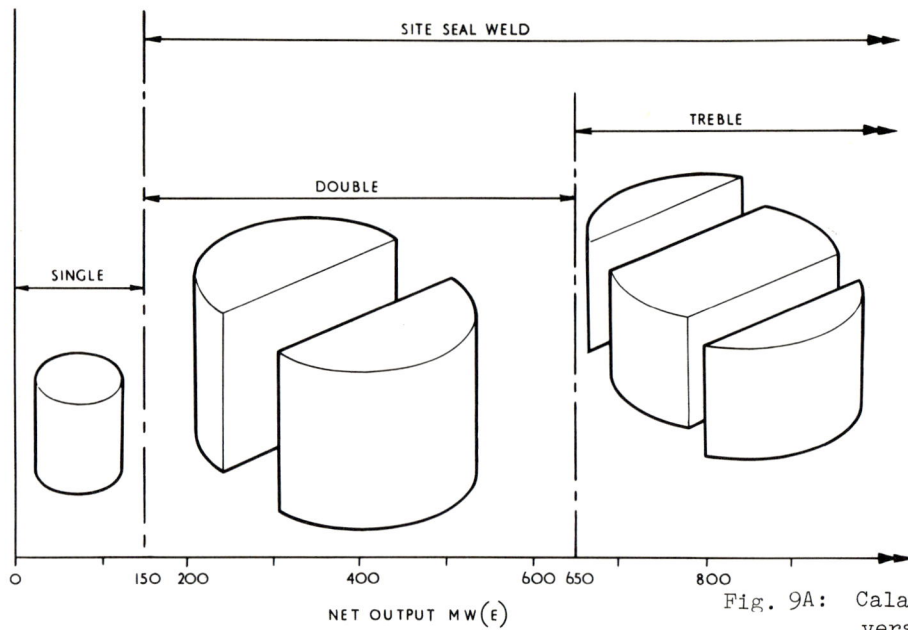

Fig. 9A: Calandria units
versus size

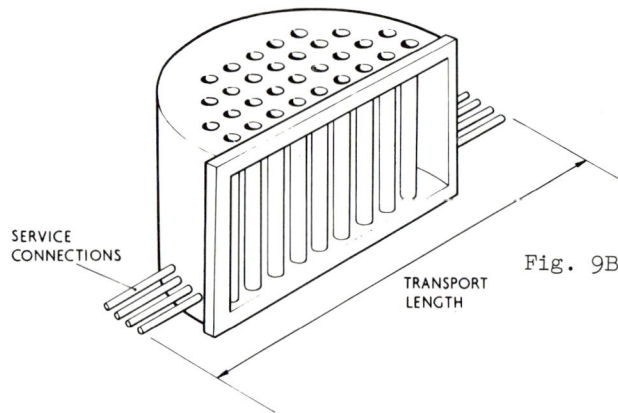

SERVICE
CONNECTIONS

TRANSPORT
LENGTH

Fig. 9B: Calandria fabrication
of tailpipes

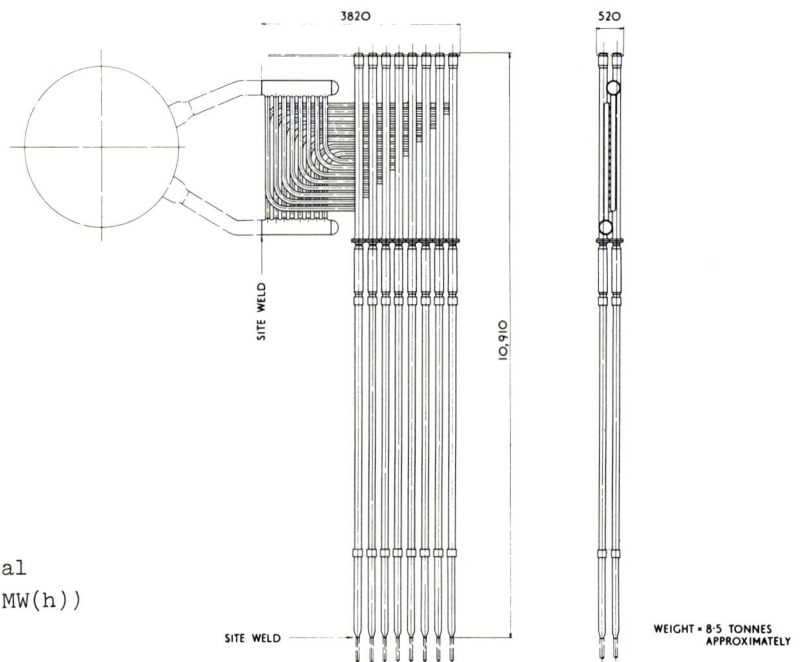

3820

520

SITE WELD

10,910

Fig. 10: Arrangement of typical
channel units (1500 MW(h))

SITE WELD

WEIGHT = 8·5 TONNES
APPROXIMATELY

24

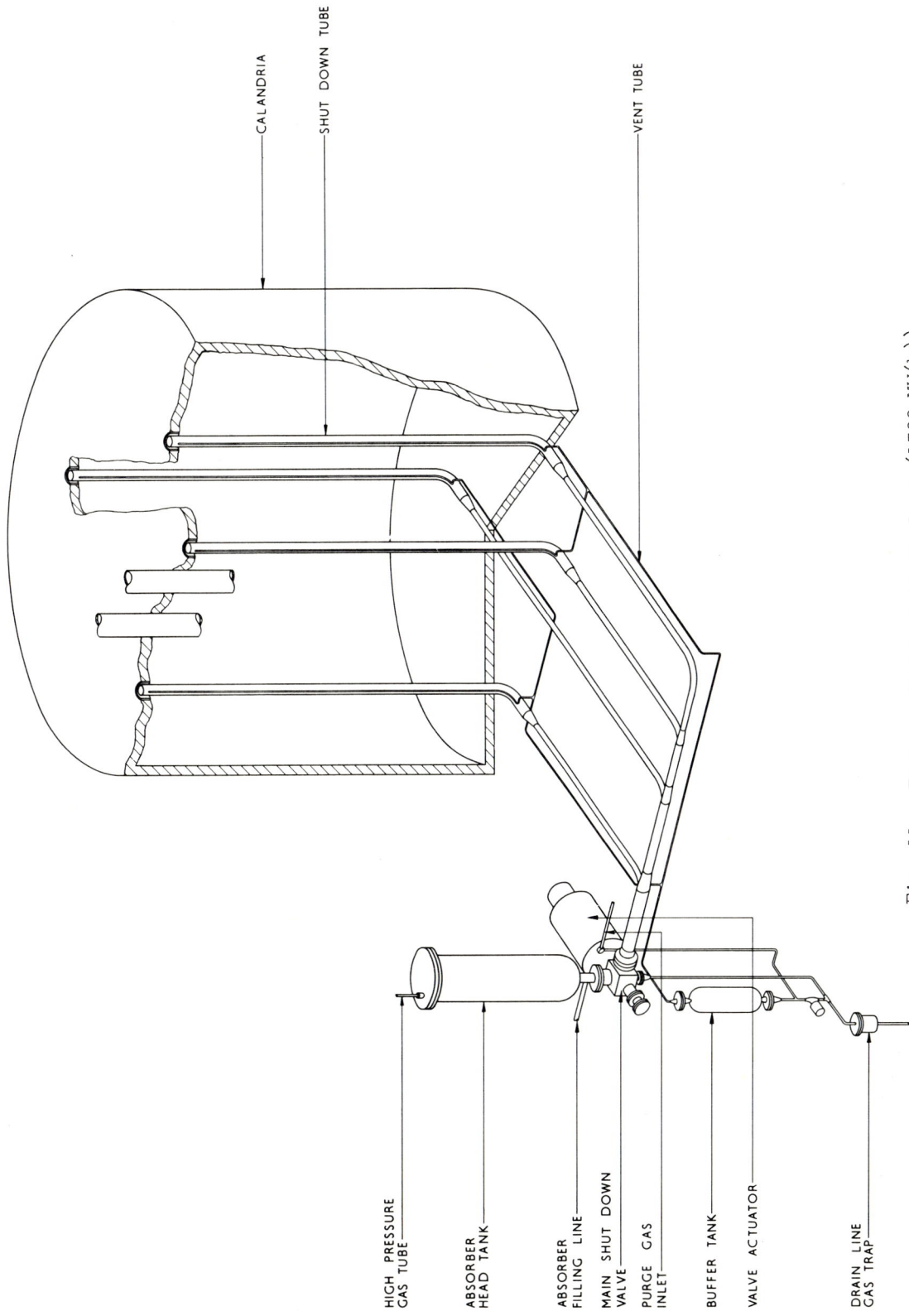

Fig. 11: Typical fluid shutdown loop (1500 MW(h)).

CALANDRIA

SHUT DOWN TUBE

VENT TUBE

HIGH PRESSURE
GAS TUBE

ABSORBER
HEAD TANK

ABSORBER
FILLING LINE

MAIN SHUT DOWN
VALVE

PURGE GAS
INLET

BUFFER TANK

VALVE ACTUATOR

DRAIN LINE
GAS TRAP

Winfrith, 12 liquid shutdown control valves, (the number being chosen to meet arguments of failure and redundancy) with these 12 valves supplying up to 48 liquid shutdown tube positions in the core. These positions in the core are distributed in such a way that failure of one valve does not make a significant reduction to the coverage in any area of the core, see Fig. 11. The ancillary circuits of the Winfrith liquid shutdown system are designed to re-use the borated solution and also require manual operation for refilling the poison vessels. Later designs discharge the absorber solution to waste and employ semi-automatic resetting of the system. These changes enable the shutdown system to be reset in 30 minutes.

Refuelling

45. The individual standpipes, each serving its own channel and fitted with seal plugs, simplify refuelling, whether for 'on-load' or 'off-load'. 'On-load' refuelling machines are complex and expensive, and call for high standards in operation and maintenance.

46. For these reasons an important area studied in the development of the system for commercial stations was refuelling. Optimization studies on suitable fuel cycles pointed to long irradiation allowing fuel to remain in the reactor for over 3 years, and this led to a detailed study of 'off-load' refuelling culminating in the present system.

47. A typical proposal is based on a nine-batch fuel cycle which closely approaches the economics of continuous refuelling. Fuel is replaced at the optium irradiation of about 21,000 MWd/tU which corresponds to a replacement of one ninth of the fuel in the core every 130 full power days (twice per year at 80% load factor). As the fuel is changed whilst the reactor is shutdown and depressurized, there are no reactivity problems since the heavy water will have been drained from the calandria and the liquid shutdown is undisturbed but cocked during refuelling operations. For reactors up to at least 600 MWe, the equipment is designed to permit refuelling over a long weekend, see Fig. 12.

48. The main feature of the refuelling system is the refuelling pond which is situated immediately above the standpipes, as shown in Fig. 13. The tops of the standpipes are built into a membrane plate which forms the boundary of the pond during refuelling operations. During normal operation of the reactor, the tops of the standpipes are isolated from the pond water by a removable dished plate which normally forms the base of the pond. When refuelling is to take place, this plate is removed after the volume between it and the tops of the channels has been flooded.

49. The channel stringer comprises two main components: the fuel element and the seal plug stringer. The refuelling machine consists of a light travelling gantry spanning the pond and carrying a grab served by a hydraulic ram. On the first movement, the seal plug stringer (seal plug, tie rod and scatter plug) is removed and stored on the machine. The spent fuel element is then discharged and replaced by a new element. The pond water acts as the cooling and shielding medium. Operations are visual and directly controlled by the operators with the simplest of equipment.

Emergency cooling system

50. The emergency cooling system of the prototype depended upon a gas pressurized supply for its emergency feed. This system tends to be rather expensive on account of the pressurized tanks which are large and heavy in order to hold the necessary volume of water at the correct pressure for the relatively long blowdown period required. Design has therefore developed in the direction of using the pumped supply described for primary circuit emergency feed requirements. Steam driven turbine pumps taking decay heat produced steam from either circuit and drawing water from the pond are used to replenish feed supplies or to cool the fuel in the event of a burst circuit.

CONCLUSIONS

(i) The 100 MWe prototype power station is now operating. All its critical features are designed so that direct incorporation in any larger station is immediately possible.

(ii) The pressure tube concept has allowed all components to be shop fabricated and leads to easy erection and short construction periods. Development of commercial designs has been aimed at even greater use of shop facilities and a further reduction of site erection work. It has been found possible to keep component sizes down to such weights and dimensions that in all cases the power plant equipment of the Station dictates transport and lifting requirements.

(iii) The Winfrith SGHWR is fully instrumented and incorporates numerous facilities which will be employed to provide advanced testing and exploitation of long term development features for the SGHWR system.

(iv) In designing the Winfrith SGHWR, the maximum use of developed equipment has been made—in fact

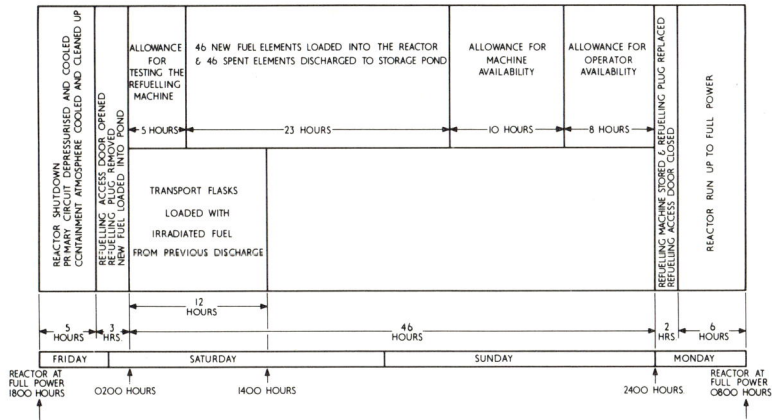

Fig. 12:   Refuelling schedule (1500 MW(h))

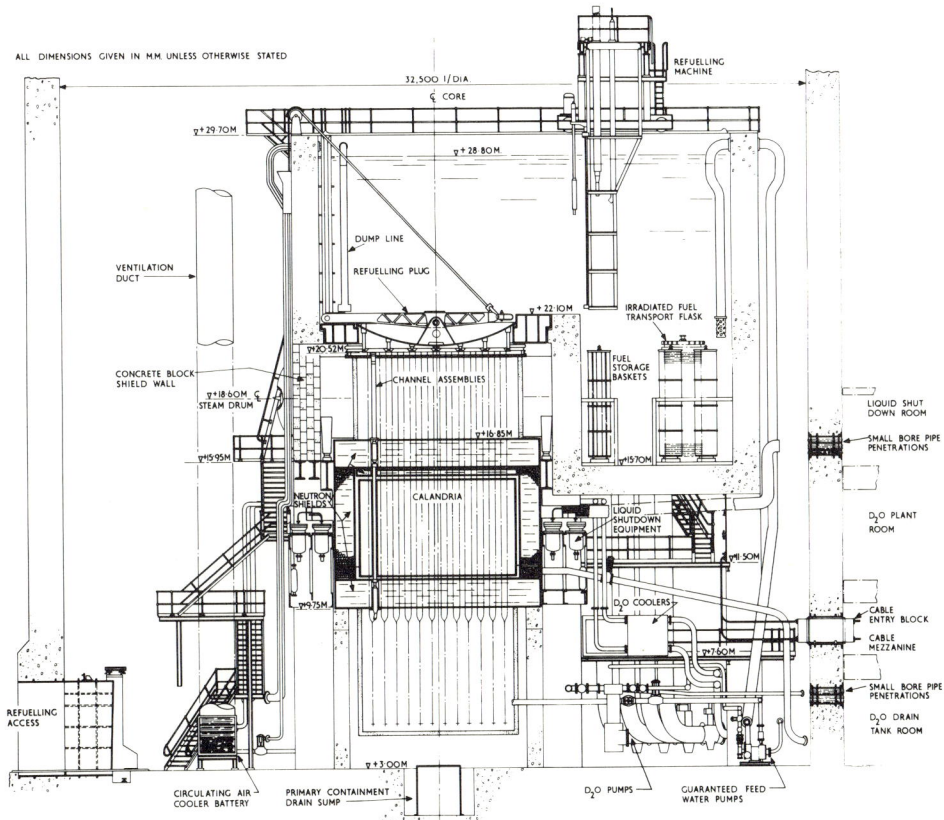

Fig. 13:   Cross section through reactor (1500 MW(h))

27

the main circuit closely resembles
a forced circulation boiler. By
this means, component development has been minimal and
confidence in equipment maximal.

(v) A simple off-load refuelling
system with negligible outage
penalties is available for all
versions.

ACKNOWLEDGEMENTS

51. This paper is published by kind
permission of the Managing Director, The
Reactor Group, UKAEA, Risley. Thanks are
due to the many colleagues at Risley
responsible for the work reported.

REFERENCES

1. FIRTH A and HOLMES J.E.R. SGHW
Prototype. Reactor Nucl. Engineering,
1964, Vol. 9, No. 93, pp.46/49.

2. SGHW Symposium, I. Mech. E., May 1967.
Calandria and neutron shields (Paper 3).

3. SGHW Symposium, I. Mech. E., May 1967.
Channel tube assemblies (Paper 2).

4. SGHW Symposium, I. Mech. E., May 1967.
Reactor primary circuit (Paper 5).

5. BRADLEY N. et al. Some engineering
problems of the SGHW 100 MW(e) Prototype
Reactor. Third International Conference
on the Peaceful Use of Atomic Energy,
United Nations, Geneva 1964, Paper 143.

6. SGHW Symposium, I. Mech. E., May 1967.
Fast-acting liquid shut-down system
(Paper 4).

7. SGHW Symposium I. Mech. E., May 1967.
Refuelling machine (Paper 7).

8. SGHW Symposium, I. Mech. E. May 1967.
Rotating shields (Paper 6).

9. SGHW Symposium, I. Mech. E. May 1967.
Steam turbine and associated plant
(Paper 8).

SGHWR fuel design and materials

D. O. PICKMAN, BA, AIM   UKAEA, Springfields

SYNOPSIS   The general design features of the fuel element developed for the Winfrith SGHWR, its operating parameters and design limits are described. Reference is made to the important differences between this and the fuel element currently under development for a natural UO_2 fuelled version of the reactor. Reasons are given for design decisions made during the course of development.

Development work on materials, manufacture, fuel pin design and fuel element design and associated irradiation testing are described.

Future trends in fuel element design and materials are considered and details are given of the extensive experimental fuel programme included in the first core of the Winfrith SGHWR and the longer term developments on which work has started.

INTRODUCTION

1.   The design of fuel elements for nuclear power reactors is circumscribed by many limitations, both technical and economic. There are complex interactions between various factors, such that once the basic concept has emerged and fuel and cladding materials have been selected, extensive optimization exercises involving neutronics, plant capital cost, fuel cost and fuel operating limits are required.

2.   The methods used in this optimization and the derivation of the physics data and thermal performance data are described in other papers to this conference (refs 1, 2).

3.   Arising from the results of the optimization study, the fuel designer is presented with the key parameters around which the final detailed design must be developed. These incorporate the assumptions which he has fed in on limits for operation of the selected materials and on fuel cost. In the final stage of development of the fully detailed design, some changes in design limits may be introduced as a result of new data, where this can be done with advantage but, in general, any major changes are reflected in new designs which will go through a sequence of large scale irradiation proving followed by selection as a preferred design for future replacement fuel.

4.   This paper is concerned in the main with the development of the detailed reference design fuel element for the Winfrith SGHWR, but some specific aspects of fuel for a natural feed version are discussed and the final section outlines developments expected during the commercial exploitation of the system.

ENRICHED UO_2 FUEL ELEMENT DESIGN

Materials and general description

5.   The SGHWR fuel elements operate in a boiling H_2O environment and are contained in circular pressure tubes. Compatibility considerations led to the early selection of UO_2 as the fuel material, a decision that has never been seriously challenged except in the context of a natural feed reactor.

6.   The candidate materials for fuel cladding were a stainless steel or a zirconium alloy. From an economic point of view. considering feasible minimum can thickness as 0.010 in (0.25 mm), there was a strong incentive to use a zirconium alloy to reduce enrichment. Subsequent experience in the USA has shown that there is a form of stress corrosion cracking in stainless steel operating in boiling water which would make this an undesirable choice regardless of economics (ref. 3). It was possible to select a zirconium alloy with some confidence based on general experience and Zircaloy-2 was designated as the preferred alloy for the boiling water environment.

7.   Existing experience on fuel designs for AGR, and general world experience on water reactor fuels, led to the initial selection of a multi-rod bundle rather than any alternative configuration. The optimization studies indicated a preference for a 37-rod geometry, and full core length fuel pins were selected because the manufacturing cost saving more than balanced out any advantage to be gained from axial shuffling.

Table 1
Main details of the SGHWR reference design fuel element

Fuel	UO$_2$ pellets	
Cladding material	Zircaloy-2	
Overall length	167 in	4.24 m
Fuelled length	144 in	3.66 m
Weight of fuel per cluster	0.198 tU	
Number of fuel pins	36	
Pin diameter	0.63 in	16.0 mm
Nominal can-pellet gap	0.005 in	0.13 mm
Cladding minimum wall thickness	0.025 in	0.635 mm
Volume of gas plenum	1.28 in^3	21.0 ml
Minimum pin to pin spacing	0.08 in	2.0 mm
Number of intermediate grids	10	
Type of intermediate grids	Brazed, stainless steel ferrule	
Grid spacing	12 and 15 in	305 and 381 mm

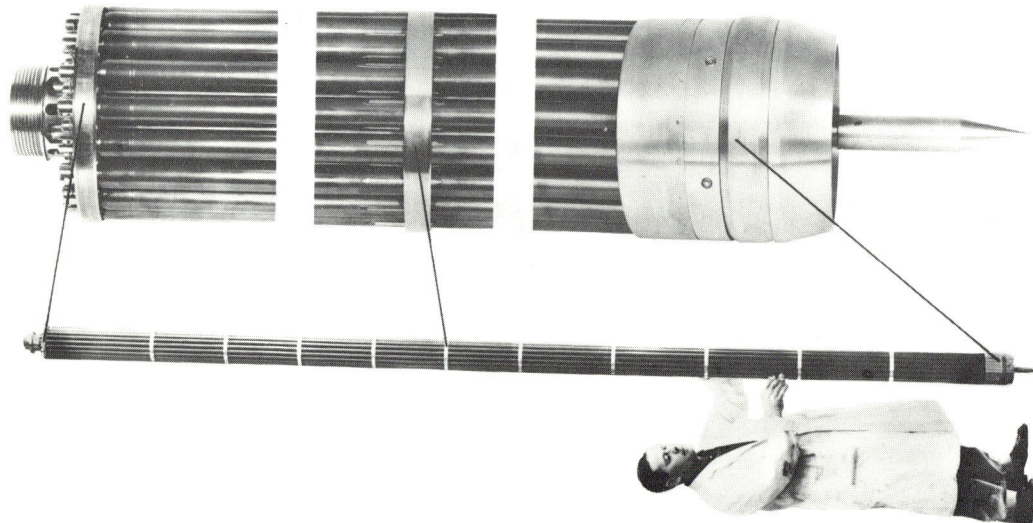

Fig. 1: General view of prototype
fuel element

Fig. 2: Prototype fuel element.
Intermediate spacer grid, showing
attachment to centre tube

Fig. 3: Prototype fuel element.
Top plate

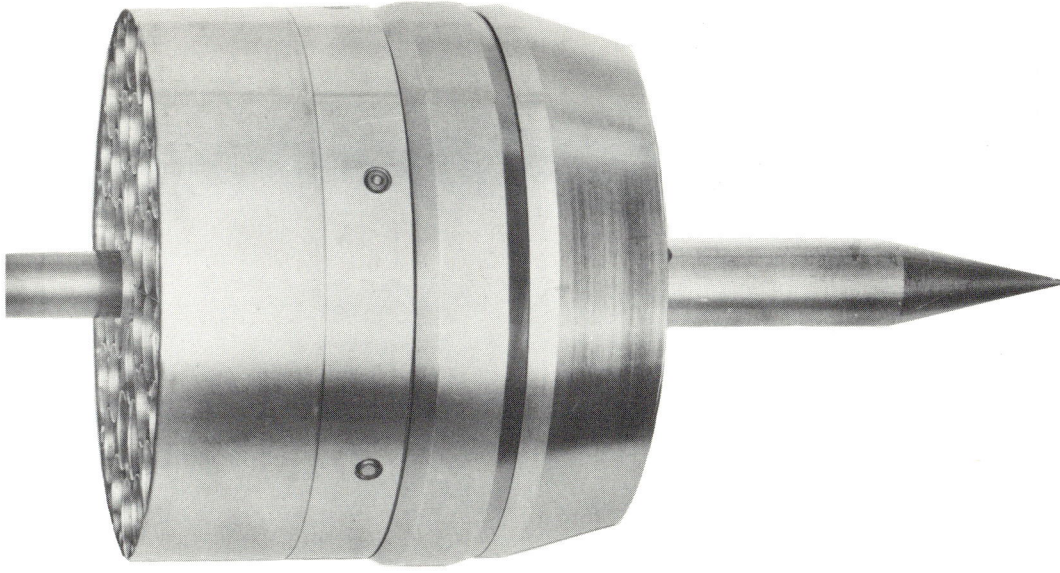

Fig. 4: Prototype fuel element.
Bottom nose unit

8.   The fuel element is illustrated in Fig. 1 and the main details are given in Table 1. The central rod of the bundle is unfuelled, it serves to support the intermediate spacer grids, which are riveted to it, Fig. 2, and as a means for supplying emergency cooling water to the fuel element via a series of drilled holes. The 36-fuelled rods (fuel pins) are arranged in three rings of 6, 12 and 18 respectively; they are attached by bolting to a stainless iron top plate of robust design, which has coolant passages machined into it, Fig. 3. Each fuel pin is held in a unique orientation by means of a small indexing key integral with the top end cap and fitting into a machined slot in the underside of the top plate. The bottom ends of all fuel pins float freely in a bottom nose unit which is attached to the centre tube, Fig. 4. Space is provided for axial extension of the fuel pins downwards relative to the centre tube assembly, but stops are provided to prevent them dropping further. The nose unit has an external split ring whose free diameter is slightly larger than the pressure tube internal diameter. This serves to centralize the fuel element in the pressure tube at its lower end and to prevent it vibrating. The fuel pins, which have wear-pads on the external can surface, are supported by ten intermediate spacer grids, fabricated by brazing from stainless steel ferrules. There are three regularly spaced wear pads on each pin at each grid position; these are shown in Fig. 5. They are of Zircaloy-2, brazed to the can with a Zr-5 ^{W}/o Be brazing alloy. The spacing of the 10 intermediate grids is varied, those in the upper half being 12 in (30 cm) apart, the others 15 in (38 cm). It was shown that grids spaced more closely in the upper half has a beneficial effect on heat transfer. The spacing at the lower end is determined only by the need to prevent fuel pin bowing.

Operating parameters

9.   Some operating parameters of SGHWR fuel elements are given in Table 2. The first column refers to the reference design fuel, the second to an uprated experiment based on the same design, and the third to a natural fuel design experiment. These two experiments are being run in duplicate in four channels which are supplied with boosted coolant flow by means of an auxiliary water pump.

10.   Points to note are the nearly 50% increase in peak fuel rating for the uprated experiment as compared with standard fuel, and the large increase in internal gas pressure; the burn-up and gas pressure quoted for the experimental designs are at the end of one year only, when the first fuel will be discharged for examination. In the 'natural' design experiment the peak fuel rating is reduced compared with standard, because of dryout limitations, despite an almost 50% increase in mass velocity to a value of 3.2×10^6 lb/ft^{2}h. In this case also the gas pressure is significantly increased at a channel burn-

up of 4380 MWd/tU, which will be reached in one year.

Design limits

11.   The basic design limits for the reference fuel are set by heat transfer (dryout) and centre melting of UO_2. Neither of these is permitted after applying the necessary margins for uncertainties, overpower and reactor faults. In fact, the reference fuel element design is dryout limited and at current maximum channel power, the UO_2 centre temperature is a long way from the limit. However, revised estimates of channel dryout power now permit major uprating and, with the same rod cluster design, the permissible uprating will take peak UO_2 centre temperature close to the melting limit.

12.   The fundamental limit to be applied in this type of reactor is set by the maximum permissible tensile stress in the can during normal operation, the concept being that no significant creep of the can away from the fuel should be permitted. A stress level of 12,000 lb/in^2 is assumed for this case, which corresponds to a gross internal pressure of some 1900 lb/in^2. With the reference design, the total internal gas pressure is well within this limit.

13.   Clad thickness has been set by creep and corrosion requirements. Although the cold fuel/can gap is fully taken up at peak rating positions at full power, it is not taken up at all positions and, moreover, a gap can exist at all positions when power is reduced below about 75%. It is a requirement that the creep down of the can in either of these situations should be minimized in order to avoid undesirable can straining on returning to full power. When the life history of the fuel is considered, a low cycle fatigue problem could exist if rapid can creep occurred during every power excursion. The can stress limit of 12,000 lb/in^2 has been set for the purpose of avoiding this problem, which has led to the minimum can thickness of 0.025 in (0.63 mm). This thickness is consistent with a maximum permissible bulk hydrogen content in the cladding at end of life of 300 ppm, the estimated 1000 day H_2 content being only 90 ppm, based on work by Pashos et al. (ref. 4).

14.   The validity of the cladding thickness limits is being explored in pilot irradiations of experimental fuel having cans of wall thicknesses 0.030, 0.022, 0.015 and 0.010 in. These represent cladding compressive hoop stresses of 10,000, 14,000, 20,000 and 30,000 lb/in^2 and H_2 contents (1000 days) up to 200 ppm.

15.   As a compromise between total can strain and gas release, fuel pins have been designed to permit some interference between UO_2 pellets and can at peak rating positions at full power. The SGHWR reference fuel design limit is 0.5% for

Fig. 5: Brazed wear pads on fuel pin.
Pickled and autoclaved

Fig. 6: General view of one 3 ft 9 in
(1.14 m) element of the
natural design

Table 3
Main details of a natural SGHWR fuel element design

Fuel	UO$_2$ pellets	
Cladding material	Zircaloy-2	
Overall length of element	45 in	1.14 m
Fuelled length of element	44.3 in	1.125 m
Number of elements per channel	4	
Weight of fuel per channel	0.34 tU	
Number of fuel pins	36	
Pin diameter	0.704 in	17.88 mm
Nominal can-pellet gap	0.005 in	0.13 mm
Cladding minimum wall thickness	0.015 in	0.38 mm
Minimum pin-pin spacing	0.030 in	0.76 mm
Number of intermediate grids per element	4	
Type of grid	Machined Zircaloy-2	
Grid spacing	9 in	0.23 m

Table 2
Operating parameters of SGHWR fuel elements

		Standard	Uprated	Natural
Channel power	MW(th)	3.8	5.0	3.5
Weight of fuel per channel	tU	0.198	0.197	0.247
Linear heat rating (max)	kW/ft	15.7	22.1	18.4
Linear heat rating (max)	W/cm	515	726	603
Fuel rating (max)	MW/tU	35	48	30
Surface heat flux (max)	Btu/ft^2h	390000	459000	412000
Surface heat flux (max)	W/cm^2	123	145	130
$\int_{T_S}^{T_o} k(\theta)d\theta$ (max)	W/cm	41	52	45
Discharge burn-up - (channel)	MWd/tU	14000	7300*	4380*
Discharge burn-up - (max pin)	MWd/tU	17600	9800*	5860*
Discharge burn-up - (max pellet)	MWd/tU	25200	14000*	8400*
Neutron flux (fast)	n/cm^2s	3.3×10^{13}	4.58×10^{13}	3.16×10^{13}
Neutron flux (total)	n/cm^2s	1.073×10^{14}	1.27×10^{14}	1.36×10^{14}
Coolant pressure (channel inlet)	lb/in^2 abs	984	1020	1028
Coolant pressure (channel inlet)	kg/cm^2	69.2	71.7	72.3
Coolant temperature (channel inlet)	^oC	272	272	272
Coolant flow	lb/h	1.37×10^5	2.06×10^5	1.37×10^5
Coolant flow	kg/h	6.2×10^4	9.3×10^4	6.2×10^4
Mass velocity	lb/ft^2h	2.18×10^6	3.3×10^6	3.2×10^6
Mass velocity	kg/cm^2s	0.30	0.45	0.43
Exit quality	% weight	11.26	9.0	10.2
Pressure drop over fuel	lb/in^2	20	34	65
Pressure drop over fuel	kg/cm^2	1.4	2.4	4.6
Fuel centre temperature	^oC	1515	2400	1759
Fuel surface temperature	^oC	375	515	416
Can internal gas pressure at discharge	lb/in^2	58	300*	119*
Can internal gas pressure at discharge	kg/cm^2	4.1	21.1*	8.4*

*At the end of 1 year

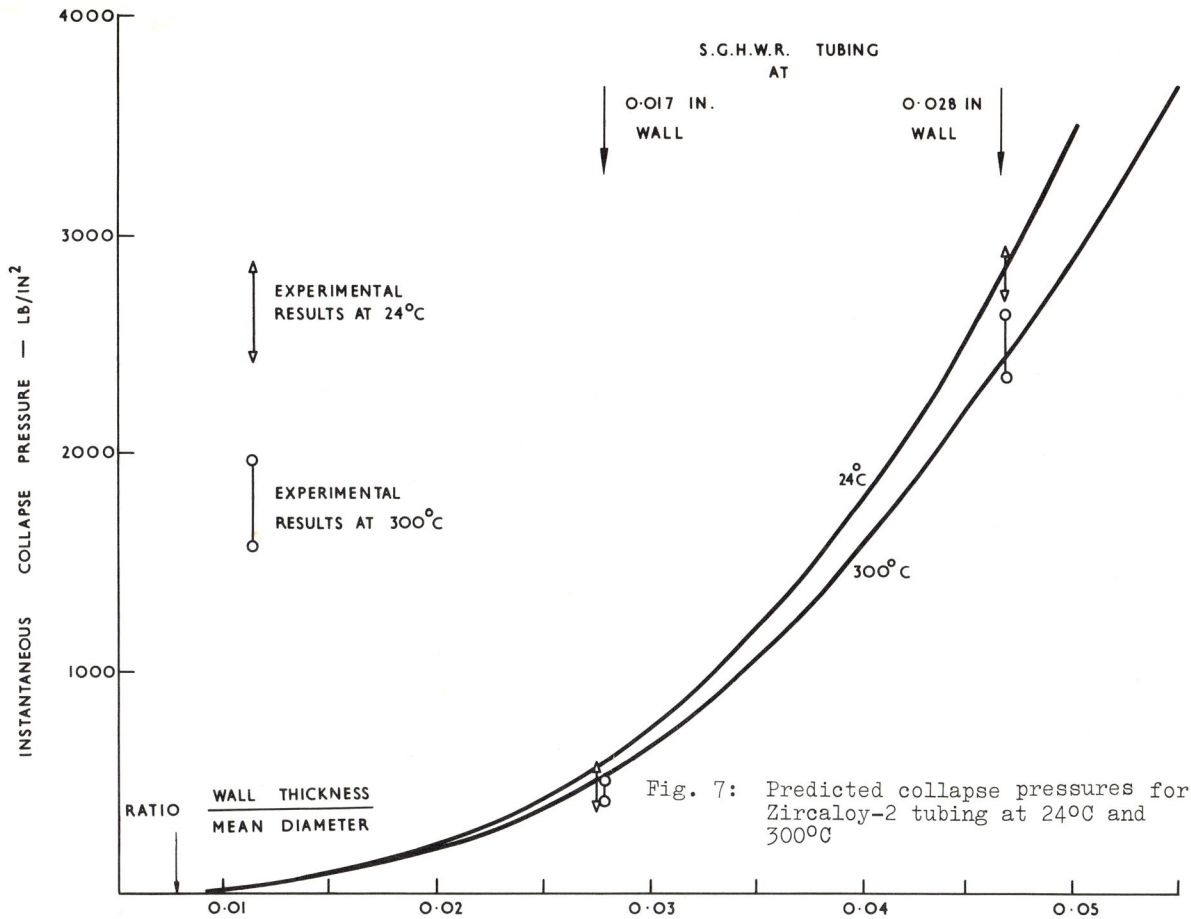

Fig. 7: Predicted collapse pressures for Zircaloy-2 tubing at 24ºC and 300ºC

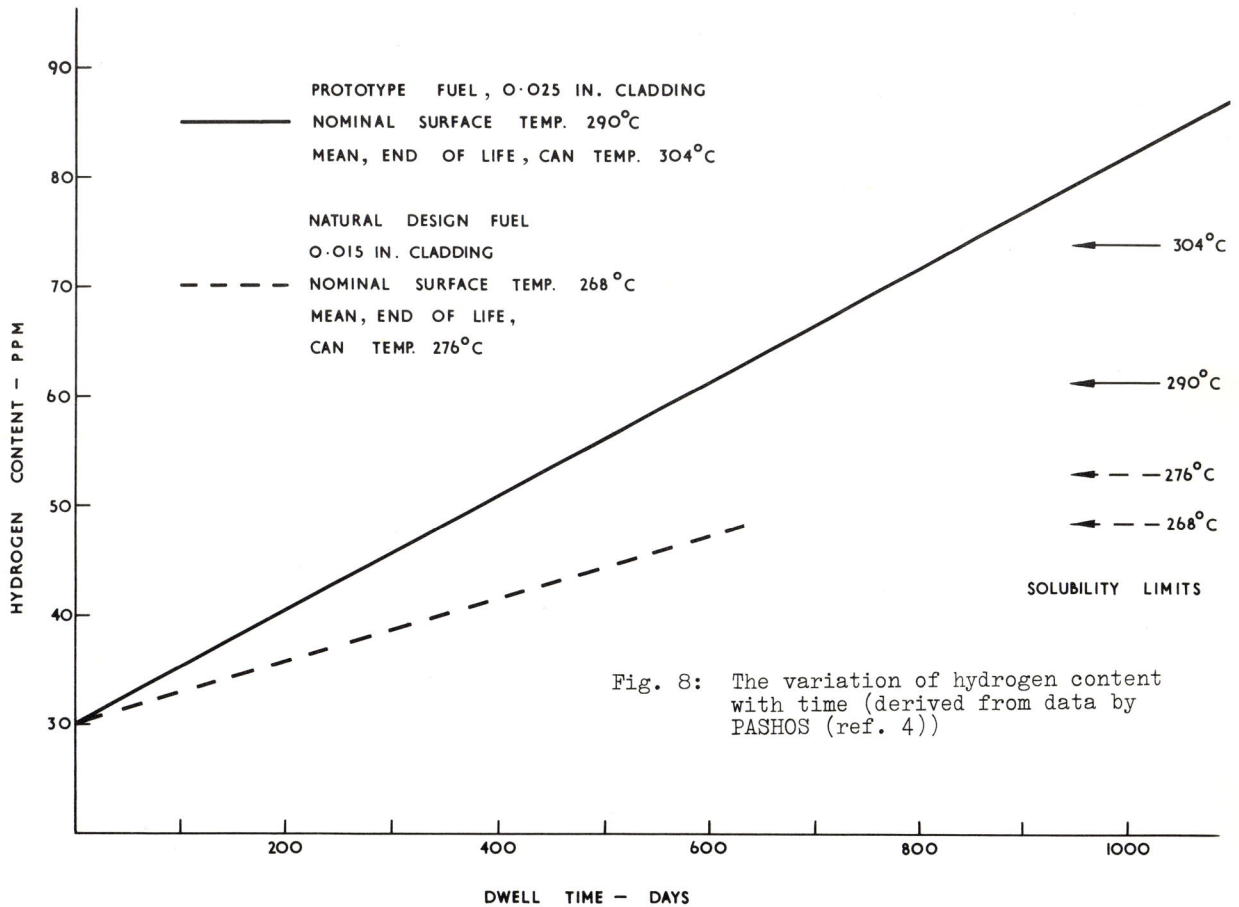

Fig. 8: The variation of hydrogen content with time (derived from data by PASHOS (ref. 4))

this thermal expansion strain, but in some experiments it will exceed 1%. The hot diameter is calculated using an effective temperature of $\frac{2T_c + T_s}{3}$, which has been shown to somewhat overpredict the diameter increase, probably because it assumes no plastic flow of the high temperature UO_2 in the centre. However, when there is fuel/clad interaction, circumferential ridges form at pellet interfaces and this effective temperature model predicts the diameter at these ridges quite closely. Plasticity of UO_2 becomes more important at high ratings and Notley and Lane have indicated the void volume to apply to limit can strain (ref. 5). This void in the form of a central hole or end dishes accommodates the plastically deformed UO_2. Depending on how the void volume is distributed however, the amount of accommodation achieved is also a function of rate of rise of power. The other factor affecting can strain is the irradiation swelling of UO_2. An additional allowance of 0.5% strain is made in SGHWR reference fuel, bringing the total can strain, elastic plus plastic, to a limit of 1%. In some experiments, the total strain limit will approach 2%. Westinghouse basic data on the swelling of UO_2 have been applied in a model which assumes swelling is temperature invariant and UO_2 non-plastic below 1000°C (ref. 6); this leads to the conclusion that any swelling allowance in the form of pellet dishing is ineffective. In practice however, an additional 1.5% void volume as double ended pellet dishing has been provided to cover uncertainty and to minimize thermal expansion strains. In arriving at the limiting burn-up for 0.5% clad strain induced by UO_2 swelling, the residual micro-porosity in the UO_2 is taken to be fully effective and restraint by the cladding is ignored. This leads to a maximum permissible burn-up in the reference fuel of 25,000 MWd/tU for the pellets which are of 10.65 g/ml maximum density.

NATURAL UO_2 FUEL ELEMENT DESIGN

16. The fuel element under development for the natural UO_2 fuelled version of SGHWR differs in a number of ways from the design described for the enriched reactor. In this version the retention of H_2O cooling puts a premium on neutron economy in order to achieve an economically viable burn-up. Further, it is necessary to achieve a more uniform burn-up of the fuel, and some axial segmentation and shuffling has been accepted.

17. The quantity of H_2O in the channel has been reduced to minimize absorption and the minimum pin-to-pin spacing is 0.03 in (0.76 mm) compared with 0.08 in (2.03 mm) in the enriched design. This has led to a change in the method of pin spacing, wear pads on the fuel pins being dispensed with in favour of direct contact between fuel pin and a machined cellular grid in Zircaloy-2. Out-of-pile loop tests on this type of design have given encouraging results from the standpoint of fretting.

18. A 3 ft 9 in (114 cm) long element of this type is shown in Fig. 6. The 37-rod geometry of the enriched design is retained, pin diameter being increased to 0.704 in (17.88 mm) outside diameter to fit in the same size pressure tube. The central rod is again unfuelled and serves to support the spacer grids and for the supply of emergency cooling water. Four such elements, spring loaded together on a central tie rod, form a 15 ft (4.57 m) fuelled length channel assembly. Alternatively, 2 or 3 longer elements may be finally selected.

19. The main parameters of the design are given in Table 3. Fuel cladding thickness has not been finally selected, but is expected to be in the range 0.010 in to 0.018 in (0.25 mm to 0.45 mm), depending on the load following required of the reactor.

20. The rating of this fuel design is limited by thermal performance at a lower peak rating than the enriched reactor fuel, even though the coolant mass-velocity is increased. Fission gas release also approaches the limit (1100 lb/in^2 max. internal pressure for 0.015 in (0.38 mm) can thickness) for the larger diameter pin with no gas plenum. The optimum coolant pressure for this reactor is lower, at 650 lb/in^2 channel inlet, than for the enriched reactor and channel pressure drop is high, about 75 lb/in^2.

21. The natural fuel has a much reduced burn-up, the peak being estimated to occur in the range 7000-9000 MWd/tU, so that very little UO_2 swelling is expected and the gas release problem is eased. The same can strain limit (1% total) is proposed as for enriched fuel, but, depending on can thickness, the initial can/pellet gap may have to be reduced to preserve stability in the initial hot, pressurized, situation. The cumulative strain, due to creep strain reversals arising from power changes, may however be the critical factor in determining the endurance of the can. Another factor of importance is that the cladding on this fuel is elastically unstable, even at the upper end of the thickness range. Elastic collapse pressures for cans have been determined by Slattery and are given in Fig. 7 (ref. 7). Irradiation experiments have indicated generally satisfactory behaviour for such cladding for the proposed natural SGHWR service, but more frequent pressure reductions during fuel lifetime may prove to be deleterious as a result of a ratchetting type mechanism.

22. Corrosion effects in the thinner cladding, operating at the reduced system pressure and for the shorter dwell time, are expected to be less important than in the enriched reactor. The lower corrosion rate and shorter time, more than offset the reduction in thickness of cladding in terms of H_2 pick-up. Fig. 8 shows the expected variation of H_2 content with dwell time for

Table 4
Fuel pellet details for the SGHWR reference design

Fuel material		UO_2	
Density		10.6 ∓ 0.05 g/cc	
Pellet diameter		0.57 in	14.5 mm
Pellet length		0.6 in	15.2 mm
Dish volume, cold		2.175%	
Typical pellet analysis	C	20 ppm	
	Ca	20 "	
	Cr	10 "	
	F	10 "	
	Fe	75 "	
	N	20 "	
	Si	45 "	
O/U ratio		2.001-2.002	
Grain size		3.5 to 6.6 μm	

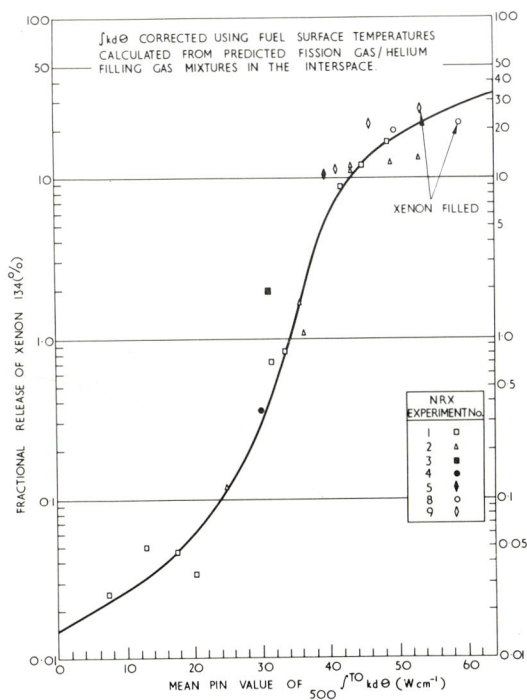

Fig. 9: Fission gas release measurements from NRX irradiation experiments

the natural and enriched reactor cladding operating under neutral conditions and the solubility limits corresponding to the clad temperatures in the two cases.

23.   Alternative fuel materials have been given serious consideration for the natural SGHWR system, where peak burn-up does not rule out metallic fuels and where high uranium density is important. Of the alternatives considered, a uranium-silicon alloy, corresponding to U_3Si in composition, has attractive properties. It has good compatibility with water below $400^{\circ}C$, favourable conductivity and expansion to minimize clad strain, very low fission gas release and freedom from cracking under irradiation. It can be cast and fabricated into fuel pin size rods without difficulty. The only real problem seen with this alloy is irradiation induced swelling, but specimens having a central void have now been successfully irradiated to 10,000 MWd/tU, the order of burn-up that will be required if it is to be used successfully in a natural SGHWR.

FUEL ELEMENT DEVELOPMENT AND IRRADIATION TESTING

Fuel

24.   High density stoichiometric UO_2 in the form of sintered pellets is the fuel used in SGHWR. The pellet design incorporates double trapezoidal shaped dishes providing some 2% void volume. Typical parameters for the pellets are given in Table 4. It has not been possible during development irradiations to establish swelling behaviour for this fuel, but useful information on fission gas release has been obtained and is summarized in Fig. 9. Valuable information on release mechanisms has been established by comparison of predictions, based on various assumptions, with experimental results, and by studies of micro-structural features of irradiated UO_2. Considerable interlinking grain boundary porosity develops at temperatures above about $1300^{\circ}C$ and this temperature limit reduces with burn-up. Fine gas bubble porosity is also seen within the UO_2 grains at higher temperatures, becoming smaller and finally disappearing at about the $1500^{\circ}C$ isotherm. These features are illustrated in Figs 10 and 11.

25.   The various criteria adopted for gas release prediction have been built into a series of computer programmes with the code name SUPATRICE. The assumptions in the version currently used for SGHWR predictions are:-

(a)   recoil release from geometric surfaces (very small);

(b)   diffusion controlled release at all temperatures, increasing with burn-up;

(c)   enhanced release in equiaxed grain growth region, $1600-1800^{\circ}C$.

Assumed to increase from zero to 30% over 150 days;

(d)   enhanced release in columnar grain growth region above $1800^{\circ}C$. Assumed 100% over total life.

26.   The number of major radial pellet cracks present during full power operation has some influence on the power cycling endurance of fuel and may be of importance in arriving at an improved model of gas release. A macro-photograph of a pellet irradiated at a rating of 34 MW/tU, $\int kd\theta = 41$ is shown in Fig. 12.

Cladding

27.   Early development samples of Zircaloy-2 cladding obtained from various sources in the UK and abroad, and made by different processes, were studied by Hindle and Slattery to investigate the orientation of hydrides formed as a result of corrosion in H_2O (refs 8, 9). It was found that un-supported sinking of the tube during manufacture, especially in the later stages, led to the formation of radially oriented hydride precipitates, and that these could have a major effect on ductility at low temperatures, leading to complete brittle-ness if long platelets were present. Examples of good and bad tubing are shown in Figs 13 and 14. This work led to the development of acceptable manufacturing processes and to the checking of hydride orientation on all batches by cold expansion tests of hydrided samples. The terminal solubility of H_2 in representative Zircaloy-2 cladding and in other alloys of interest has been determined by Slattery (ref. 10). The development of radial hydride precipitates in satisfactory cladding tubes can occur if this limit is exceeded and if the hydrides are formed while the cladding is under a hoop tensile stress. The extent of such re-orientation is a function of stress level and this has been found to vary widely in otherwise satisfactory tubing. Limits of stress between 10,000 lb/in^2 and 20,000 lb/in^2 are found, and it is now believed that this variation depends on basal pole orienta-tion, a radial orientation being most favourable in resisting re-orientation.

28.   Precipitation of hydride while the can is under tensile stress can be largely avoided by control of reactor operation. If radial hydrides are developed, it is particularly important to avoid stressing the can while at low temperature, say below $200^{\circ}C$, since zirconium hydride exhibits some ductility above this temperature (ref. 11). The margins against failure originating from gross radial hydride formation are increased for reactors with higher coolant temperature, and on start-up clad temperature should be raised to the maximum before significant power is raised.

29.   The corrosion behaviour of Zircaloy-2 cladding tubes has been studied extensively during SGHWR fuel development and this work has been reported by Allen et al. (ref. 12).

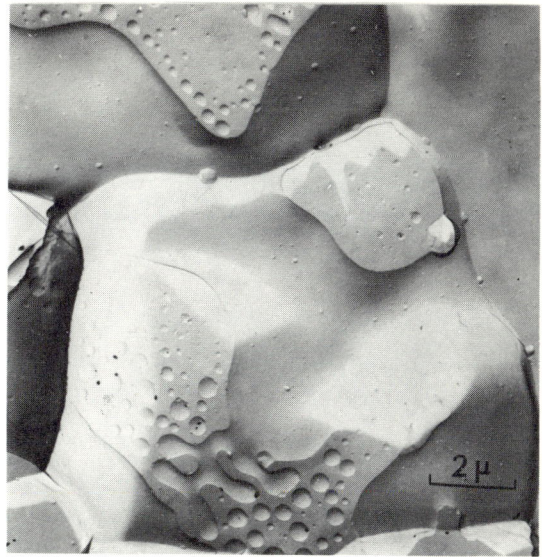

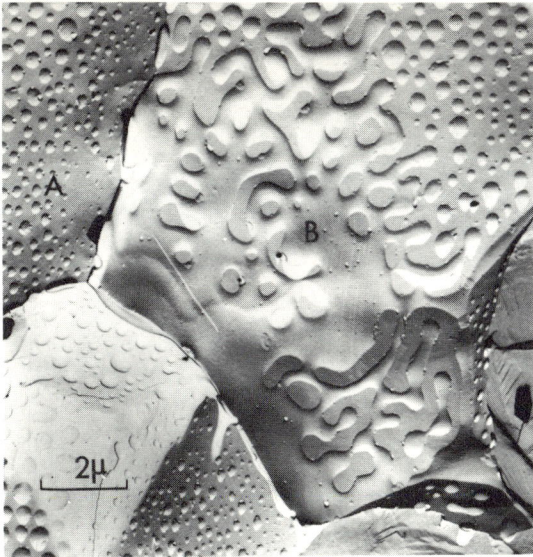

Fig. 10: Electron-micrograph of irradiated UO₂ from Halden irradiation. Burn-up 8500 MWd/tU, rating 34 MW/tU (time-average), centre temperature ζ 1500°C. Structure near pellet centre, showing discrete pores (A) most of which contain solid fission product precipitates, and interlinked pores (B)

Fig. 11: Same specimen as Fig. 10, showing extensive grain boundary fissuring caused by interlinking of discrete pores. Solid fission product precipitates remain on fissured surface

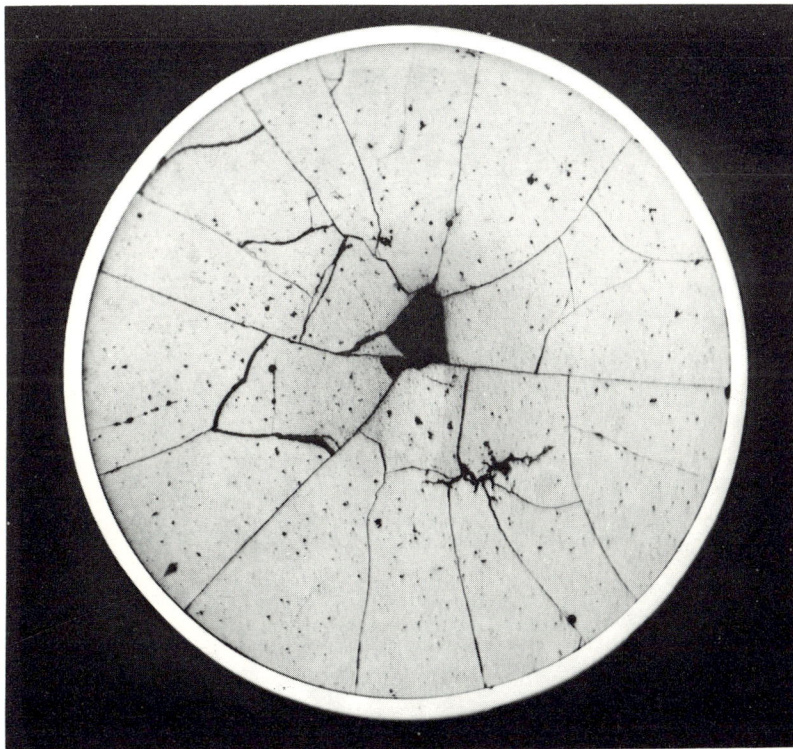

Fig. 12: Fuel structure in a pin irradiated at 34 MW/t (time-average) to 8500 MWd/tU burn-up in Halden BWR. Some loss of fuel has occurred during preparation of the section

Fig. 14: Transverse section of hydrided Zircaloy-2 cladding tube. Shows radial hydride typical of unacceptable tube

Fig. 13: Transverse section of hydrided Zircaloy-2 cladding tube. Shows circumferential hydride typical of good quality tube

The influence of micro-structure on corrosion rate has been shown to be pronounced, large or widely spaced precipitates of $Zr(Cr,Fe)_2$ and Zr_2Ni give high corrosion rates in some conditions and are best avoided by a β quenching operation at the billet stage (ref. 13).

30. A considerable amount of work has been carried out on conditioning treatments for cladding, as a result of which HF/HNO_3 pickling followed by 24 hour low pressure steam autoclaving at $400^\circ C$ was adopted. This process is of very limited value as a proof test for the material. Its main value lies in putting down a protective film of ZrO_2 which is much less susceptible to subsequent contamination than the base metal, e.g., from handling, which gives some protection from scratching during assembly, and which ensures that the initial corrosion layer is put down under controlled conditions. The $400^\circ C$ autoclaving in steam does, however, increase the H_2 content of the can and may have a slight accelerating effect on subsequent corrosion rate at lower temperatures.

31. Extensive in-pile corrosion studies have been carried out by numerous workers. Some of the UK work is described by Nichols (ref. 14). The view that emerges is that the effect of irradiation on corrosion weight gain is predominantly due to radiolysis in the coolant and is very much influenced by water chemistry. Under neutral chemistry conditions (high O_2) a factor of x 20 is used on out-of-pile corrosion weight gain for fuel design purposes. Corresponding fractional H_2 pick-up is low. probably 20-30% in the early stages, reducing to less than 10%. UK irradiation data have not yet gone far enough to establish the latter figure reliably, but it is well established from US and Canadian data (refs 4, 15). Under reducing conditions, acceleration factors are generally found to be lower and fractional H_2 pick-up much higher. It is now doubted whether total H_2 pick-up will be less under reducing conditions than under neutral conditions in a typical power reactor.

Fuel pin

32. The fuel pin comprises the assembly of can, end-caps, UO_2 pellets and plenum support spring where used. This spring also serves to prevent movement of the UO_2 pellets relative to the can during handling and transport; it is made of 18/8 steel and is of the self-locking type, so that there is no reaction on the end-cap during second end welding.

33. Out-of-pile studies have been carried out on can collapse behaviour, both elastic and plastic and Fig. 15 shows how maximum permissible hot can/pellet gap is fixed in relation to pressure and can t/d ratio (ref. 7). The criterion is that the can should not wrinkle by creep deformation, but that limited ridging may be permitted. In fact for the prototype reference fuel

the creep is so small that ridging does not occur with the maximum possible gap. When can/pellet interference is permitted at peak rating positions, as in the SGHWR design, deformation of the can results in an increased gap under low power operating conditions. This may impose limitations for thin cladding designs if the increased gap leads to rapid wrinkling.

34. Increased can/pellet gaps can be tolerated in the reference design with its free-standing can and experiments having gaps up to 0.015 in (0.38 mm) are included in the first fuel charge. The decision to minimize the gap at the expense of some interference, was based on the view that small strains, of the order of 0.5%. were readily accommodated in cladding at the start of life and that fission gas release could be minimized in this way. Experience so far has shown this approach to be justified, but larger gaps may be required in fuel designed for non-base load operation.

35. Attempts to induce ratchetting between UO_2 pellets and cans in out-of-pile experiments have failed to show any means of producing progressive length changes. Nevertheless, with elastically unstable cans, particularly those on the borderline, and with the rating gradients present in fuel pins, such a phenomenon does seem possible if power reductions are accompanied by pressure reductions. This situation arose during the Halden BWR irradiation experiments where the assemblies that showed end failures had in the range 10-15 full power cycles with pressure reduction, as well as many more cycles during which pressure was maintained. Typical length changes on irradiated 6 ft long (1.8 m) fuel pins are in the range 0.02 in (0.5 mm) to 0.1 in (2.5 mm), but these have not correlated well with design and operating variables.

36. The end sealing welds of the fuel pin are magnetic force resistance welds which as made have a considerable 'flash' inside and out. This is machined off externally. Mechanical tests on such welds in the as manufactured and hydrided conditions, at room temperature and at $150^\circ C$, $200^\circ C$ and $290^\circ C$, show that under most conditions failure occurs in the can wall away from the weld. Only with hydrided specimens (2-300ppm) at the lower temperatures did some weld zone failures occur. With the exception of certain fuel pins irradiated in the Halden BWR, no weld failures have occurred in experimental irradiations.

37. The power cycling behaviour of SGHWR fuel is of particular interest in terms of future requirements for commercial reactors. Experimental irradiations have concentrated on the endorsement of fuel for the base load operation of the Winfrith Heath Prototype, in which a typical history will involve some 20-30 major power cycles during the fuel life. This number of cycles, of which about 10 may involve reactor depressurization, have been successfully achieved by reference design fuel (0.025 in, (0.625 mm) cladding) and

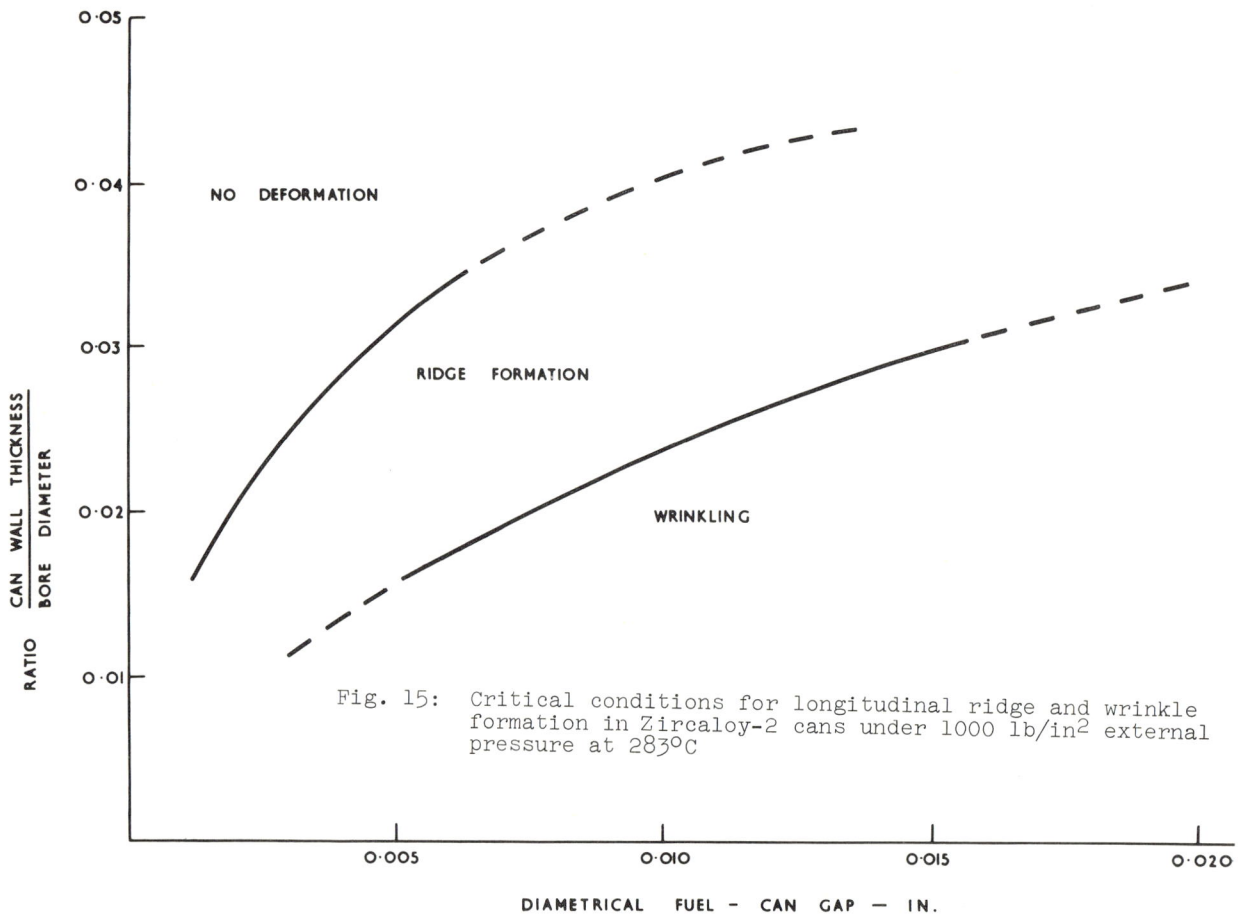

Fig. 15: Critical conditions for longitudinal ridge and wrinkle formation in Zircaloy-2 cans under 1000 lb/in^2 external pressure at 283°C

Fig. 16: Brazed wear pads on a Zircaloy-4 clad fuel pin irradiated for 261 full power days in Halden BHWR

Table 5
Fuel element experiments in NRX

		Peak rating		Peak burn-up
		$\int k d\theta$ w/cm	MW/tU	MWd/tU
1.	Short pins, clad in 0.016 in Zircaloy-2, Zr-Nb, and pre-hydrided Zircaloy-2	51	45	1800
2.	Short pins, as above	51	45	1300
3.	6 ft pin clad in 0.025 in Zircaloy-2, wire wrapped	42	37	1450*
4.	6 ft pin, as above	41	36	1400
5.	6 ft pin, 0.025 in Zircaloy-2, brazed wear pads	49	43	4900
6.	Ditto	47	41	2900
7.	Defect test	66	55	800
8.	Short elements filled with helium or xenon	59	52	900
9.	Ditto but some pins with thin cladding	55	51	1050
10.	Large can-pellet gaps, includes some vibro-compacted fuel	62	54	1150
11.	6 ft pin with 0.015 in Zircaloy-2 cladding	57	48	500
12.	Trefoil of close-spaced (0.040 in) pins clad in 0.015 in Zircaloy-2	45	38	3500

*Pin failed by dry-out

<u>Table 6</u>
Data from NRX experiment 5

Pin length 6 ft   (1.8 m)
Peak ∫k(θ)dθ   49 w/cm
Peak burn-up   4900 MWd/tU
Residence time   115 full power days

Visual appearance	Clean with some lightly crudded patches Dull and rougher over top 12 in
Length change	+0.056 in (1.4 mm)
Diameter increase: (a) mid-pellet (b) pellet ends	 0.001 in (0.025 mm) at end → 0.002 in (0.05 mm) at centre 0.002 in (0.05 mm) at end → 0.004 in (0.1 mm) at centre
Oxide thickness on can	Generally 1 μm mean, occasional patches up to 7 μm. Over top 12 in, 3 μm mean, occasional patches up to 10 μm
H_2 pick-up	Inlet end 10-15 ppm Peak rated position 20-25 ppm Exit end 40 ppm Wear pads 40 ppm
UO_2 structure	Grain size near periphery 11 μm Columnar grain growth region 0.22 in (5.6 mm) dia.
Fission gas release	Fractional xenon release 9.9%

fuel with reduced cladding thickness
(0.015 in (0.375 mm)). Calculations of the
endurance of the cladding under the
fatigue strain arising from power cycling
indicate that certainly down to cladding
thickness of 0.020 in (0.5 mm) many
thousands of major power cycles could be
tolerated. Experiments are planned to
confirmed these predictions and to investigate the importance of can/pellet gap in
this context.

38. The main fuel pin irradiation experiments in the SGHWR fuel development have
been in the X-6 loop in the NRX reactor at
Chalk River. These experiments are
summarized in Table 5. Apart from length,
6 ft (1.8 m) compared with 12 ft (3.7 m),
the main fuel pins in experiments 5 and 6
were exact replicas of SGHWR pins, although
they were run in these experiments with
about a 15% increase in peak fuel rating.
Of the earlier experiments, 3 and 4 were
tests of wire wrapped fuel pins which
featured in the fuel design at that time.
Experiment 3 failed by local dryout downstream of a wire wrap at a position just
above the peak rating. This, together with
adverse heat transfer test results and
fretting behaviour, led to the change to
wear pads and spacer grids. Most of the
more recent irradiations, apart from
experiment 12, have used NH_3 dosed coolant.
No excessive crudding has been seen in any
of the series, and deposition appears to
be a function of circulating crud content
rather than of water chemistry per se.
Circulating crud levels in the loop have
varied between 5 and 73 ppb with NH_3 dosing
and 4 and 200 ppb with neutral operation.
Projection of these results to higher burn-
up does not lead to any serious concern
about the effect of crud on fuel performance, although interpretation of crudding
data from some BWR irradiations, and from
various models of crud deposition, leads to
predictions of very significant can temperature increases. In view of this, can
temperature will be monitored on special
pins in SGHWR in order that the magnitude
of the effect can be assessed and any
consequences taken note of in future
designs.

39. Some of the data obtained from
experiment 5 is given in Table 6. One of
the features noted is that circumferential
ridges of height up to 0.0015 in (0.04 mm)
form over the more highly rated part of
the fuel pin, where can/fuel interaction
exists. These have been seen in all
similar irradiations, the height of the
ridges does not increase with time and they
are apparently generated on first raising
to power. Similarly, length changes do not
vary much with time and the value given is
typical. Clad corrosion and hydriding has
already been discussed. The increase in
oxide film thickness close to the top of
the can of experiment 5, indicates that the
5-10 ppm NH_3 content was not quite sufficient to maintain reducing conditions
throughout. On the other hand, the low
rate of corrosion in the reducing region
may be accounted for by the relatively low
fast flux (2 x 10^{12} n/cm^{2}s > 1 MeV) in the
X-6 position in NRX.

40. The Halden irradiation experiments are
summarized in Table 7. In many respects
these are unrepresentative of an enriched
SGHWR, but they give useful information
relative to proposals for the natural
version running at reduced pressure. The
pressure in the Halden BWR during these
experiments was 28 atm (420 lb/in^{2}a;
29.50 kg/mm^2) and the saturation coolant
temperature 230°C. The peak rating of
48 W/g in experiment 10 is almost 40% above
the prototype reference design SGHWR, and
comparable to that in some of the high
rated fuel experiments. This assembly had
reached 8500 MWd/t at the end of the 1964-
66 programme and irradiation is being
continued under the new programme. The
four failures comprise three weld failures
and one body failure. The reason for these
failures is not known with certainty, but
it is thought to be related to the reduced
saturation temperature and to the selection
of a can on the borderline of elastic
instability. There can be little doubt
that in the first three cases stressing of
the end caps has arisen from can/pellet
interaction under conditions in which a
brittle weld failure has resulted.

41. The condition of the brazed-on wear
pads after irradiations in NRX and Halden
has been excellent, Fig. 16. The braze
metal fillet has a grey appearance and
undergoes a little more corrosion than the
can, but the actual penetration is very
small. The H_2 concentration in the wear
pad is up to 50% greater than in the can,
presumably because of the lower temperature.
Specimens having brazed wear pads attached
have been irradiated in the Dounreay Fast
Reactor (DFR) to total neutron doses of
2.5x10^{22} without any noticeable effects on
micro-structure. Mechanical tests on
similar samples are being carried out.

Fuel element

42. The fuel element comprises the fuel
pins, centre tube/spacer grid assembly and
top and bottom support grids. No irradiation testing of complete elements has been
possible because of lack of suitable
facilities. The main features requiring
proving are the strength of the various
grids and their attachments, the resistance
to fretting corrosion at pin/grid contacts
and the thermal performance. The thermal
performance work is all carried out at
Winfrith and is described by Holmes et al.
(ref. 2).

43. A high pressure 2-phase loop is
installed in the Springfields Laboratories
for out-of-pile endurance testing of full
size fuel elements and is known as the
SWEL loop. A general view of this
facility is shown in Fig. 17. Endurance
tests in this loop, and in a similar
facility operated by Babcock & Wilcox at
Renfrew, have been used in arriving at the
present design. In addition, the strengths
of various competing spacer grid designs
have been compared on a weight basis by
simple mechanical tests, and by recipro-
cating pins through them in a high pressure

Table 7
Summary of experiments in Halden BWR

	Brief description	Peak pellet burn-up MWd/tU	
1.	Zr-2 clad pins and machined Zr-2 grids	3400*	These experiments used 5 pin assemblies having, except where otherwise noted, 0.018 in thick Zircaloy-2 cladding, brazed wear pads, and brazed S.S. grids.
2.	Ditto	3600	
3.	Ditto but Zr-Nb cladding	3800*	
4.	First wear padded design 4 pins clad Zr-Nb	2600*	
5.	1 pin Zr-Nb, 3 pins welded wear pads	6250	The operation conditions were:-
6.	4 pins Zr-4, 2 of them 0.015 thick cladding. One pin hollow pellets	8500*	Peak rating 39 w/g Peak surface heat flux 120 w/cm^2
7.	2 pins Zr-4	7150	
8.	1 pin Zr-Nb, 1 centre UO$_2$ thermocouple, 1 fission gas pressure transducer	5950	Peak $\int_{T_S}^{T_O} k(\theta)d\theta$ 40.3 w/cm
9.	End pellet variants and stack length indicators	860	
10.	3 pins hollow pellets, stack length indicators	8500	Peak rating - 48 w/g Surface heat flux - 150 w/cm^2 $\int k(\theta)d\theta$ - 50.3 w/cm
11.	3 pin assembly, Zr-2 clad U metal fuel	1800	Peak rating - 12 w/g Surface heat flux - 31 w/cm^2

*One pin failed

Fig. 17:   SWEL two-phase endurance test loop

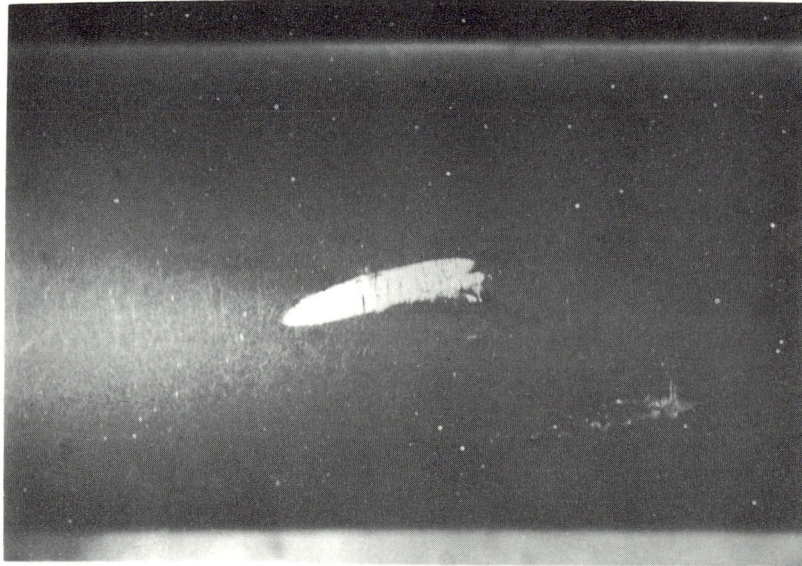

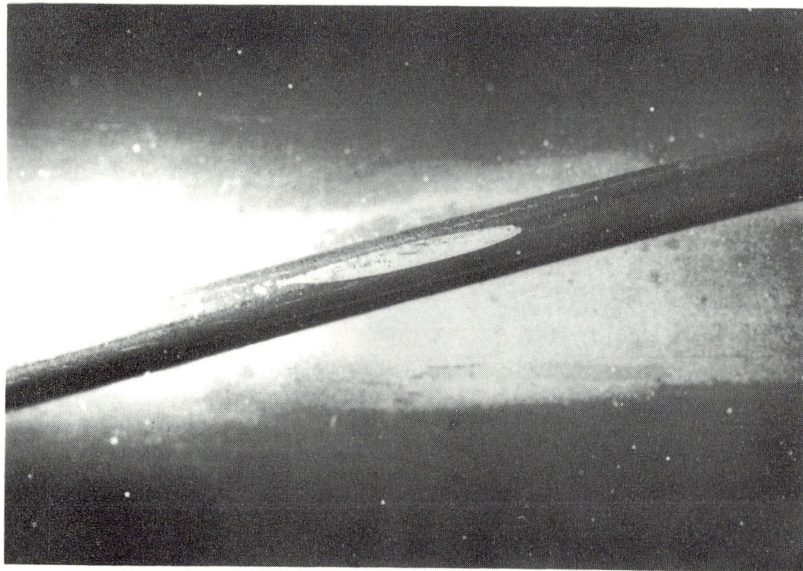

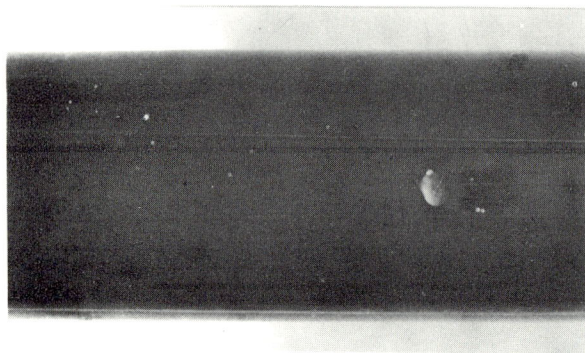

Fig. 18: Fretting produced during endurance tests.
Top: can body, wire wrap design
Centre: wire wrap
Bottom: can body, spring grid design

Fig. 19: Spacer grid and wear pads after 2000 hours endurance test.
Prototype design

autoclave. The grid made by brazing together stainless steel ferrules, when strengthened by the insertion of six radial arms, proved marginally better than two alternative machined grids.

44. The endurance loop testing procedure has been to test elements at the correct mass-velocity and exit voidage, pre-mixing circulated steam and water, for periods of about 2000 hours with preliminary examination after about 300 hours. The initial design with wire wrapped pins, externally banded together, gave considerable fretting at contact points between wires and cans. A later design with single cantilever springs, aimed at a nominal 2 lb load from each of four springs on a pin, also showed substantial amounts of fretting. This design concept was not ruled out completely, but it was preferred to base the reference design on a more positive principle for the present. Examples of fretting damage from these test series are shown in Fig. 18.

45. The present reference design has shown no evidence of any fretting damage on wear pads in tests up to 2000 hours. Early tests showed some distortion of grid ferrules and these were strengthened (thickness increased from 0.010 in (0.25 mm) to 0.013 in (0.33 mm) and radial arms inserted). The condition of some typical wear pads and a spacer grid, after such a test, is shown in Fig. 19.

46. Some difficulty was experienced in early tests with grids catching on minor protrusions in the charge path (which is a close simulation of that in the reactor) and being tilted. The external grid band was chamfered as a result and no further difficulty has been experienced.

47. Fuel pin and fuel element stability tests have been conducted both in air/water and freon loops, in the latter case under nucleate boiling conditions. These tests have all shown the fuel pins to be inherently very stable in the reference design, but have revealed some cluster vibration at about 7 c/s which is initiated by flow around the neutron scatter plug. An early type of twisted strip scatter plug was rejected because it set up torsional oscillations in the fuel; the current torpedo shaped plug can be stabilized by a device already developed, but this will not be applied to reactor fuel unless the instability proves to be damaging to fuel or pressure tubes.

MANUFACTURE

48. Manufacturing processes for SGHWR fuel were developed in the Reactor Group Laboratories at Springfields, and the first reactor charge was manufactured by Production Group, Springfields Works. All components except the UO_2 pellets were bought in from outside manufacturers against UKAEA designs and product specifications.

49. Fuel cladding was manufactured by tube reduction from extruded hollows and wear pads were attached by brazing. Fuel pins were made up using magnetic force resistance welding for end cap attachment and pins were then flash pickled and autoclaved (24 hours, $400^{\circ}C$ steam, 150 lb/in^2) in a vertical position. Final assembly was done by hand. The centre support tube is screwed and locked to the top and bottom support grids and intermediate spacer grids are attached by six rivets.

50. Stringent inspection is carried out on incoming cladding to control dimensions, freedom from defects, corrosion resistance, and mechanical properties. Wear pad braze fillets are visually inspected for freedom from blow holes and lack of wetting. Weld quality is assessed primarily by monitoring of machine operating parameters and secondly by visual examination. Radiography has not proved useful with this type of weld. Freedom from excessive interpellet gaps is determined by tight dimensional control with a check by gamma absorption. Autoclave film quality is assessed visually against a series of standards. The increased grain size in the heat affected zone extending over each set of wear pads results in a different appearance.

FUTURE DEVELOPMENT

Design

51. In order to maintain the present competitive status of SGHWR, fuel design developments must match those of other systems. This situation had been anticipated and an extensive irradiation programme on fuel design variants for both enriched and natural reactors has been included in the first charge, and in the experimental facilities in the reactor. The core channel, boosted channel and loop experiments are listed in Table 8.

52. Of major importance is the desirability of pushing fuel rating to its limit, taking full advantage of the results on dryout heat flux coming from the unique 9 MW heat transfer rig at Winfrith. Rating of the enriched design can be increased by over 30%, to a 5 MW channel, with only minor design changes to prevent can strain and gas release limits being exceeded. In the uprated experiments in boosted channels, the main design change is to increase can/pellet gap. In order to run similar experiments to higher burn-up, the gas plenum and UO_2 density must also be adjusted. Experiments are included on low density UO_2, and on the use of further increases in can pellet gap, as alternative means of extending burn-up without exceeding permissible can strain limits.

53. Several experiments are included in which can thickness is varied, 0.015 in (0.38 mm), 0.022 in (0.55 mm) and 0.030 in (0.57 mm) in core channels and 0.010 in (0.25 mm) in a small loop, and in

Table 8
Fuel element experiments in SGHWR

Number of clusters	Planned irradiation years	Object
Core channels in the first charge		
4	1, 2, 3 & 3	Behaviour of thin cladding in Zircaloy-2, Zircaloy-4 and Zr-Nb.
3	1, 2 & 3	Behaviour of Zircaloy-2, Zircaloy-4 and Zr-Nb. Includes some hollow pellets, and some electron-beam welded wear pads.
2	3 & 5	Assessment of larger fuel-can gap, and lower pellet density as a means of providing swelling accommodation.
3	1, 2 & 3	Behaviour of unground pellets with respect to fuel-cladding interactions.
3	1, 2 & 3	Comparison of projection welding wear pad attachment with the standard, induction-brazing method.
4	1 & 2	Behaviour of non-wear-padded designs using spring grids and machined grids.
2	1 & 3	Behaviour of vibro-compacted fuel.
3	5	Longer term behaviour of standard fuel.
5	1, 2 & 3	Use of knitmesh pellet to reduce axial strain on end welds.
2	3	Behaviour of internal autoclaving as a protection from fission gas attack.
8	1, 2, 3 & 5	Irradiation of specimens of zirconium alloys for measurements of corrosion and mechanical properties.
Replacement core channel		
8	3	Comparison of machined, and spring leaf, grid designs.
4	3	Ditto, but using thicker (0.030 in) cladding.
5	3	Ditto, but using thinner (0.015 in) cladding.
5	3	Intermediate grids at wider spacing (24 in).
Boosted channels		
2	1 & 2	Standard design operated at higher power.
2	1 & 2	Natural design.
Cluster loop		
2	1 month	Dry out experiment, one for detailed measurements, the other for continued core irradiation after a single dry-out transient.
1	½	Uprated natural design.
Pencil loops		
	½	Trefoil, testing features of natural designs (0.010 in cladding).
	½	Short pins with high density fuel.
		U_3Si defect tests.
		Trefoil dryout tests.

which the performance of alternative alloys, such as Zircaloy-4 and Zr-2½ ^{W}/oNb, will be studied. The aim of such experiments is to better understand design limits for future exploitation.

54. In addition to the spacer grid arrangement selected for SGHWR, alternatives, including a spring grid based on well tried BWR and PWR principles, are being tested. Axial separation of spacer grids will also be varied, since wider separation leads to a useful saving in fuel cost.

55. It is believed that in the future vibro-compacted UO_2 fuels may show some advantages over pelleted UO_2, both functional, e.g., minimizing or preventing circumferential ridge formation, and in terms of fuel cost. This may apply particularly in cases where UO_2 pellet density has to be reduced to around 90% theoretical density to avoid swelling limits at high burn-up. In view of this, assemblies of vibro-compacted UO_2 are included in the first charge and will be taken to a peak burn-up of about 30,000 MWd/tU.

56. Although the general arguments on which the full core length pins in SGHWR were adopted still apply, flux shaping considerations may lead to some advantage for designs in which the pins are half-core length with gas plena at their outboard ends. Such a design, incorporating a central tie-rod, is being produced for early irradiation proving.

57. Extension of design outside the 37-rod geometry, or to different pin spacing layouts, e.g., hexagonal pitch, have been considered and will be the subject of future studies aimed at improved utilization of the coolant. Differential enrichment within the cluster is also being assessed by heat transfer experiments. It seems likely that the various possibilities for increasing channel power now showing promise will inevitably lead to some reduction in fuel pin diameter. The next natural configuration is 61-rods, but possible intermediates exist which must be assessed. Alternatively, a reduction in bundle diameter with 37-rods will be assessed.

58. Pilot design and manufacturing studies have been carried out on nested tubes and tube-in-shell type assemblies, but the immediate aim will be to fully exploit the rod cluster before turning to serious assessment of such major changes which currently show no obvious advantage.

Manufacture

59. Future manufacturing development will have the twin aims of improving the integrity of fuel pin containment and cheapening components, assembly processes and inspection.

60. In the former category, cladding manufacturing processes will be further developed with the object of improving mechanical properties and corrosion resis-

tance. Of particular importance are resistance of stress induced re-orientation of hydrides, creep strength and rupture ductility. Any development which can lead to a major reduction in hydrogen pick-up will also be of importance.

61. The present magnetic force resistance welding process appears to be basically most satisfactory, but it has limits of application to thin cladding. Some developments of the process are in hand at the present time aimed at extending its use and at detailed improvements in weld design.

62. In the field of component manufacture, spacer grids have been made in small numbers by tape controlled machining. This process is competing with improved brazing techniques as the most economic for future manufacture.

63. Reference was made earlier to proof testing procedure and its present role. It is probable that there will be a change in procedure, or that pickling and autoclaving will eventually be dispensed with altogether. This will have the effect of reducing the initial H_2 content of fuel cladding and eliminating pickling losses.

Materials

64. The most important area of materials development for the future is that of improved cladding alloys. UKAEA work is concentrated on cladding alloys suitable for higher temperature service, since these show some promise of permitting operation with reduced margins, i.e., with a higher probability of hot spots occurring due to local peaking or under faults such as a circulator outage. The alloys being studied are based on the Zr Cr Fe alloy developed by Klepfer and the Russian oshennite-0.5 alloy, both of which show promise for service at $400^{\circ}C$ or at higher temperatures for short periods of time (refs 16, 17).

65. Work is also proceeding on alloys for improved creep resistance, including dispersion hardening, which is expected to make an important contribution to fuel for operation under onerous power cycling conditions. Irradiations under such conditions have started and it is proposed to add further in-reactor facilities for more extensive tests.

66. Materials for manufacture of the brazed spacer grid and capable of being precipitation hardened after the brazing operation are under consideration. Such alloys could result in stronger grids for the same neutron absorption, or grids of lower absorption. Spring materials for spring spacer grids are being surveyed to find the most suitable alloy. Springs in grids made for the first charge experiment were in Nimonic PE16.

67. No change from UO_2 as a fuel for the enriched SGHWR is contemplated, but improvements are expected, particularly with res-

pect to gas release, swelling and plasticity. Attempts to improve thermal conductivity, potentially a most beneficial improvement, have so far been disappointing, but further work in this field will be pursued.

ACKNOWLEDGEMENTS

68. This paper is published by kind permission of the Managing Director, the Reactor Group, UKAEA, Risley. Thanks are due to the many colleagues at Springfields, Windscale and Risley responsible for the work reported, and especially to Mr. D.H. Willey for his assistance in preparing the paper and to Mr. J.A.G. Holmes for helpful comments and criticisms.

REFERENCES

1. HICKS D., JOHNSTONE I and O'DELL P. Nuclear design. BNES International Conference on Steam Generating and Other Heavy Water Reactors, May, 1968, Paper 4.

2. HOLMES J.A.G., OBERTELLI J.D. and ROBERTS H.A. BNES International Conference on Steam Generating and Other Heavy Water Reactors, May 1968, Paper 5.

3. DUNCAN R.N. Stainless steel failure investigation programme, 1966. Quarterly Report No. 6, GEAP 5281.

4. PASHOS T.J., WILLIAMSON H.E. and DUNCAN R.N. Fuel performance in boiling water reactors. Nuclear Applications, 1966, 2(Dec), 510.

5. NOTLEY M.J.F. and LANE A.D. Factors affecting the design of rodded UO_2 fuel bundles for high power outputs. IAEA Symposium on Heavy Water Reactors, Vienna, September 1967, Paper SM-99/35.

6. DANIEL R.C., BLEIBERG M.L., MEIERAM H.B. and YENISCAVICH W. Effects of high burn-up on Zircaloy clad bulk UO_2 plate fuel element samples. 1962, WAPD-263.

7. SLATTERY G.F. The prediction of collapse pressures for anisotropic Zircaloy-2 tubing using tensile stress-strain data. UKAEA Report 1966, TRG 1476(S).

8. HINDLE E.D. and SLATTERY G.F. The influence of processing variables on the grain structure and hydride orientation in Zircaloy-2 tubing. J. Inst. Metals, 1966, 94,.245.

9. HINDLE E.D. and SLATTERY G.F. Preferred orientation in Zircaloy-2 tubing manufactured by various routes. J. Inst. Metals, 1964/65, 93, 565.

10. SLATTERY G.F. The terminal solubility of hydrogen in zirconium alloys between $30^{\circ}C$ and $400^{\circ}C$. J. Inst. Metals, 1967, 95, 43.

11. PARRY G.W. and EVANS W. Occurrence of ductile hydride in Zircaloy-2. Nucleonics, 1964,22(11)65.

12. ALLEN P.L., MOORE D.A. and TROWSE F.W. The relation of proof testing to long term corrosion behaviour of zirconium alloys. UKAEA Report, 1966, TRG 1134(S).

13. SCHEMEL J.H. New heat treatment cuts Zircaloy-2 corrosion, hydrogen embrittlement. Nucleonics, 1963, 21(11), 70.

14. NICHOLS R.W. BNES International Conference on Steam Generating and Other Heavy Water Reactors, May 1968, Paper 8.

15. PAGE R.D. Engineering and performance of Canada's UO_2 fuel assemblies for heavy water power reactors. IAEA Symposium on Heavy Water Power Reactors, Vienna, September 1967, Paper SM-99/48.

16. KLEPFER H.H. Specific zirconium alloy design programme. Summary Report, 1964 (May), EURAC/GEAP 4504.

17. AMBARTSUMYAN R.S., KISELEV A.A., GREBENNIKOV R.V., MYSHKIN V.A., TSUPRUN L.J. and MIKULINA A.F. Mechanical properties and corrosion resistance of zirconium and its alloys in water, steam and gases at high temperatures. A/CONF., 15/P/2044 (1958).

Session A : Discussion

PAPER 1

Mr P.H. Margen, AB Atomenergi, Stockholm

1.   Past UK policy seems to have been to
consider the AGR as the unit for large outputs and the SGHWR as that for small outputs. However, the <u>marginal</u> cost (i.e.,
cost increase resulting from increase in
output/increase in output) with increasing
unit size is dominated by the fuel cycle
cost component: reactors with low fuel
cycle costs tend to attain their strongest
competitive position at large outputs.
HWRs (particularly variants with D_2O
coolant, but to some extent even SGHWRs)
have lower fuel cycle costs than AGRs or
LWRs. Hence they should be preferred for
large outputs. I notice that more mention
has been made at this conference of SGHWRs
for large outputs than has been the case
in the past. Does this indicate a change
in UK policy?

2.   HWRs (particularly natural uranium
variants with D_2O coolant) have a Pu
production higher than LWRs and much higher
than AGRs and HTRs per kWh generated.
Countries such as the UK which have a very
strong development programme on fast
breeder reactors will need vast quantities
of Pu if they are to reap the benefits of
their development efforts by a rapid introduction of fast breeder reactors and the
export of these to other countries. To
what extent will the effect of this be
taken into consideration in the choice of
convertor reactors for the coming UK
stations, e.g., the choice between the
SGHWR and those which produce less Pu?

Authors' reply: Paper 1

3.   Our ideas for commercial SGHWRs were
initially centred round the 300-400 MWe
size. Paper 2 describes some aspects of
the commercial designs quoting 500 MWe or
even greater. Mr. Booth in his opening
address has said that the CEGB are considering the possibility of including the
SGHWR in their network and I am sure that
in this connection they will wish to consider units larger than 500 MWe.

4.   In reply to Mr Margen's second point,
plutonium production is a matter which is
taken into account when assessing reactors,
and selection of reactor systems to fit

into the network. It comes about in two
ways: first a price for the plutonium
credit of the reject fuel must be assumed;
then the build-up of the reactor installation programme must be considered. I would
expect this factor to be taken into account
when assessing the overall strategy relating to thermal reactors versus fast
reactors.

PAPER 2

Mr H.M. Carruthers, Central Electricity
Generating Board

5.   Mr Bradley emphasizes the relative
simplicity of extrapolating from the prototype to larger sizes of SGHWR: I think it
would be of general interest if he could
say something of the need for spatial
control in larger reactors, and of how this
might be achieved.

Mr J.C. Bennett, Atomic Power
Construction Ltd

6.   My first question is about the construction of the calandria and the different alternatives illustrated in Fig. 9A
of the Paper. The Authors refer to site
problems and the limitations imposed by
transport. Does site welding of a calandria for this application require site
procedures outside the range of normal
practice? What is the setting up required?
Is there a need for training of welders and
control of the operation? What are the
inspection and leak testing requirements?
Are special requirements imposed by the
nature of the material and geometry, by the
need for very high pitch accuracy, or by
any effects arising during service?

7.   My second question concerns the refuelling arrangements illustrated in the
1500 MW(th) reactor illustrated in Fig. 13.
The new fuel and the irradiated fuel for
disposal use the same route, which appears
to be contrary to accepted practice on most
other nuclear stations. Does this raise
any question concerning contamination of
new fuel entering the reactor? Would
damaged fuel elements be discharged through
the same route? Will the design impose
purification or filtration requirements on
the pond water beyond those which exist for
segregated routes?

Mr A. Forbes Gower, Central Electricity Generating Board

8. Could the Authors say who imposes the 15 ft transport limitation on components? Has the use of special transporters such as the CEGB's hover cushion transporter for moving heavy transformers, been considered?

9. Perhaps they could also indicate why old fuel is to be removed in a transporter during the refuelling operations. There seems no reason for not doing this either a month earlier or a month later when the two teams would not risk getting in each other's way.

Mr P.G. Boiron, Groupement Atomique Alsacienne Atlantique

10. I would like to ask the Authors a question concerning the design of the neutron shield. In association with the German firm Interatom and the Italian firm Montecatini Edison my company are studying an organic cooled heavy water moderated station of about 250 MW gross electric power for the Euratom ORGEL prototype concourse. We consider that for any type of reactor it is important to be able to repair everything both during erection and after the start of operating the irradiated core. From this point of view the situation is not generally as good for D_2O reactors as for light water reactors. For this reason we have chosen an alternative solution for the thermal shield design. In our project this is provided by a cylindrical water pool in which the reactor vessel is mounted. This gives additional advantages:

    (a)   the construction is very simple;

    (b)   there is no transportation problem for the pool, which is site-welded;

    (c)   the reactor vessel is cooled during all operating conditions;

    (d)   it is possible to position the ionization chambers easily and to modify their position if necessary.

I would therefore like to know if it is possible to repair defects in the thermal shield in the SGHWR concept.

Authors' reply: Paper 2

11. Mr Carruthers is correct in his suggestion that there is an instability problem with reactors in the 300-500 MWe range. This can easily be corrected by very small amounts of reactivity variation in the three 120° sectors of the core. This is done by varying the level in the three sectors relative to one another by changing the helium blanket pressure. Fig. A1 shows diagrammatically how this is achieved. Dividing curtains are installed at the top of the calandria so that different helium pressures can be applied in the different zones. This requires only a

small change in the calandria design and control valve equipment in the existing helium system.

12. The latest development in this direction is to use a number of gas control rods dispersed throughout the core. These would be coupled together in the three zones to permit automatic spatial instability control. Hand control of individual rods is also provided to give the flux shaping over the core and to improve the radial form factor. Neither method introduces any safety problems because of the low reactivity content involved. Both methods are fairly straightforward from the point of view of engineering, design and manufacture.

13. Concerning Mr Bennett's questions, the site work involved in welding the two modules of the calandria together is very small, as only a seal weld joining the two halves is required; for this we would import a factory welder. To fabricate the calandria itself on site would be possible but very undesirable as it would virtually involve setting up a factory at the site. While this has been done on many current reactor systems we are trying to achieve the complete opposite for this system. There is no difficulty in making the calandria in the factory and we have found that with the method of construction adopted, the tolerances achieved were to a higher degree of accuracy than those specified.

14. On his second question, in the refuelling scheme described in Fig. 13 of the Paper, the new fuel uses the old fuel discharge route only after fuel is inserted into the pond. Since this water is common with the core water during refuelling there is little purpose in trying to segregate new and old fuel from this point onwards. The system resembles that in a gas cooled reactor where new fuel is put into the refuelling machine which has previously contained defective or old fuel. When defective fuel is withdrawn from the core it is immediately put into a tube which is sealed. The tube is then handled in the same manner as an old fuel element which is not defective. Old fuel leaves the pond in the fuel transport flask, and while this has slight contamination from pond water, American experience shows that this is not likely to present any difficulty in local site handling.

15. The quality of the pond water has to be kept very high in order to give viewing during the refuelling procedure. The standards on the prototype reactor are very good and we have so far had no difficulty in achieving this requirement. Our chemical advisers say that the quality we obtain is adequate for reactor purposes during the shutdown period or at low power operation. At full power, the water quality would need to be improved somewhat, but this can easily be done by coupling the pond clean-up plant into the reactor circuit to polish up the reactor water. There is no general circulation of water from the pond to the reactor core during the re-

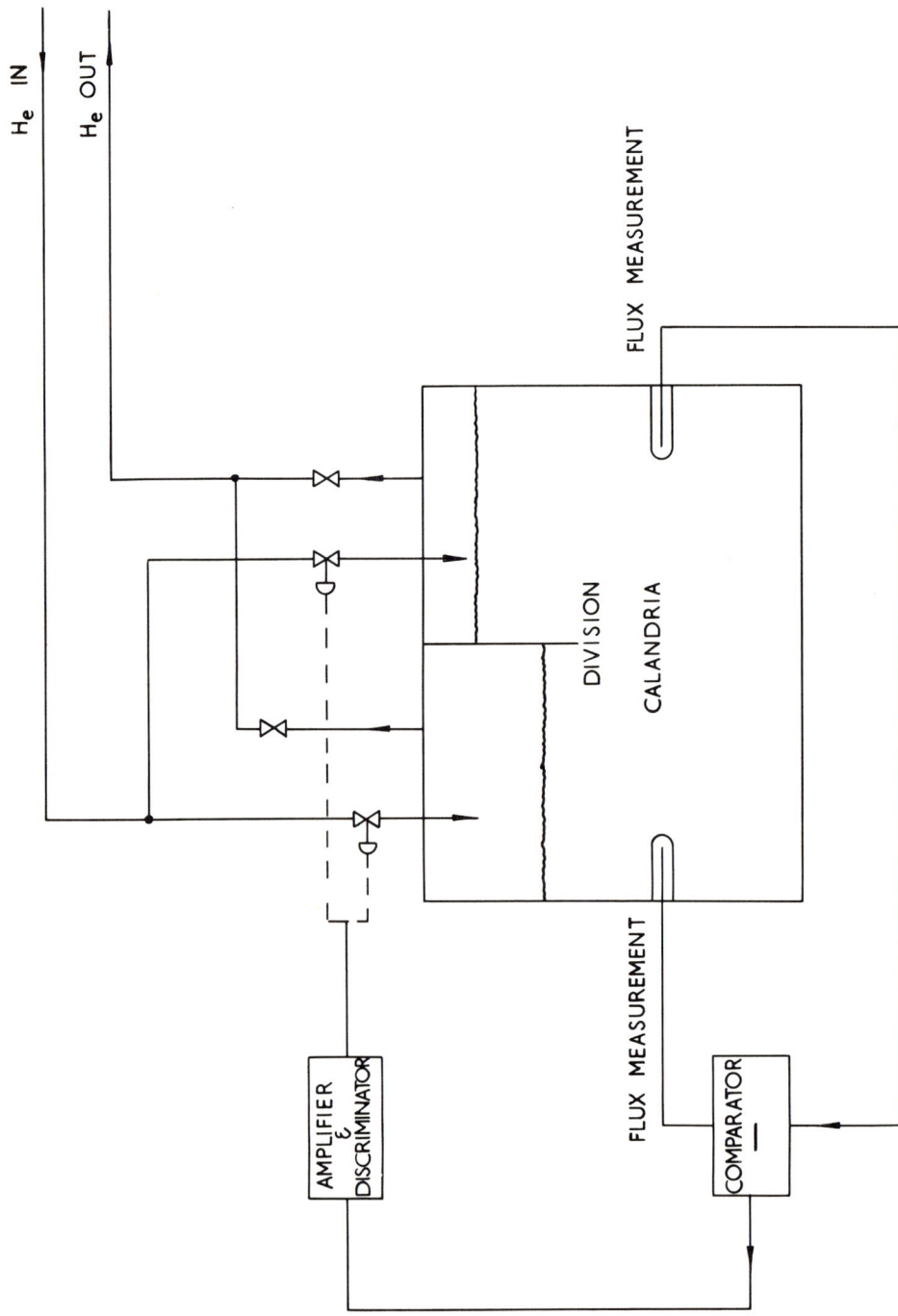

Fig. Al. Spatial control

56

fuelling operation, the core being separately cooled during this period. Only small quantities of pond water are likely to find their way into the core.

16. In response to Mr Forbes Gower, the road transport limitations are very difficult to pin down, and it is usually necessary to give a specific problem before they can be accurately determined, since each site has to be surveyed. We therefore adopted ourselves a 15 ft wide limitation as being a figure that could normally be met under most circumstances. The CEGB methods of transport have been considered, but the problem of transport is basically one of bulk rather than weight, except for the neutron shields. In the case of the calandria, once the site is known, providing the overall diameter will allow the component to be transported as a whole, we should certainly consider building it as one complete unit, although this would involve investigating different equipment for machining the vessel due to its larger size. It is quite possible that this alone would deter us from making it as one unit even if it could be transported.

17. The need to remove the spent fuel from the fuel pond at the same time as refuelling arises because with the scheme shown in Fig. 13 there is no access to the containment building while the plant is in operation. With other forms of containment which have been investigated it is possible to carry out the handling of old fuel from the site independent of the actual fuel changing.

18. With regard to Mr Boiron's remarks, the neutron shields are designed and constructed so that they are extremely robust and under low pressure. The water is dosed to inhibit corrosion. We do not therefore make any special provision for repairing them. In the case of the calandria there is provision for replacing the thinnest section - the calandria tube itself. The remainder of the vessel is extremely thick in section and no provision is made for replacement. During the latter phases of the construction of the SGHWR prototype it was found that some corrosive substance had been introduced into the calandria by persons unknown. The repair involved cutting a hole through the neutron shields into the calandria. Access inside the calandria was practical and several sections which had been badly corroded were removed and repaired. As a result of this experience provision will probably be made on future designs for access up to completion of the construction stage but not beyond that time. During flights of fancy we have studied what would be needed to rebuild the core completely, and while this is practical, the probability of such a requirement is so small that it has never been treated seriously.

PAPER 3

Mr L.M. Wyatt, Central Electricity Generating Board

19. One major advantage claimed for the SGHWR reactor is its suitability for load following. This would, of course, involve a considerable amount of power cycling in the fuel elements. Could the Author say how much data are available on this point, and what is the maximum number and amplitude of the cycles which have been withstood by fuel under irradiation?

Mr A. Forbes Gower, Central Electricity Generating Board

20. Fabrication costs are three or four times greater with steel pin bundles than for Magnox fuel. Has the use of extruded Zr finned fuel cans, together with larger diameter pins, been considered?

Mr E.F. Masters, Messrs Preece, Cardew and Rider

21. The maximum can temperature has not been specified. Is there a figure above which it is not advisable to go?

Authors' reply: Paper 3

22. We believe that the fuel is good in a power cycling role. Experience with fuel undergoing one or more major cycles per day is limited to about 100 cycles. A major cycle in this context is defined by the fuel shrinking away from the cladding by an amount such that 'can creep-down' is not limited by the UO_2. Typically this occurs in SGHWR fuel at a power reduction of about 25%. Greater power reductions therefore have no additional effect. During the period of low power operation the can creeps down by a finite amount and the strain is reversed when fuel power is restored. Extensive theoretical studies have been made and it is concluded that one major cycle per day during the fuel life will exhaust something less than 1% of the available fatigue endurance of the cladding. The conclusion is that the standard design of fuel has excellent prospects of meeting any likely load following requirement of utilities. To confirm these predictions it is proposed to introduce a regular daily power cycle of the SGHW reactor, and further to install special power cycling rigs in a small number of reactor channels.

23. In reply to Mr Forbes Gower, if the present pin diameters are increased substantially, the fuel centre temperatures will increase to the melting point of the UO_2. We regard centre temperature as being a limit at the moment. In the future, some centre melting may be permitted, but this does introduce new problems and requires initial testing on an experimental basis. In a film boiling regime the heat transfer is good and there is no advantage in having finned surfaces, which would hardly effect the normal can temperatures. In the event of a dryout excursion, finned surfaces would have a beneficial effect in reducing

can temperature, but unfortunately the
heat transfer coefficient is low and can
temperature would be greatly in excess of
that permissible in operation.

24. Mr Masters asks for the limit on the
maximum fuel can temperature. Normally
this is little affected by the life or
rating of the fuel. It can only change
significantly by oxidation of the zirconium
or by the deposition of crud. In steady
state operation, having set the reactor
pressure and therefore the saturation temperature of the coolant, the can surface
temperature follows from this. The surface
temperatures of cans are about 304°C and
are very far from the limits of the
material. It is common, for instance to
operate Zircaloy-2 at surface temperatures
up to 360°C. I do not consider that can
temperature is ever likely to be a limit in
this type of saturated reactor.

Nuclear design of SGHWRs

D. HICKS, MA, DPhil, UKAEA, Winfrith

I. JOHNSTONE, BSc, UKAEA, Winfrith

F. P. O'DELL, BSc, UKAEA, Risley

SYNOPSIS   The factors influencing the choice of lattice design parameters are reviewed. It is shown by comparison with experimental data from zero energy assemblies that the interplay of these parameters is well understood and that in particular the coolant void coefficient of reactivity can be predicted accurately. The representation of the complete core of the Winfrith SGHWR is discussed and it is shown that the validity of the techniques used have been experimentally demonstrated. Finally the nuclear design aspects of larger SGHWRs including those designed for operation with natural uranium fuel are reviewed.

INTRODUCTION

Scope

1.   The object of this paper is to review the nuclear performance aspects of SGHWRs from the point of view of reactor design. There are three main areas to consider, namely, the choice of lattice parameters to give appropriate reactivity characteristics, the choice of a core loading pattern to give an acceptable power distribution, and the interactions which occur between the nuclear and thermal-hydraulic performance due to the presence of steam voids. A fourth topic, i.e., the question of the fuel replacement strategy forms a subject in itself and is dealt with in a separate paper (ref. 1).

Approach to performance problems

2.   In the early days of the SGHWR project it was realized that the nuclear performance of the reactor would be dominated by the choice of lattice parameters. Since the parasitic absorption present in the structural materials tends to be fixed by asking the mechanical designer to minimize his requirements, the nuclear designer has essentially three main parameters at his disposal:

  (a) H_2O/UO_2 volume ratio;

  (b) D_2O/UO_2 volume ratio;

  (c)   enrichment level.

These had to be chosen to achieve an acceptable economic performance and to result in a steam void reactivity coefficient compatible with the limitations set by control system design and fault transient analysis.

3.   A first essential was, therefore, to develop a lattice physics model which would

trace the influence of the main parameters and in particular provide a good estimate of the void coefficient of reactivity. The model was embodied in the METHUSELAH code and descriptions have already appeared in the literature (refs 2, 3).

4.   In order to optimize overall design, it was necessary to combine the METHUSELAH predictions with estimates of U-235 enrichment costs, D_2O inventory charges, thermal performance limitations and plant costs. This led to the LIMBO code which was developed as a direct aid to the design office.

5.   Later in the project after the main parameters had been fixed it was necessary to build up a detailed picture of the expected performance tracing the interactions between the nuclear and thermal hydraulic aspects. This led to the development of the PATRIARCH scheme (see Fig. 1) of computer codes which forms a set of modular compatible programmes designed to cover all performance aspects. It was of course necessary to relate the development of PATRIARCH very closely to the flow of data arising from the experimental reactor physics programme and from the thermal and hydraulic rigs (ref. 4).

LATTICE PHYSICS

Methods development

6.   Reference has already been made to the METHUSELAH code which has formed the basis for SGHWR nuclear design. The code uses a five-group model of the neutron physics and relies on an extensive library of effective group cross sections deduced from nuclear data. The first version came into operation towards the end of 1961 (refs 2, 5). Some revisions of the nuclear data libraries and improvements in the representation of the thermal spectrum were

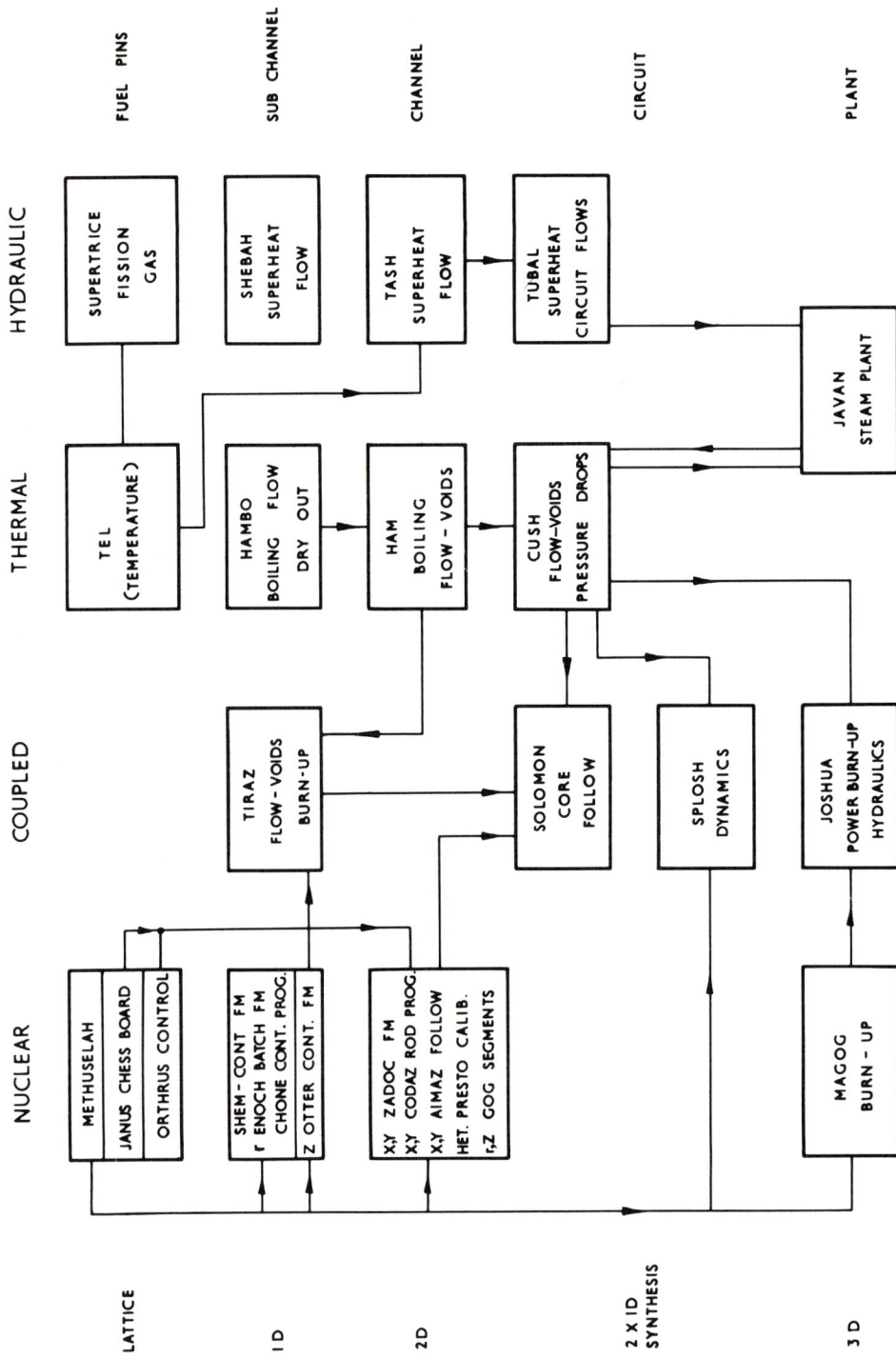

Fig. 1: Patriarch

60

included in the Mk. II version which was introduced in 1964 (refs 3, 6). At the present time, a Mk. III version containing further data revisions, particularly in the treatment of fission product poisons, and many extra facilities linking it to other modules of the PATRIARCH scheme is coming into service.

Survey calculations and parameter choices

7. As soon as the METHUSELAH code became available, survey calculations were undertaken to determine the lattice parameters for an SGHWR. The objectives were mainly:

(a) to achieve a design with a void coefficient of reactivity which would be slightly negative;

(b) to balance D_2O inventory charges against U-235 enrichment costs to give an acceptable economic compromise.

It was found that designs with volume ratios

$$H_2O/UO_2 \simeq 1$$
$$D_2O/UO_2 \simeq 7$$

would satisfy both criteria and would need enrichment levels of about 2% to give economically attractive burn-ups ($\sim$20,000 MWd/TeU) in large commercial reactors.

8. Within this broad generalization, it was found that the actual magnitude of the void coefficient depends in an extremely complicated way on the detailed design of the fuel element and lattice structure, the enrichment level, the degree of burn-up and the concentration of boron poison dissolved in the moderator (ref. 7). Whilst it was recognized that a good deal of these uncertainties could be removed by zero energy experimentation, it was decided to provide for contingencies in the design of the Winfrith SGHWR. The control system was, therefore, designed to operate with a range of void coefficients

$$- 0.02 < K_V \leqslant + 0.02$$

where $K_V = \left(\dfrac{dk}{k}\right)\Big/\left(\dfrac{d\rho}{\rho}\right)$

k = effective reproduction factor

ρ = coolant density.

An array of so-called moderator displacement or interlattice tubes located between the pressure tubes within the calandria were provided. These tubes could be emptied if necessary to bring an excessively positive void coefficient into the desired range. An excessively negative void coefficient could be corrected by increasing the H_2O impurity in the D_2O moderator. In the event, the calculations of void coefficients have proved to be very accurate and it has not been necessary to resort to either of these measures. Interlattice

tubes are not, therefore, included in current reactor designs.

9. It is not appropriate here to describe in detail the optimization studies which led to the final choice of lattice parameters. Considerations of dryout heat fluxes, centre temperature limitations and fuel pin fabrication costs fixed the fuel pellet size at 0.57 in (14.5 mm). An examination of the savings achieved by using fewer larger pressure tubes suggested that a 37-rod configuration (with 36 fuelled pins) would be appropriate. Thus, with a suitable allowance for clearances the pressure tube internal diameter came out at 5.14 in (130.6 mm). The D_2O/UO_2 volume ratio requirement then fixed the lattice pitch at about 10.25 in (260 mm) which was acceptable on engineering grounds. This outline is of course a gross simplification of the process of optimization but it indicates the broad pattern.

Lattice parameter experiments

10. Although some testing of the calculation methods was undertaken against published data for other systems using either heavy or light water moderators none of this was directly relevant to the geometrically complex two-moderator SGHW system where about 30% of the moderation occurs in the light water coolant (ref. 5). A special programme of experiments using both critical and sub-critical assemblies was therefore initiated at Winfrith. A detailed description of the first phases has already appeared and they will only be reviewed in outline here (ref. 8). These early experiments made use of available fuels which had originally been fabricated for other purposes. The UO_2 pellets covered the enrichment range 0.91-1.78% U-235, pellet diameters from 0.3-0.5 in (7.6 mm to 12.7 mm) and were arranged in clusters containing between 37 and 90 fuel pencils. The main objectives were as follows:

(1) to provide a basis for the estimation of reactivity levels in SGHWR type lattices to an accuracy of $\pm$1% or better;

(2) to measure sufficient isotopic reaction rates to check the details of the theoretical picture and ensure that overall agreement was not fortuitous;

(3) to measure void coefficients of reactivity and ensure that predictions could be made to an accuracy significantly better than the control system tolerance. This implies an accuracy of say $\pm$0.01 in predictions of K_V;

(4) to check that power distributions over the large enriched rod clusters could be calculated to the accuracy ($\sim$5%) required in thermal design calculations.

Table 1
Average discrepancies between METHUSELAH II and experiment in regular cluster lattices

Parameters	Coolants	No. of lattices studied	METHUSELAH II - Expt. % Expt.	
k-effective (sub-critical cores)	AIR	6	+2.10	±0.44
	MIXTURE	4	±0.51	±0.35
	WATER	6	+0.07	±0.57
k-effective (critical cores)	MIXTURE	7	+0.01	±0.89
	WATER	4	-0.24	±1.35
U-238/U-235 fast fission ratio (FR)	AIR	4	-4.30	±4.1
	MIXTURE	6	+0.80	±2.0
	WATER	9	0.00	±2.8
Relative conversion ratio (RCR)	AIR	4	-1.80	±0.70
	MIXTURE	7	-1.20	±1.98
	WATER	9	-0.60	±0.53
Maximum/average manganese reaction rate	AIR	4	+0.30	±1.24
	MIXTURE	8	+1.20	±1.83
	WATER	11	+1.90	±3.18
Maximum/average U-235 fission rate	MIXTURE	4	+4.30	±1.53
	WATER	3	+6.00	±0.42
Normalized Pu/U fission rate	MIXTURE	8	+2.10	±0.97
	WATER	9	-1.40	±1.78

Table 2
Effect of plutonium build-up on reactivity and void coefficient predictions

Lattice reference	% Pu fissions	Predicted K_{eff} H_2O METH II	METH III	K_V Calculated	Measured	
SG19	0	1.003	0.999	+0.009	+0.007	±0.002
SGP1	30	1.001	1.000	+0.007	+0.006	±0.002
SGP2	70	0.990	0.995	-0.006	-0.007	±0.005

11. A summary of the principal results is included in Table 1. In order to provide data on void coefficients the experiments were conducted with coolants with different slowing down powers; these were air, (light) water and 'mixture', the latter being a mixture of light and heavy water with an effective slowing down power equivalent to boiling light water with a density in the range 0.4-0.6 g/cm^3.

12. In general, the errors are seen to be small. In the rather extreme case of the air 'coolant', leakage and streaming account for some 20% of the neutrons in a typical experimental core although this effect would be much less in a large power reactor. In high leakage situations, METHUSELAH II tends to overestimate the reactivity of the cores with air 'coolant' but, in the more representative liquid cooled cores, it predicts k-effective to within $\pm\frac{1}{2}$%. The small magnitudes of the discrepancies between the measured and predicted reaction rates in the fast, resonance and thermal energy regions demonstrate that this excellent agreement does not arise from a number of cancelling errors. This point is further demonstrated by the success obtained in the prediction of the void co-efficient, which is a delicate balance of positive and negative effects. The average discrepancy between METHUSELAH II and experiment for integral void coefficients found by differencing corresponding WATER and MIXTURE coolant eigenvalues is

$$K_v = +0.003 \pm 0.003$$

which implies an accuracy of calculation well within the control system tolerances. The objectives of the first series of lattice experiments were therefore all attained and there was a corresponding degree of confidence in the selection of lattice parameters for the Winfrith SGHWR.

Experiments with plutonium bearing fuels

13. The predictions for power reactor performance required an assessment of the effects of burn-up on lattice properties, particularly the effect of plutonium build-up. Although application of the METHUSELAH code to burn-up data from other reactors showed an encouraging measure of agreement the special complexities of the SGHWR again suggested that it would be prudent to mount an experimental programme to explore the effects of plutonium build-up (ref. 9).

14. Three sets of critical experiments were conducted with identical lattice geometry but with fuels ranging from 1.35% UO$_2$ to a PuO$_2$/UO$_2$ mixture in which 70% of the fissions occurred in the plutonium. This work showed that, as pre-dicted, the void coefficient became rather more negative with plutonium build-up. This is because the large thermal cross section of Pu-239 reduces the importance of the thermal utilization perturbation due to coolant voiding. The plutonium experiments also demonstrated the advantage of changing the value of the Pu-239 2000 m/s η built

into the METHUSELAH II library from the old 'World Consistent Set' value of 2.091 to the higher value emerging from more recent studies under the auspices of the IAEA which is used in METHUSELAH III (ref. 10). A fuller discussion will be found elsewhere, the main results are summarized in Table 2.

NUCLEAR DESIGN OF THE WINFRITH SGHWR

Core layout

15. It has been shown that the basic parameters for SGHWR lattices were fixed by arguments which are rather independent of reactor size. In order to generate the 100 MW(e) required of the Winfrith reactor, the core layout shown in Fig. 2 was adopted. The 104 boiling channels are fuelled with 3 basic fuel enrichments in a manner described in another paper on fuel manage-ment (ref. 1). Irregularities in the basic scheme are introduced by the presence of irradiation experiments (ref. 11).

16. In addition to the standard boiling channels, the core contains superheat channel positions, liquid shutdown tubes, two small irradiation loops and the moderator displacer tubes for void coef-ficient control.

17. All the features listed above had to be represented in the nuclear design analysis. It was clear at the outset that particular attention would have to be devoted to the problem of core representa-tion if the overall objectives of pre-dicting reactivity levels and void coef-ficients accurately, as already achieved in simple lattices, were still to be attained in the actual reactor core. Moreover, there was the problem of predicting the power distribution to an accuracy of about 5% of the peak value in order to satisfy the requirements of thermal hydraulic design.

Core representation models

18. The problems presented in achieving an overall picture of the nuclear performance of SGHWR cores were tackled in three ways:

(i) special computer codes for rapid calculations using coarse mesh, 2-group homogeneous reactor theory were produced, special emphasis being placed on the ability to represent burn-up changes;

(ii) the application of the source-sink heterogeneous formalism to SGHWRs was considered;

(iii) since any workable design scheme seemed likely to involve approximations of uncertain validity, a series of critical experiments representing specific situations of interest was undertaken.

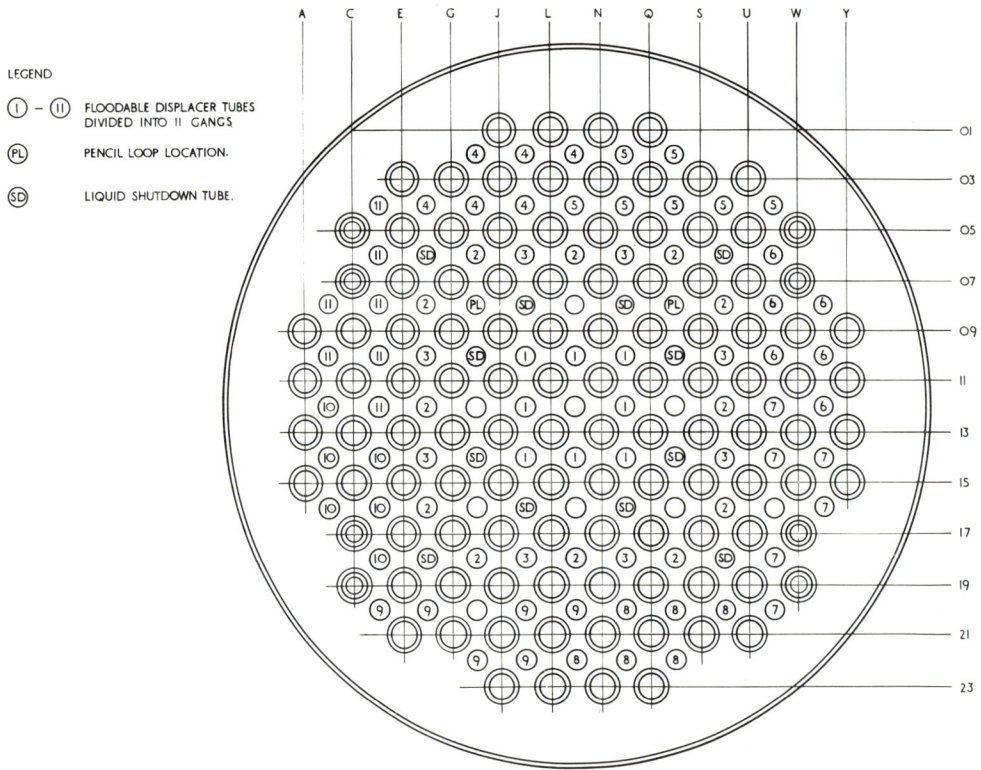

Fig. 2: Core layout Winfrith reactor

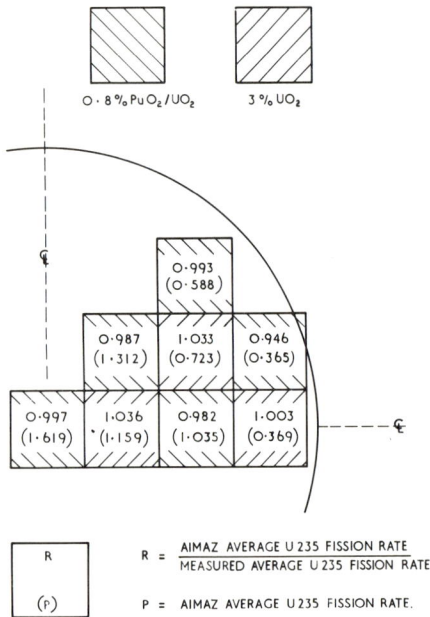

Fig. 3: Typical power distribution in JUNO core

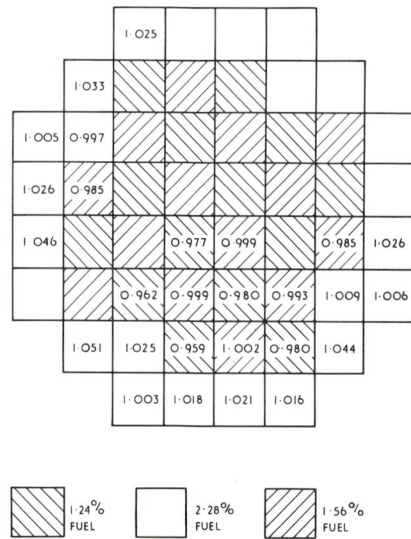

Fig. 4: SGHWR core mock-up power distribution

19. The developments of coarse mesh homogeneous theory were begun with the ZADOC code (ref. 12). It was found that, if two mesh lengths per cell side were used to represent the reactor, the truncation errors compared with using larger numbers of mesh points produced only small discrepancies of 2-3% in the power predictions for channels on the core periphery. Two mesh lengths per cell side also splits the lattice cell into quadrants and so provides a convenient framework for the assignment of modified group cross sections representing the presence of interlattice perturbations.

20. In addition to the adoption of a two mesh lengths per cell side standard, it was argued that it would be preferable to normalize the neutron group parameters so that they would give cell reaction rates when multiplied by the average flux on the cell edge (refs 13, 14). This is in contrast to the more conventional normalization based on the average flux but is more appropriate to the problem of joining dissimilar cells and reflectors where it is evidently the cell edge flux and current that are continuous.

21. Heterogeneous source-sink codes have been developed as part of the PATRIARCH scheme. It has proved necessary to use dipole corrections to allow for the finite size of the fuel clusters and computer running times in cores with a limited degree of symmetry have been correspondingly long. The accuracy attained in power distribution calculations has not, in general, proved better than the coarse mesh homogeneous theory and so heterogeneous methods have not been extensively used for routine design analysis.

Core representation experiments

22. In order to provide a basis for the estimation of nuclear performance of complex core loadings, a major series of experiments was undertaken in the DIMPLE and JUNO critical assemblies (refs 15, 16). The fuel elements used were specially recanned for the SGHWR programme and covered the U-235 enrichment range from 1.35-3%. Plutonium bearing fuels were also used in the JUNO programme. Since the Winfrith reactor lattice parameters had by this time been frozen, the work was carried out with a reasonably close simulation of the actual lattice.

23. Five groups of cores were studied, i.e.,

(i) Uniform - to provide a basis for comparison.

(ii) Two-zone - with radial enrichment variation.

(iii) Chess-board - in which the 'black' and 'white' channels have different enrichments and/or types of fuel.

(iv) Three-batch roundelay - in which a central chess-board is surrounded by an outer annulus of channels at a higher mean enrichment.

(v) Perturbed - in which one or more fuel channels or other lattice components is non-standard.

24. Some typical results of reactivity calculations made with coarse mesh homogeneous theory for these critical cores are shown in Table 3. This shows that k_{eff} values were being estimated with a similar degree of accuracy to that attained with regular lattices. Experiments with different effective coolant densities showed that the accuracy attainable in void coefficient predictions was closely similar to that obtained with the regular lattices.

25. Fission power distribution measurements were made in these complex lattices and the comparison with predictions showed an accuracy within the design tolerances. The result of one of the more stringent experiments is illustrated in Fig. 3. The core loading in this case is a chess-board of 3% enriched UO_2 alternated with PuO_2/UO_2 containing 8 kg/TeU of plutonium. This represents a situation which could develop under fuel management in an SGHWR running to irradiation levels well in excess of 20,000 MWd/TeU. It is seen that even in this case the maximum discrepancy is only 5.4% of the local power on a peripheral channel.

26. The perturbation experiments provided such useful data on the effects of control absorber tubes, moderator displacement tubes, empty channels, non-standard fuel elements and the loading of dummy superheat channels. It was found that the effects could be represented to adequate accuracy within the coarse mesh design scheme though errors of about 10% in the local power distribution were encountered with some of the larger perturbations in regions of high flux gradient near the core periphery.

27. A series of experiments was carried out by using a hot loop which enabled one channel near the centre of the JUNO core to be raised to full operating temperature and pressure. This loop was used to explore the variations of isotopic reaction rates with temperature with particular emphasis on plutonium fuels. An analysis of the reactivity changes with temperature observed with both uranium and plutonium fuelling, showed that, in common with other water systems, the SGHWR has a coolant temperature coefficient less negative than predicted by $3-4 \times 10^{-5}$ $\Delta K_{eff}/^{\circ}C$ (ref. 17). The origin of this discrepancy is obscure, but its existence has been confirmed by observations on the Winfrith SGHWR (ref. 11).

Table 3
Calculated k-effective values for critical cores

Core Number	Core type	Central core fuel	Calculated k-effective
DIMPLE			
SG15/E3	Uniform	1.35% UO_2	1.004
SG15/E4	Uniform	1.35% UO_2	0.996
SG17/E8	Two-zone	1.35% UO_2	1.004
SG16/E5	Chess-board	1.35% UO_2/3% UO_2	0.985
SG18/E13	Three-batch roundelay	1.35% UO_2/1.8% UO_2	1.009
JUNO			
SGP1/1	Uniform	0.25% PuO_2	0.999
SGP1/2	Uniform	0.25% PuO_2	1.000
SGP2/1	Two-zone	0.8% PuO_2	0.996
SGP4/1	Chess-board	3% UO_2/0.8% PuO_2	0.993
SGP4/2	Reflected chess-board	3% UO_2/0.8% PuO_2	1.002
SGP4/3	Reflected chess-board	3% UO_2/0.8% PuO_2	1.004

Table 3
Calculated k-effective values for critical cores

The performance of the initial core loading

28. The experience emerging from the core representation experiments enabled the design calculations for the Winfrith SGHWR to be made with steadily increasing confidence. The METHUSELAH II-ZADOC coarse mesh representation was developed into a special code known as AIMAZ specifically designed to represent the various types of perturbation present. As the work proceeded fuel management considerations became of paramount importance (ref. 1). It also became necessary to consider interactions between the nuclear and the thermal-hydraulic performance. Iterative calculations, notably between the AIMAZ (nuclear) and CUSH (core and primary circuit hydraulic models) were needed to reach final estimates of overall reactor power distributions and void coefficients.

Mock-up of the Winfrith SGHWR core

29. A final check on the nuclear design predictions was made by using the actual reactor fuel elements in a core mock-up experiment in DIMPLE. These experiments also provided an opportunity to make calibrations of flux wires, evaluate approach to critical procedures and make isotopic reaction rate elements with special demountable fuel pins. This resulted in the saving of in-line time during the commissioning of the reactor.

30. The DIMPLE tank was able to accommodate a maximum of 68 channels on the standard square pitch of 10.25 in (260.35 mm) and the experiments were, therefore, carried out with smaller cores simulating the important features of the initial power reactor core loading of the power reactor. Mock-ups representing fuel irradiation experiments with non-standard fuels were introduced to examine perturbation effects.

31. The main conclusions reached during the series of mock-up experiments were:

(1) Reactivity level. The reactivity levels of cold lattices in the mock-up are about 0.5% k_{eff} lower than predicted. The JUNO temperature coefficient measurements (see para. 27) suggested that this bias would just disappear at operating temperature.

(2) Void coefficient. Experiments with H_2O/D_2O mixtures to simulate coolant voids showed the following accuracy:

$$\Delta K_v = 0.000 \pm 0.003.$$

(3) Power distribution. In cores with a regular loading pattern the power distribution was well predicted (see Fig. 4 for a typical result). It was found that in the channels on the core edge, the calibration factor linking the central flux wire to

the total fission power was dependent on the local flux gradient. Errors of up to 7% would have been introduced if this effect had been ignored. The methods of calculation originally developed for multipole source-sink calculations were found to be useful in representing these effects.

(4) Effects of perturbations. A wide range of perturbations were studied including different fuel geometries, high enrichment channels, dummy superheat channels, dummy pencil loops and a reactivity oscillator. In each case, the reactivity change produced by the perturbation was measured together with the effect on the power distribution. Over the whole series, the standard AIMAZ calculation scheme predicted channel power variations to an accuracy of $\pm6\%$ though there were cases of perturbations near the core edge with power errors of 10-12%.

COMMERCIAL REACTORS

Enriched fuel versions

32. The nuclear design characteristics of the larger commercial reactors are closely similar to those of the Winfrith SGHWR. This follows from the fact that the later reactors will be constructed from the same size pressure tubes and fuel assemblies engineered into a larger calandria. There are some marginal differences arising from higher operating power levels, small changes in neutron leakage contributions to the void coefficient and shifts in the appropriate levels of enrichment.

33. Nuclear design studies for reactors in the size range 300-500 MW(e) have been made using the core representation techniques originally developed for the Winfrith SGHWR. This involved a considerable expenditure of computer time and there is a strong incentive to evolve more efficient types of core representation particularly for use in large coupled nuclear-thermal-hydraulic calculations. Some advances in this direction have already been made and a single line of mesh points is normally used to represent a channel in the JOSHUA 3-dimensional coupled code.

Natural fuel versions

34. The larger enriched reactors have been seen to introduce no essentially new nuclear design aspects, though some difficulties associated with the scale of the calculations have been noted. However, reactors designed to operate on natural fuel differ significantly from the enriched version in the following respects:

(1) the short burn-up (~7-8000 MWd/TeU) attainable requires a higher

accuracy in reactivity calculations for a given percentage
precision in the estimate;

(2) fuel elements are sub-divided
axially and an axial fuel management scheme is required to even
out the fuel irradiation distribution and so achieve maximum
efficiency in irradiation performance;

(3) natural uranium fuelled reactors
will have significantly positive
void coefficients; these increase
the importance of nuclear-
thermal-hydraulic couplings.

35. A special programme of reactor physics
experiments is in progress with the objective of improving the accuracy of nuclear
calculations for natural uranium SGHWRs by
providing calibration data.

36. The coupled code JOSHUA is of particular importance in the natural uranium
SGHWR project. It has been used to show
that the fuel management scheme may be
designed to offset some of the consequences
of the positive void coefficient. Since
steam voids increase reactivity there is a
tendency for the power to peak towards the
channel exit. This may be corrected by
loading fresh fuel at the lower end of the
channel and moving the parts of an axially
sub-divided element upwards during irradiation.

CONCLUSIONS

37. The evidence presented in this paper
and the references cited demonstrates that
the factors influencing the nuclear design
of SGHW reactors are now well understood.
A comprehensive system of computer codes
has been developed to assist in the design
process and evaluated against experimental
data. A firm basis now exists for the
design of larger enriched reactors;
experimental and theoretical work currently
in progress will place the nuclear performance estimates for natural uranium
versions on a similar footing.

ACKNOWLEDGEMENTS

38. This paper is published by kind
permission of the Managing Director, The
Reactor Group, UKAEA, Risley. Thanks are
due to the many colleagues at Risley and
Winfrith responsible for the work reported.

REFERENCES

1.   O'DELL F.P., ALLEN F.R. and
HOPKINS D.R. (Paper 7 to this conference.)

2.   ALPIAR R. METHUSELAH I - A universal
assessment programme for liquid moderated
reactor cells using IBM 7090 or STRETCH
computers. AEEW - R 135, 1964.

3. BRINKWORTH M.J. and GRIFFITHS J.A.
METHUSELAH II - A Fortran programme and
nuclear data library for the physics
assessment of liquid moderated reactors.

4.   HOLMES J.A.G., OBERTELLI J.D. and
ROBERTS H.A. (Paper 5 to this conference.)

5.   ALLEN F.R. and HICKS D. The validity
of METHUSELAH I in reactivity predictions.
AEEW - R 233, 1962.

6.   HICKS D. and HOPKINS D.R. The validity
of METHUSELAH II in water moderated lattice
calculations. AEEW - R 397, 1964.

7.   McMILLAN R.N.H., O'DELL F.P. and
WRAY D. The physics and control of the
Steam Generating Heavy Water Reactor.
TRG Report 1343(R), 1966.

8.   BRIGGS A.J., JOHNSTONE I.,
KEMSHELL P.B. and NEWMARCH D.A. Further
reactor physics studies for SGHWRs - Part 1.
Uniform cluster lattices containing UO_2 or
PuO_2/UO_2 fuel. Journ. Brit. Nucl. Energy
Soc., January 1968.

9.   FLOYD M. and HICKS D. An analysis of
water reactor burn-up data with the
METHUSELAH II code. AEEW - R 399, 1967.

10. WESTCOTT C.H. et al. At. Energy
Review. 3. 3-60, 1965.

11. Paper 11 of this conference.

12. ALLEN F.R. ZADOC - A two-group, two-
dimensional fuel management programme for
IBM 7090 or STRETCH. AEEW - R 425, 1965.

13. ALLEN F.R. and NEWMARCH D.A. Core
representation in SGHW reactors. Paper 17,
Joint International Conference on Physics
Problems in Thermal Reactor Design, London,
1967.

14. ALLEN F.R. (To be published.)

15. BRIGGS A.J., HICKS D. and HOPKINS D.R.
Fuel management in SGHW reactors. Paper 41,
Joint International Conference on Physics
Problems in Thermal Reactor Design, London,
1967.

16. BRIGGS A.J., JOHNSTONE I, KENDELL K.C.
and NEWMARCH D.A. Further reactor physics
studies for SGHWRs - Part 2. Multizone
cores for fuel management studies.
J. Brit. Nucl. Energy Soc., April 1968.

17. FAYERS F.J., KEMSHELL P.B. and
TERRY M.J. An evaluation of some uncertainties in the comparison between theory and
experiment in regular light water lattices.
J. Brit. Nucl. Energy Soc., April 1967.

Thermal and hydraulic design of SGHWRs

J. A. G. HOLMES AMIMechE, AFRAeS UKAEA, Risley

J. D. OBERTELLI   BSc(Eng), AMIMechE UKAEA, Winfrith

H. A. ROBERTS   AKC, BSc(Eng), AMIMechE UKAEA, Winfrith

SYNOPSIS   This paper first reviews the thermal design features which influence the performance of SGHWR systems. Whilst, in general, the questions that arose are similar to those which had been met and resolved both with other reactor types and in other related fields of technology, some extrapolation from previous experience was required. Inevitably, there were initially uncertainties in the prediction of thermal-hydraulic behaviour particularly when closely coupled with neutronic effects. An extensive theoretical and experimental programme was, therefore, undertaken in support of the design. This work is discussed together with the main conclusions that resulted. It is shown that predictions can now be made of the thermal-hydraulic behaviour of SGHWR systems with satisfactory precision thereby allowing the potential of the concept to be appropriately exploited.

INTRODUCTION

Scope

1.   This paper covers the heat transfer from fuel to coolant and the hydraulics of the primary circuit. Necessarily it is difficult to discuss these topics in isolation since there are strong linkages to the nuclear design on the one hand and the overall plant design on the other. The paper reviews the factors influencing the choice of design parameters, the development of suitable calculation methods to aid the design process, and the experimental studies carried out to establish uncertain parametric data. It concludes by reviewing the expected performance of commercial Steam Generating Heavy Water Reactors.

Factors influencing selection of parameters

2.   The principal reactor parameters influenced by considerations of thermal-hydraulic performance are fuel geometry, fuel channel diameter and length, channel power output, coolant flow rate and inlet enthalpy, coolant pressure and also the primary coolant circuit design. There are no technical issues associated with selection of these parameters which are greatly different from those encountered in any other reactor system using a two-phase coolant. The major concern is to select a self-consistent set of parameters which lead to the most economic design within the allowable physical limitations, based on current ground rules in use in the United Kingdom.

3.   Fuel geometry is influenced by fuel temperature and heat transfer considera-
tions and also by the quantity of light water in the fuel channel. This latter is due to the neutron moderating and absorption properties of the coolant and, therefore, its influence on fuel cost. The combination of oxide fuel and attainable fuel rating leads to a fuel geometry based on a cluster of comparatively small diameter pins. Spacing between pins, and therefore coolant cross sections within the channel is determined largely by reactor physics considerations which differ significantly for the enriched and natural uranium variations of the reactor. In a design where enrichment is permitted, the generation cost is minimized by utilizing the coolant to contribute significantly to the moderation of neutron energy, thus saving heavy water requirements. Pin spacing is therefore comparatively large. However, in the reactor using natural uranium only, close pin spacing is essential because it is of over-riding importance to minimize neutron absorption in the coolant. Fuel pin diameter, and consequently the number of pins in the channel is determined by the allowable limit on fuel centre temperature. It is therefore dependent both on the channel diameter and power output.

4.   Channel diameter is governed by interactions between reactor physics and engineering considerations. In the enriched reactor, the optimum volumetric ratio of heavy water to fuel is approximately 7.5, giving a fairly close channel lattice pitch. The space between the channels of a single-pass design is, however, physically limited by the engineering considerations of the space required for passing riser pipes between channels and accommodation of the rolled joints combining the component sections of the pressure tube assemblies. This leads

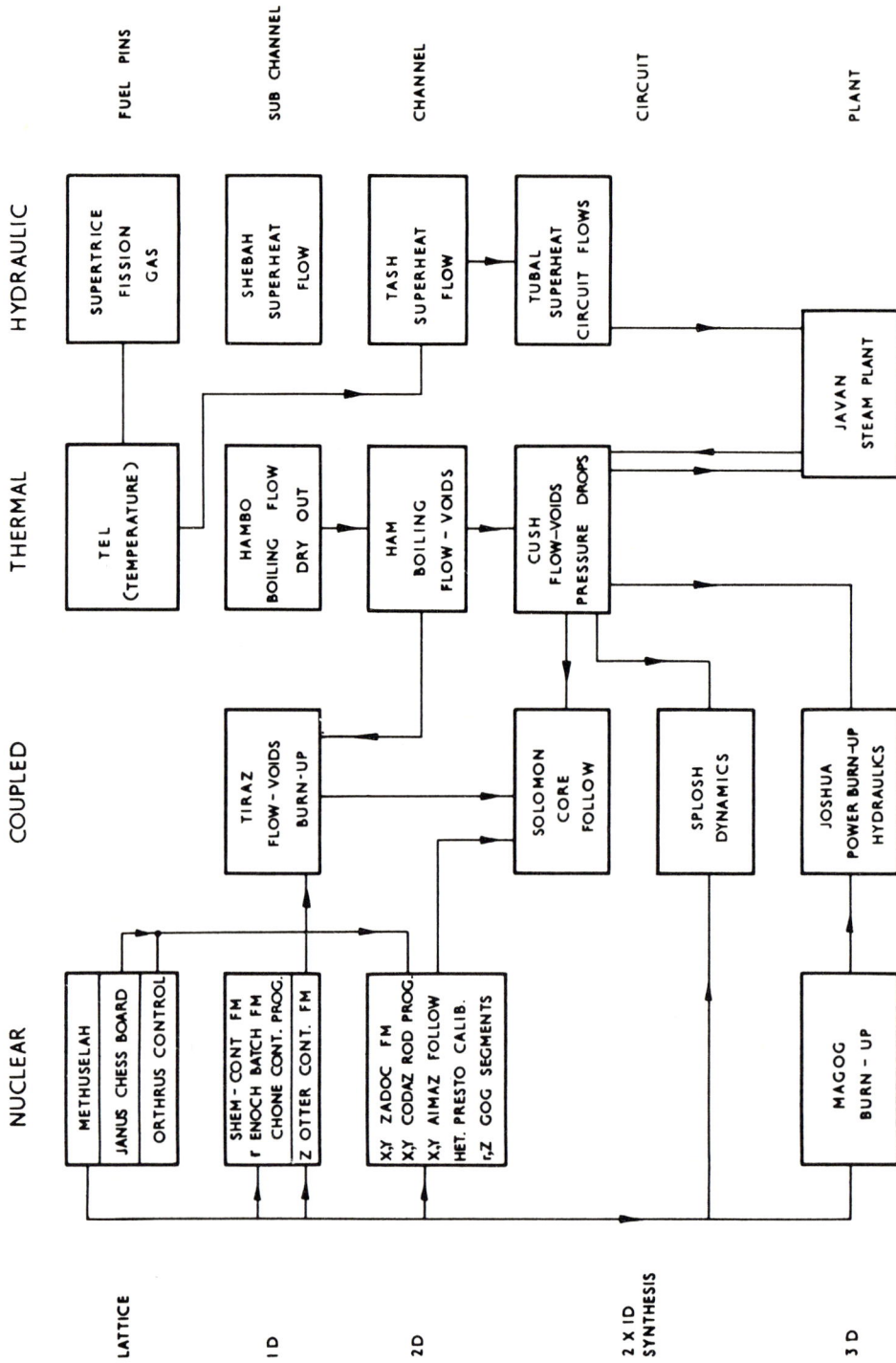

Fig. 1: Patriarch code scheme for SGHWR

to a minimum practicable channel diameter for the optimum value of heavy water to fuel ratio. Adoption of a larger channel diameter might be expected to reduce capital cost by reducing the number of channels to be fabricated. This, however, is offset partly by the need for thicker pressure tube components if the coolant pressure is held constant but also by an increase in maximum to average fuel rating within the channel resulting from greater depression of neutron flux toward the centre of the channel. Thus, the average fuel rating is reduced for a constant value of allowable peak rating.

5.   Optimization of the balance between neutron leakage and heat transfer performance determines active core height and hence channel length. Experimental heat transfer data have shown that over the range of heated length of interest there is very little increase in allowable channel power output for a substantial increase in length. Thus, as channel length is increased, the allowable fuel rating must decrease, raising both fuel and capital cost. However, too short a length results in high neutron leakage. Channel length is, therefore, selected to obtain an optimum balance between these factors.

6.   The choice of operating channel power output and coolant flow rate must be made against considerations of the margins to dryout and the onset of hydrodynamic instability. The former is defined as an abrupt change in the heat transfer regime leading to overheating of the fuel clad, while the latter is initiated by the differences in pressure drops between single and two-phase flow regimes. In general, dryout is the more stringent limitation. The coolant flow rate required to maintain a constant margin against dryout is approximately proportional to the square of the power output. The cost of circulating the coolant therefore rises disproportionately compared to channel power and an optimum balance between power output and coolant flow rate must be found.

7.   Considerations of steam cycle efficiency and cost of the pressure circuit influence selection of coolant pressure. Heat transfer performance has not been a contributory factor in determination of pressure as there is no significant change in performance over the range of interest. Higher thermal efficiency leads to a requirement for higher coolant pressure which increases the pressure circuit cost, largely due to the influence of the zircaloy pressure tubes. In addition to capital cost, fuel cost is also affected because of neutron absorption by the thicker pressure tube. Circuit pressure is therefore selected to obtain the optimum balance between these factors.

Method of attack

8.   The preceding discussion demonstrates that the selection of an economically attractive design and the evaluation of its

performance calls for the ability to predict a variety of effects, notably fission gas pressures, the conditions for dryout, coolant flow distribution and hydrodynamic stability margins. There was therefore a need at the outset of the project to develop a comprehensive set of calculation methods and appropriate computer codes to cover the effects in a self-consistent manner. At the same time, it was clear that many of these codes would have to depend on parametric data which could only be generated experimentally. A balanced programme of experimental and theoretical studies was therefore undertaken with results that will be reviewed below.

ASSESSMENT MODEL DEVELOPMENT

The PATRIARCH scheme

9.   The development of methods of calculation for thermal-hydraulic design has proceeded in close association with the work on nuclear design methods. The complete system of digital codes now available for steady state performance analysis is known as PATRIARCH (see Fig. 1). Descriptions of the functions of the reactor physics codes appear in a companion paper. The approaches used in the thermal-hydraulic codes will be reviewed briefly below. In the space available, it is only possible to outline the basis of the more important codes.

Fuel pin model - SUPATRICE

10.   The SGHWR project has been able to make use of the extensive experience of oxide fuel irradiation behaviour obtained in the course of the AGR programme. This experience has been correlated into the SUPATRICE code which follows the life history of a fuel pin subjected to a specified irradiation history. Fuel temperatures, fission gas pressures and clad strains are calculated through life.

Fuel cluster hydraulics model - HAMBO

11.   The flow distribution problem within the sub-channels of the rod cluster fuel elements is solved by the HAMBO code using a power distribution derived from the reactor physics calculations. The effects of flow mixing between sub-channels and the influence of grids on pressure drop are included through experimentally determined parameters. Dryout limits to performance are determined by the use of special empirical correlations which describe the performance of the individual sub-channels. HAMBO is used to predict the overall channel properties for use in simpler one-dimensional models and to indicate the dryout limits on channel output.

Multichannel primary circuit model - CUSH

12. Once the individual channel properties have been derived from the HAMBO sub-channel analysis, it is necessary to consider the flow distribution problem in the primary circuit. This question arises because the higher power channels tend to contain more steam and offer a greater resistance to flow than the low power channels. Moreover, there are differences in the pipe runs to and from the channels which can cause small but significant differences in flow.

13. The CUSH code has been developed to provide a complete representation of a primary circuit containing several hundred channels with appropriate pumps, steam drums, headers, tail pipes and other features associated with a practical arrangement. Each channel is represented one-dimensionally and such aspects as the appropriate single- and two-phase pressure drops and coolant density distribution are calculated. A three-dimensional speci-fication of the nuclear power distribution is required as input to CUSH. Specifica-tions of the feed-water flow for a given steam output are also needed to determine the sub-cooling at channel entry and may be derived from the JAVAN complete steam plant model.

Coupled calculations

14. It is evident from the preceding discussion that there must be iterations between the nuclear and thermal-hydraulic codes of the PATRIARCH scheme to achieve consistent solutions. The thermal codes need power distributions which are in turn dependent on the coolant density distribu-tion.

15. Special coupled codes have been developed for this purpose. These range from the TIRAZ single channel model, through the SOLOMON synthesis scheme for the Prototype, to the full three-dimen-sional coupled nuclear thermal hydraulic code JOSHUA. In the enriched SGHWR designs the coolant void coefficient is close to zero, the cross couplings are relatively weak and only a single cycle of iteration is necessary for acceptable accuracy. On the other hand, the significantly positive void coefficients of the natural uranium designs imply a greater need to study coupling effects and the full three-dimensional JOSHUA code has been exten-sively used in these circumstances.

Dynamic effects - SPLOSH

16. Two dynamic problems are of particular interest in the design of SGHWRs which are not covered by the overall plant analogue computer control studies. These are the questions of hydraulic stability and the behaviour of the coolant flow following pump failure. The SPLOSH code has been developed to study these and related problems. Essentially the code provides a coupled nuclear-thermal hydraulic model of an average core channel and the primary circuit. The dynamic response of the system to various types of disturbance is calculated. Provision is made to follow the flow changes in slave channels of different power outputs under the influence of changing pressure drops fixed by the average channel properties.

EXPERIMENTAL PROGRAMME

Outline

17. In the previous sections, it has been shown how the various phenomena bearing on thermal hydraulic design have been repre-sented by a modular system of computer codes. This structure would be valueless if it did not rest on a sound basis of experimental data particularly as many significant features such as, for example, pressure drops in components, or the onset of the dryout phenomenon, must, in the present state of the art, rest on formalisms with empirically determined coefficients. An extensive series of experiments specifically geared to the needs of the SGHWR programme was, there-fore, launched covering the following features:

    (1) measurement of flows and pressure drops in full size heated fuel assemblies;

    (2) measurements of steady state dry-out powers in fuel bundles including full size fuel assemblies;

    (3) dryout studies under transient conditions;

    (4) dynamic response experiments to explore hydrodynamic instability problems;

    (5) measurement of pressure drops in circuit components, for example, flow manifolds;

    (6) simulation of the emergency spray cooling system;

    (7) studies of post dryout heat transfer;

    (8) calibration of flow and steam quality measuring instruments.

18. It is not possible to cover all these topics here but some of the more important items will be reviewed briefly.

Experimental facilities

19. A number of high pressure electrically heated test rigs have been used during the experimental programme. The most important of these are the 1 MW and 9 MW test rigs located at the UKAEA's Winfrith Establishment. Full-size fuel elements may

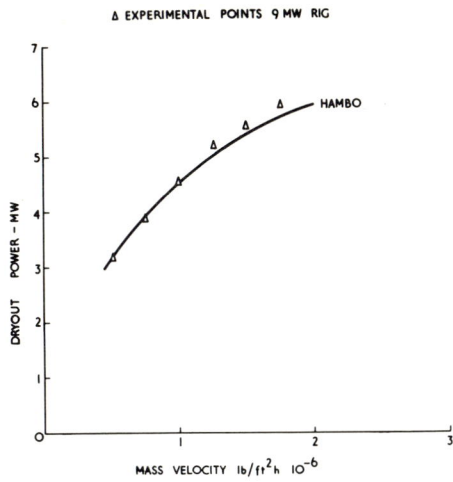

Fig. 2: Comparison of HAMBO prediction of dryout power with experimental results using a typical full-scale channel assembly for an enriched reactor system

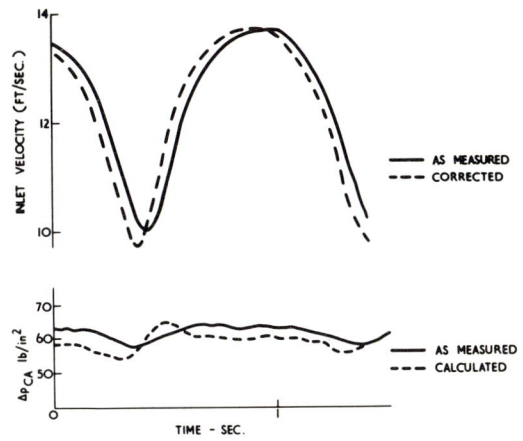

Fig. 3: Comparison with SPLOSH predictions of measured response of pressure drop between boiling channel inlet (C) and steam drum (A) in a test rig to forced oscillations in flow at 1 cps

Table 1
Comparison of channel pressure drop predictions with experiment in the then 6 MW rig using full-scale channel assembly

Channel power MW	Mass velocity lb/ft²h 10⁻⁶	Pressure drop predictions lb/h²			Experimental values lb/h²
		CUSH	HAMBO	SPLOSH	
2.86	2.36	19.2	21.1	21.7	20.2
4.02	1.97	19.7	21.6	22.6	20.5
6.00	1.50	20.0	22.1	23.7	22.0

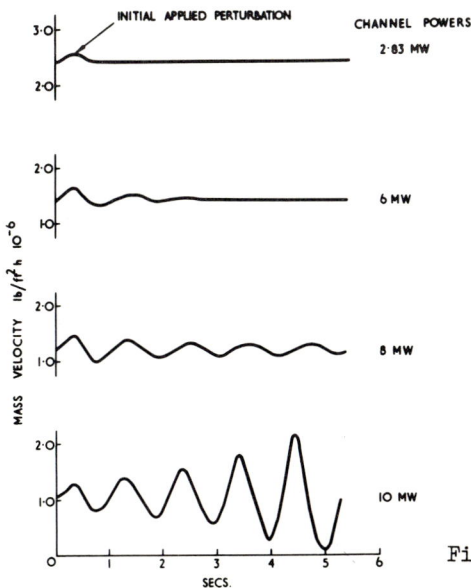

Table 3
Dryout probabilities estimated for a typical channel power distribution in the Winfrith SGHWR at reactor overpower

Fractional reactor power	Power dryout margin	Dryout probability
1.0	1.56	0.0000
1.1	1.43	0.0000
1.2	1.32	0.0000
1.3	1.22	0.0015
1.4	1.15	0.0280
1.5	1.08	0.2400

Fig. 4: Predicted responses of typical Winfrith SGHWR channels to flow perturbations when operated at various power levels

be tested in the latter which is an up-rated version of the earlier 6 MW rig. Experience has shown that full scale testing is essential and large extrapolations from small-scale test data can be very misleading.

20. In the 9 MW rig, power is supplied to a simulated full size fuel element, in the form of low voltage, ultra high direct current, a maximum of 75,000 amperes being available. The use of direct rather than 3-phase alternating current has many advantages and readily permits all the rods to be connected in parallel to form a single electrical load. Such a system avoids insulation and electrolysis problems resulting from voltage gradients between the rods and enables the spacer grid arrangements to be made identical to those used in the reactor fuel element. Furthermore, by using heated tubes of different wall thickness in the various rings of rods forming the cluster, a simulation can be provided of the radial heat production profile across the cluster. This process can also be extended to model the relevant axial heat flux profile by variation of the nominal thickness along the length of each element.

Steady state dryout tests

21. In a typical test series, with a particular fuel element geometry, pressure drop characteristics and dryout powers are measured for a range of flow rates, inlet sub-coolings and operating pressures. A range of fuel element configurations appropriate to both enriched and natural fuelled designs has now been tested and the following generalizations may be made.

(a) As expected dryout was first attained on the outer ring of most highly rated rods. The results from a given rod cluster are very reproducible, the typical standard deviation being only $1\frac{1}{2}\%$. The standard deviation for re-builds of essentially the same geometry is about $2\frac{1}{2}\%$.

(b) Dryout power depends linearly upon the sub-cooling of the coolant below saturation temperature at channel inlet. It is approximately proportional to the square root of mass velocity at zero sub-cooling and is constant to within $\pm 5\%$ over a wide range of operational pressure.

(c) Final optimization of rod positions within a given pressure tube can give increases of up to about 10% in thermal performance.

(d) The consequences of pin heat flux tilt and of the fuel element being slightly eccentric within the pressure tube have little effect on the cluster dryout power.

22. Fig. 2 shows a comparison between the rig data and the HAMBO predictions for a typical design of fuel element for an

enriched reactor. In general, the HAMBO correlations have been optimized to fit a wide range of cluster dryout data to an RMS error of about 6%.

23. It has been found that the predictions of dryout power made with HAMBO are not unduly sensitive to the remaining uncertainties in the hydraulic model, particularly in the assumptions made concerning turbulent mixing between sub-channels and slip ratio. These uncertainties correspond to an error of about $\pm 4\%$ in predictions on clusters similar to those chosen for the enriched SGHWR reference design. Larger uncertainties could arise in situations where there is a potentially larger degree of imbalance between the sub-channels.

24. For many purposes, particularly in survey calculations, the extra complexity of sub-channel analysis is not justified and correlations of the Macbeth-Barnett type have been found to be suitable.

Pressure drop measurements

25. Table 1 shows comparisons between pressure drop data for a full-scale channel assembly and the PATRIARCH code predictions. The latter have been based on empirically determined two-phase friction multipliers which seem to have a wide range of validity under SGHW conditions. In general, three two-phase pressure drop friction factors for rod clusters lie between the predictions of the Martinelli-Nelson and Thom correlations for single round tubes.

Transient dryout measurements

26. Transient dryout has been studied experimentally either by producing a step increase in rig power or by a run-down in coolant flow. These tests demonstrated that (within an instrument resolution of about 100 ms) dryout occurs at the instant when the local conditions at the point of dryout matched those at the steady state conditions. This supports the assumptions made in the SPLOSH transient analysis. Measurements of fuel pin temperatures made in the rigs during the post dryout phase are consistent with heat transfer appropriate to the local steam flow. Closer agreement with experiment can be achieved by using a more comprehensive theory allowing for water droplet evaporation. There is still however some uncertainty concerning the mechanism of the rewetting process and this is the subject of present work.

Hydraulic stability experiments

27. The margins against parallel channel hydraulic instability in the Prototype reference design are so large that it has not been possible to initiate instabilities in the full-scale test rig when modelling the Winfrith SGHWR performance.

Table 2
Thermal and hydraulic design parameters

Parameter	Units	Prototype		Representative commercial reactors			
				Enriched		Natural	
Channel diameter	in (mm)	5.13	(130)	5.13	(130)	5.13	(130)
Core height	in (mm)	144	(3660)	144	(3660)	180	(4572)
Fuel pin outside diameter	in (mm)	0.63	(16)	0.63	(16)	0.70	(17.8)
No. of fuel pins in channel		36		36		36	
Flow area	ft^2 (cm^2)	0.063	(58.4)	0.063	(58.4)	0.043	(39.8)
Maximum channel heat to coolant	MW	3.8		5.0		4.6	
Maximum channel coolant mass velocity	lb/ft^{2}h (g/cm^{2}s)	2.23x10^6	(305)	2.65x10^6	(362)	2.05x10^6	(278)
Coolant inlet sub-cooling	Btu/lb (J/g)	20	(47)	23	(54)	20	(46.5)
Coolant inlet pressure	lb/in^{2}a (kg/cm^{2}a)	984	(69.2)	855	(6.02)	665	(46.8)
Coolant exit quality (maximum) channel	%	11.0		12.6		24	
Pressure drop over fuel	lb/in^2 (kg/cm^2)	20	(1.7)	26	(2.2)	81	(5.7)
Total circuit pressure drop	lb/in^2 (kg/cm^2)	57	(4.0)	91	(6.4)	140	(10)
Ratio:- $\dfrac{\text{Coolant pumping power}}{\text{Core thermal power output}}$		0.005		0.007		0.005	
Equilibrium peak surface	Btu/ft^{2}h (W/cm^2)	390,000	(123)	456,000	(144)	366,000	(115)
Equilibrium peak fuel centre temperature	$^{\circ}$F ($^{\circ}$C)	2730	(1500)	3800	(2100)	3630	(2000)

28. Dynamic experiments to test the features of the SPLOSH model used to predict stability thresholds have however been undertaken. Fig. 3 shows the measured response of a test rig to forced oscillations in flow at 1 cps compared with SPLOSH predictions. These results show satisfactory modelling at the frequencies at which unstable behaviour would be initiated.

PERFORMANCE LIMITATIONS IN THE WINFRITH SGHWR

Nature of limits

29. The various phenomena bearing on the thermal-hydraulic performance have now been described and the programmes of experimental and theoretical studies outlined. It emerges that there are the following important factors which represent potential constraints on the attainable thermal output from an SGHWR. These are:

    (1) the power form factors expressing the shape of the power distribution;

    (2) the build-up of fission gas within the fuel pins;

    (3) the threshold of hydraulic instability;

    (4) dryout.

30. The first two topics are dealt with in companion papers; the second two will be discussed here. As an illustration of the principles appropriate figures for the Prototype design will be presented. Table 2 summarizes the main design parameters for the Winfrith SGHWR and some representative commercial systems.

Hydrodynamic stability

31. In the general sense, the term 'instability' is used to denote a state in a system wherein disturbances tend to grow in amplitude either exponentially or as a divergent oscillation. In determining the implications of instability of a design of an SGHWR system, there are three main modes that must be considered.

(a) Circuit instability: the flow rates in all channels oscillate in phase involving systematic variation of the steam voidage throughout the core. It is necessary to consider flow perturbations in association with fundamental mode core neutronics.

(b) Parallel channel instability: pairs or groups of channels oscillate in anti-phase in such a manner as to produce no net flow disturbances in that part of the circuit which recirculates coolant from the steam drum to core inlet. Consequently, a feature that characterizes this

phenomenon is a constant pressure difference between inlet and exit plenums. Because of this constant pressure difference, it can be assumed that the hydrodynamic coupling between channels is negligible and that the only coupling arising is from neutron diffusion.

(c) Parallel channel instability involving the external circuit: this mode differs from the parallel channel instability by virtue of the fact that the anti-phase flow oscillations between channels do not cancel and consequently perturbations are induced in the external circuit flow rate. However, this mode is considered to have a lower probability because of the stabilizing effect of the coolant inertia in the steam drum and external loop.

32. The effects arising from unstable behaviour may be three-fold. First, it is possible that as a result of an instability involving a reduction in flow rate, the fuel clad surface may experience transient dryout and hence short-term increase in surface temperature. Secondly, if the margin to instability is limited, an undesirable roughness in performance levels or 'noise' can appear during operation. Finally, the influence of potentially varying coolant conditions on the nuclear performance could influence control requirements.

33. It is well known that the main coolant and thermal conditions effecting stability are as follows:

    (a) power level and channel power distribution;

    (b) the inlet sub-cooling and flow rate;

    (c) the flow rate and the driving head associated with the circuit.

34. The onset of instability may be studied with the SPLOSH code. Fig. 4 shows predicted responses of typical Winfrith SGHWR channels to perturbations when they are operated at various power levels. It can be seen that the disturbances are well damped at the channel powers of about 5 MW used in current designs. It is, therefore, concluded that hydraulic instability does not become an effective constraint on performance.

Dryout

35. The ability to achieve high heat transfer coefficients between the surface of a heat source and boiling water results, in a reactor application, in the design being based on high heat fluxes in the region 300,000 to 500,000 Btu/ft^2h (100 to 170 W/cm^2), without the cladding outer surface exceeding the saturation temperature by more than about 10 to 15°C. However, a performance limit is reached

beyond which heat is transferred primarily to the vapour phase. In this regime, the heat transfer coefficient is markedly reduced and the heat transfer rate can be maintained only at the expense of a significant rise in surface temperature. This condition is variously described as 'heat transfer crisis', 'critical heat flux', 'departure from nucleate boiling', 'burnout', 'dryout', etc. The term 'dryout', referring to the removal of a climbing film of liquid from the heated surface, at high steam qualities, is currently in general use and will be retained in the following discussion.

36. Whereas exploratory studies have indicated that the consequences of the dryout are unlikely to be catastrophic as regards massive release of fission products, nevertheless, the outage time due to fuel replacement and plant clean-up, which might result from even limited fuel clad damage are of economic importance. In the SGHWR design, the general principles adopted have been to ensure that the operating conditions are compatible with the overall design both in the nominal steady state and under appropriate transient conditions and are such that the possibility of dryout is remote. A concept of a dryout power margin (which has many parallels in other branches of technology) is used as an indication of the probability of dryout. It is defined as the factor by which the power level of the reactor could be raised before dryout is reached. It is known that dryout power and, therefore, dryout margin under steady state conditions are related both to geometrical features of the channel and fuel element and to the operating levels of various coolant parameters, such as flow rate, inlet sub-cooling and system pressure. However, it is generally found that since unavoidable short-term delays in the protective instrumentation response will permit transitory deviations from nominal design conditions, the dryout margin has its lowest value during certain fault transients. This minimum value depends on such features as operating power level, speed of response of the protective system, time-based behaviour of certain plant items such as pump run-down and reactor shutdown characteristics. The inter-relation of these parameters is assessed by analysis of appropriate transients arising in normal operation and minor fault conditions.

37. The application of these dryout margin principles requires a specification of data in the following main areas:

(a) minimum design dryout margin on which the design is to be based;

(b) dryout data for steady state and transients;

(c) identification and evaluation of plant coolant and design parameters that enter into the steady state and transient calculations. This would include a specification of transient conditions from

which the design is required to be protected.

38. In deciding on a minimum design dryout margin, it is useful to examine the statistics of the problem. Such an evaluation of the statistical significance of dryout margin requires a study of the two main problems:

(a) random deviations from the nominal conditions of all the parameters that enter into the dryout margin assessment, notably those associated with instruments, components, data and calculation techniques;

(b) steady deviations permitted by the protective instrumentation and operational procedures.

39. The random deviations lead to a statistical distribution for the estimated dryout margin. Knowing the power and flow distributions for the core, the probability of dryout for individual channels may be calculated and combined statistically to obtain the dryout probability for the reactor as a whole. Once the probability of dryout has been established as a function of reactor power, it is, in principle, possible to proceed to a discussion of the effect of steady deviations in parameters and of appropriate transients. Table 3 shows an example of probabilities of dryout at overpower estimated with a typical Winfrith SGHWR core distribution of channel powers. In assessing dryout probabilities, the values for individual channels have been combined statistically to obtain a probability of dryout appropriate to the reactor as a whole. From this table, it is clear that the reactor is highly protected against dryout at nominal full power conditions.

COMMERCIAL DESIGNS

40. The extensive development programmes which have been implemented during evolution of the reactor system design have enabled a considerable advance to be made in the thermal and hydraulic design of the fuel channel compared with the basic prototype design.

41. Data now available on fuel behaviour, coupled with improved methods of prediction, have shown that fuel operating temperature may be increased to a level at which the fuel centre is approaching its melting temperature.

42. The heat transfer and hydraulic experimental programme has given reliable data on both dryout and stability performance of the SGHWR fuel channel designs. This has enabled a reduction to be made in the margins allowed for uncertainties in prediction of dryout performance. Methods of predicting fuel surface temperature in the dryout regime have also been developed from experimental data. An indication of the consequences

of such operation on fuel cladding behaviour has been obtained, which gives confidence that a short-term dryout excursion such as may occur during some transient conditions is unlikely to lead to fuel cladding failure. This will enable a higher probability of dryout to be accepted in certain transient operating conditions. A power margin of 1.4 based on nominal operating conditions gives an acceptably low probability of dryout occurring in both the enriched and natural systems.

43. For commercial applications of the enriched reactor, these increases in available performance lead to the possibility of a considerable uprating of power output from the Winfrith SGHWR fuel and channel designs. The upper limit for the design at which the fuel temperature limitation is reached is in the range 5.5 to 6 MW. However, based on the latest available data from the then 6 MW rig on a full 36-rod cluster with uniform axial heating, the cost of circulating a sufficient coolant flow to remove this heat rating would more than offset the cost savings resulting from the increased core power density. An optimization study based on the ground rules currently in use in the UK has shown that the peak channel power rating should be increased to about 5 MW. This compares with a power output of 3.2 MW originally selected for the Winfrith SGHWR.

44. The recent experimental heat transfer data indicate considerable potential for further increasing the power density of the reactor core. The optimum power output from the most highly rated channel is likely to be greater than 6 MW, which would exceed the fuel temperature limitation of the Winfrith SGHWR fuel geometry. Methods of overcoming this limitation will therefore be required. Scope exists for reducing local peaking factors within the channel, thus enabling the power output to be increased without violating the fuel temperature limit. Alternatively, or in combination with means of reducing peaking factors, it may be necessary to modify the fuel geometry by use of smaller diameter pins to reduce maximum fuel temperature. Initial commercial designs will, however, be based on exploitation of the Winfrith SGHWR fuel geometry to its limits in order to obtain maximum advantage of direct experience already being gained in operation of this fuel design in the Winfrith SGHWR since its initial commissioning.

45. The higher ratio of channel power output to coolant flow rate which will be obtained in commercial reactors compared to the Winfrith SGHWR results in increased steam quality at channel exit and, therefore, higher pressure drop in the two-phase regime of the primary circuit. This tends to bring the system closer to the onset of hydrodynamic instability. Sufficient flexibility exists in the design of the primary circuit to enable the two-phase pressure drop to be maintained at a level which will allow an adequate margin to onset of instability.

46. In reactors fuelled with natural uranium, the neutron absorption in the light water coolant has a significant effect on design and performance of the fuel channel and coolant circuit. No incentive has been found to change the channel diameter from that of the enriched reactor. To minimize the quantity of coolant in the core a larger diameter fuel pin is used, the minimum pin-to-pin spacing being limited by physical restriction in fuel design and the pressure drop across the channel necessary to circulate a sufficiently high coolant flow rate to obtain an economic channel power output. The mean coolant density within the core is lower than in the enriched reactor in order to reduce neutron absorption. By controlling flow into groups of channels, a uniform exit quality across the core is obtained, thus avoiding any increase in density in channels at lower rating than the peak. The relationship between maximum channel power output and coolant flow rate, and hence exit quality, is also arranged to give an optimum balance between capital and fuel cost. A high ratio of flow to power could lead to high channel power output and low capital cost, but higher fuel cost, while a low ratio reduces fuel cost at the expense of capital cost.

47. Based on the latest available experimental data, these considerations lead to a maximum channel power output of about 4.6 MW from a 15 ft long fuel element. Fuel design requirements for the natural uranium reactor lead to an upper limit of about 2000°C in fuel temperature. Any increase in thermal performance which may be anticipated from continuing development work will necessitate some revision to the fuel design to maintain fuel temperature within an acceptable limit.

48. The considerations reviewed here lead to the present reference parameters for commercial designs shown in Table 3.

Comment and implications

49. The thermal hydraulic experimental programme has produced an extensive collection of empirical data covering the performance of the fuel element and the primary circuit. This has greatly reduced the uncertainties involved in evolving the overall thermal hydraulic design of the system. It has helped to establish that the Winfrith SGHWR should have a substantial margin to dryout to cover accidental overpower conditions and the possibility of various types of transient. It is claimed that experimental programmes have covered all the features which are of importance in the performance estimation and have verified the general correctness of the methods of calculation used in the design. There is, therefore a strong basis for the design of commercial SGHWRs.

ACKNOWLEDGEMENT

50.   This paper is published by kind
permission of the Managing Director,
The Reactor Group, UKAEA, Risley.   Thanks
are due to the many colleagues at Risley
and Winfrith who were responsible for the
work reported.

Control of SGHWRs

D. WRAY, BSc, MIEE UKAEA, Risley
M. H. BUTTERFIELD, BA UKAEA, Winfrith
R. N. H. McMILLAN, MA, MIEE UKAEA, Risley

SYNOPSIS   This paper describes the bases for control of steam generating heavy water reactor stations and gives some detail of the system adopted for the Winfrith SGHWR.

The basic dynamic properties of the SGHWR system are discussed first in terms of possible control actions, followed by the practical requirements for normal regulation and protection against fault conditions.

A brief description of the methods used for system design and of the SGHWR simulator is next given, simulation having proved useful not only in control design but also in training operators.

A description is provided of the station power, drum pressure and drum level controls on the Winfrith SGHWR together with the principal features of the emergency protection system.

Reference is made to commercial SGHWR designs from the point of view of control. The effects of increased size compared with the Winfrith SGHWR on overall dynamic properties and spatial reactor modes are discussed together with control system developments to improve load following capabilities.

Finally, the functions that could usefully be performed by an on-line computer are outlined although it is emphasized that this is not essential for satisfactory operation.

CONTROL PRINCIPLES AND REQUIREMENTS

Important dynamic features of the system

1.   Since it embodies a direct coolant cycle, the various dynamic properties of an SGHWR plant interact closely and, for a full understanding, require to be seen as a whole. In order to describe these dynamic properties and, at the same time, introduce the control concepts we shall consider, in turn, the input elements that are present in principle. The most important interactions are illustrated in Fig. 1.

2.   Reactivity. When a change is imposed on an SGHWR operating at power, causing it to depart from one set of steady conditions, two important influences on reactivity arise from alteration of core conditions. First is the effect of fuel temperature on reactivity which is dominated by the Doppler effect on U-238 resonance absorption. The coefficient is defined as the change in reactivity per unit rise in fuel temperature; it is negative and varies in magnitude approximately inversely as the square root of absolute fuel temperature. The second influence is due to changes in coolant density, or voidage, in the core channels. The void coefficient is defined as the change in reactivity produced per unit increase of voidage in the core, for small changes. Its value depends on many

factors including lattice design, enrichment and irradiation level but is dominated by the choice of moderator-to-fuel and coolant-to-fuel ratios.

3.   If the void coefficient is zero, the fuel temperature coefficient is important in limiting the rise (or fall) in power that follows an increase (or decrease) in reactivity imposed by any means. The effect of a variation in reactor power on coolant voidage in the core depends on the method of operation, but with fixed speed pumps (as in the Winfrith SGHWR) voidage generally increases with power. Hence a negative void coefficient acts with the fuel temperature coefficient in further limiting the steady state power variation following a change in reactivity. A sufficiently large positive void coefficient could override the fuel temperature coefficient producing an overall positive 'power coefficient of reactivity' and giving a divergent unstable condition.

4.   The rate at which heat is delivered to the coolant water and the consequent core voidage depends on the fuel temperature and, due to the thermal conduction through the fuel and its canning, follows with a time constant of order 10 s. This difference in timing between the influences of the fuel temperature coefficient and voidage on reactivity can give rise to oscillatory modes of instability for

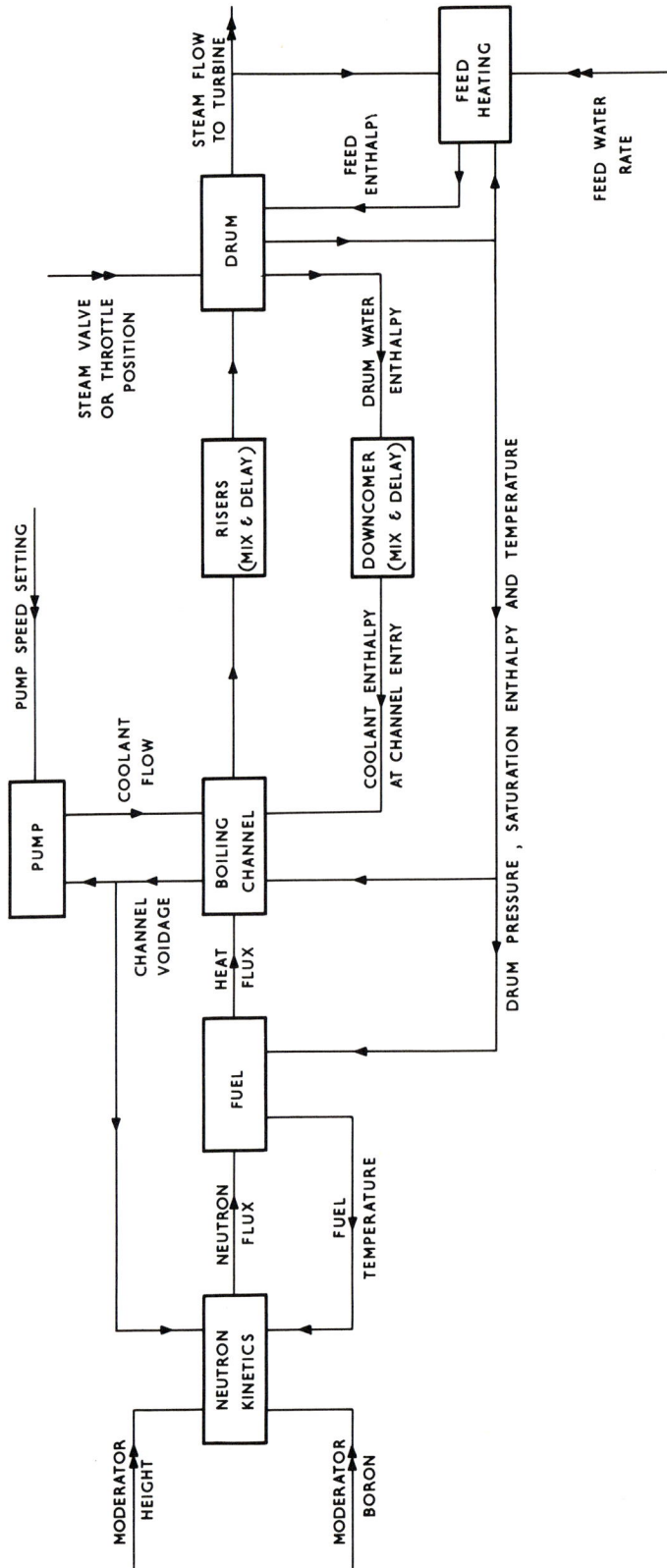

Fig. 1: Principal dynamic interactions in SGHWR system

sufficiently large values of void coefficient, positive or negative.

5. These considerations led to choice of a reactor design with a void coefficient within the range -0.02 to +0.02. This lies within the range for inherent reactor stability and the control system is designed to accept any value within these limits. Similar figures apply for all enriched designs and operating experience on the Winfrith SGHWR will enable future estimates to be made within narrower limits of accuracy.

6. An increase of reactivity leads to a rise in steady state reactor power and associated with this will be an increase in system pressure until the steam flow to the turbine rises to match the increased reactor power. Adjustment of reactivity, therefore, provides a possible method of controlling pressure; it acts via two important delay effects which are due to fuel conduction and the heat capacity of the primary circuit including the steam drum.

7. Steam flow rate. To regulate steam flow from the drum when at any specified pressure, it is necessary to insert a valve and alteration of the setting of this exercises an important influence, which also depends on the void coefficient. For example, suppose the turbine throttle is opened a little to increase the turbine loading. The system pressure would fall and, as steam flashes off from water, the voidage in the core is increased. With a positive void coefficient, an increase of reactivity follows, causing the reactor power to rise, thereby giving a degree of inherent power following and reducing the fall in pressure that would occur if voidage had no effect. However, the same disturbance with a negative void coefficient produces a fall in reactor power, magnifying the fall in system pressure.

8. In general, the rate at which pressure alters depends on the difference between the rate at which heat is being put in and taken out and also on the heat storage in the drum and primary circuit. For either a change in steam offtake or in power taken from the reactor, the pressure approaches the new steady state asymptotically with an exponential form which has a time constant ('the drum time constant') of approximately 20 s on the Winfrith SGHWR. Condensation of steam in the drum is caused, as pressure rises, when the steam demand is reduced, but this occurs less readily than the corresponding 'flashing off' of steam when the offtake is increased and pressure falls. This introduces a non-symmetry in the dynamic response. Also for either of these there is some additional delay as the heat storage in the whole circuit, not just the drum, becomes effective.

9. The minimum acceptable size of drum is decided by the need to store sufficient water to fill the voids in the core when they collapse following a reactor shutdown. On the Winfrith SGHWR, the drum time constant of 20 s given by this minimum drum

was considered to give adequate decoupling between the steam supply to the turbine and reactor condition.

10. Feed-water flow rate. The first obvious effect of a variation in feed flow is on water level in the drum which by itself would only affect the drum time constant. However, an increase in feed flow imposed on steady conditions leads to an increase in the sub-cooling at channel entry and a consequent reduction in channel voidage. The reactor power then changes according to the void coefficient, increasing in the case of a negative void coefficient.

11. Control of water level must overcome some anomalies which have their parallels in conventional water tube boilers. Thus, a rise in reactor power will increase channel voidage and this causes a slight reduction in recirculation flow; also as the new voidage is established in the channel and riser, water is displaced causing an initial rise in drum water level. But an increase in reactor power should call for an increase in feed flow and this raises the water level further. A corresponding fall in drum water level follows a reduction in power. Hence it is seen that control of drum level is not a simple function and leaves no additional freedom for feed flow as an operational control.

12. Feed-water pre-heating. The efficiency of the steam cycle in converting the heat generated into electrical power is influenced by the degree of feed heating, and, for a particular cycle, attainment of maximum efficiency requires it to be as high as possible.

13. The pre-heating of feed water is performed using bled steam from the turbine which leads to a final feed temperature below the saturation temperature corresponding to the drum steam pressure. By design choice of the method of introducing the feed water to the primary circuit and taking into account the pressure changes round this circuit, a reasonable minimum margin of sub-cooling can be arranged at input to the circulating pumps. In order to maintain maximum operating efficiency, control of feed heating is not provided as a normal means to regulate the system, since this could only reduce the feed heating. Prevention of cavitation in the pumps gives rise to limitation on the short-term system pressure changes that are permissible and may also lead to the necessity of using flow restricting valves at output from the pumps while operating at low power, when the drum water is virtually saturated.

14. Primary circulation flow rate. At any power level, a change in circulation rate has a rapid influence on channel voidage, and therefore on reactivity, leading to a change in channel power and primary loop conditions.

15. For enriched fuel SGHWRs this degree of freedom is neither essential nor appro-

priate to control the plant. It was, therefore, not provided in the Winfrith SGHWR and the pumps were arranged to run at constant speed. However, the flow rate delivered by the pumps and the pressure across them are related so that, as reactor power is increased and the channel voidage increases, the resistance to circulation also rises causing the flow to reduce. The pump design is chosen so that this flow reduction is quite small and has only a minor effect on the dynamic properties of the system.

Control requirements

16. System power level. It is clearly fundamentally important to have control of the power level at which the system is operating. This applies not only to the level of electrical power delivered to the grid but also for start-up of the reactor, and then there are limitations on the rate at which the turbine can be loaded.

17. At higher powers, it is necessary to have accurate measurements and control of system power both for satisfactory operating conditions and for commercial purposes. At lower powers and during start-up it is not so important to have precise knowledge of the actual power level but its variations must be controlled.

18. The design requirements for load following on the Winfrith SGHWR did not need to be as stringent as those which this type of reactor is capable of satisfying. Thus, the station load is required to be variable at up to 10% of maximum rating per minute and no requirements were laid down for load following of grid frequency. These aspects are considered later.

19. System pressure. For economic and satisfactory operation, some provision is essential to maintain pressure within reasonable bounds. If it is allowed to vary randomly over a wide range the channel inlet sub-cooling will also vary, with loss of efficiency and risk of pump cavitation while the effect of pressure on reactivity via core voidage would assist in making conditions too variable and indeterminate, with delivered power varying widely. The maximum pressure that can be permitted depends on the structural design of the plant. The maximum permissible rate of fall or step fall of pressure is decided by sub-cooling conditions and pump cavitation. These considerations make control of pressure a necessity for satisfactory operation. On the Winfrith SGHWR, reactor trips occur when pressure rises more than 50 lb/in^2 above the design pressure and when it falls at an effective rate of more than 1 lb/in^2/s for 40 s.

20. Drum water level. In order to provide a reasonably simple and reliable alarm and safety system it is necessary to control the level of water in the drum within fairly narrow limits. Any fault causing the drum to empty may result in channel dryout and damage to the fuel while there is also a danger in passing water to the turbine when the drum is over full. The limits at which a reactor trip is initiated are ±8 in. departure from the demanded drum water level on the Winfrith SGHWR.

21. Moderator height. It is desirable that the moderator height should be kept as high as possible during operation. This minimizes neutron leakage and reduces the importance of power limitations imposed by dryout.

22. Emergency shutdown and power set-back. The requirements of the automatic protective system are two-fold. First, and more important, it is designed to protect against the release of radioactive fission products to the atmosphere. The barriers to such a release are the fuel cladding, the primary circuit and finally the containment system. Without postulating independent, simultaneous failures of two or more of these barriers, the most significant fault is that arising from a fracture of the primary circuit. The subsequent loss of coolant could lead to cladding failure and so leave only one barrier to the release of fission products. This fault is, therefore, given special consideration in the protective system. The second function of the automatic protective system is to protect the fuel from major damage, in particular, dryout due to incidents too fast for operator intervention. In general, faults of this kind could arise in two different ways:

    (a) uncontrolled increase of reactor power due to some form of reactivity excursion;

    (b) loss of coolant flow due to circulator pump failure or cavitation.

23. The required speed of response of the fast acting shutdown system is determined by the fastest fault transient and the available margin to dryout. On the Winfrith SGHWR this fault is the loss of supplies to the main circulators and arises because of the low inertia of the glandless pumps used. Later designs under study at the moment use glanded pumps to which large inertia can be added, thereby, considerably reducing the severity of this transient. However, it is still worthwhile retaining the same speed of operation of the shutdown system to permit a reduction to be made in the dryout margin allocated for fault transients. For the Winfrith SGHWR, a period of 600 ms between supply failure and insertion of shutdown absorber requires 12½% dryout margin to allow for the transient; each further 100 ms delay requires a further 2% dryout margin.

24. Some fault conditions do not require a complete shutdown or reactor trip and furthermore, if the fault can be corrected quickly, there is a strong incentive to avoid a reactor trip and carry out a rapid power set-back instead. The most important example is the trip out of the turbo-alternator. In this case, it is an

advantage to provide an alternative steam off-take, or dump, when the turbine trip valve closes due to overspeeding, so that the pressure changes do not cause a reactor trip. Similarly, the drum water level control must be sufficiently good to avoid a trip condition. Other examples only requiring power set-back include failure of moderator cooling, low condenser vacuum and high moderator level.

CONTROL DESIGN METHODS

Simulation of the system

25. An extremely valuable contribution to control system design has been provided by the digital and analogue system simulations developed over the past years. It is, therefore, worthwhile to outline the basic content of the current wide range simulator which is programmed on a PACE analogue computer.

26. The mathematical model forming the basis of the simulation adopts a point representation of the reactor. It assumes conditions corresponding to an average channel with a description of phenomena associated with boiling derived from previous analysis of a one-dimensional channel. Hence the simulation takes into account items such as movement of the boiling boundary and corresponding voidage changes including appropriate variations of saturation conditions with channel pressure; these can be made available as signal outputs from the simulation. The reactor neutron kinetics include up to six delay groups but, with suitable choice of constants these are normally reduced to two with no appreciable errors being introduced; the principle reactivity feed-backs due to the Doppler effect and channel voidage are, of course, included. Moderator height in the simulation is derived from flow into and out of the calandria controlled by valves with appropriate stroking times and flow limits; its influence in the simulation is only as a reactivity input. Feed line downcomer and riser delays are included in the simulation. Pressures are estimated round the primary circuit giving the sub-cooling at any point required, in particular at channel entry, and also giving the circulation flow from the pump characteristics quoted by the manufacturers. The turbine steam valve characteristics are represented by expressing steam flow as simply proportional to the product of drum pressure and valve position. The valve position is the sum of the speeder gear position and governor signal, which is proportional to frequency error. Feed-water heating is simulated and is dependent on steam output to the turbine. The arrangements provided on Winfrith SGHWR for dumping steam are also simulated. All the principal control valves are included in the simulation together with stroking times or responses either quoted by the maker or derived from tests and the simulator is, therefore, able to give a reasonable representation of any auto-control system under consideration.

27. The alarms and trips based on neutron flux, pressure, drum level and their rates are available on the simulation and other failures such as circulator or turbine trips can be represented by moving appropriate input switches, and the resulting transients studied.

28. A mock-up control desk can be connected to the simulator and is used for training operators. It includes the principal manual controls such as speeder gear and moderator level, together with metered outputs and auto/manual changeover, similar to the Winfrith SGHWR.

System design

29. The outline form of control for the Winfrith SGHWR was chosen from the considerations outlined previously. The actual values of control loop gains and shaping networks used were obtained by experiment on a simulation and by frequency responses obtained digitally. Frequency responses are particularly useful in checking that the most suitable forms of shaping networks are being used and in assessing margins of stability; it is essential for any practical system to make reasonable allowance for variations in performance of control valves, measuring instruments, etc., and inaccuracies in the simulation model.

30. While frequency response methods are useful in initial basic design of control loops for stability, they do not immediately yield transient responses showing the variations that are likely, even ignoring non-linearities. Hence simulation studies are necessary at least to check the viability of a theoretical design, and in practice play a large part in getting a feel for the behaviour of the plant and formulating control philosophy.

31. Simulation provides a simple direct way of seeing that the best combination of control gains are being adopted and checking trip or alarm margins against transients that would be expected under operating conditions. As an example, use of a simulation provides the only means of checking that drum level and pressure will stay within their limits when a turbine trip occurs.

DESCRIPTION OF WINFRITH SGHWR CONTROL SYSTEM

Control freedoms required and available

32. Moderator height is maintained to cover the fuel by suitable boron addition; the remaining control requirements under normal operation are that the dependent quantities,

system power level

system pressure

drum water level

should be regulated at prescribed values.

33. In order to regulate three outputs at least three independent degrees of freedom must be physically available for control input with suitable rates. Two such control inputs already mentioned are feed-water flow rate and the steam flow rate valve controlling off-take from the drum.

34. In principle, any third independent input could be used to complete the control, for example recirculation flow rate, but its effect on reactivity is proportional to the void coefficient and it is, therefore, not suitable for an enriched SGHWR. A direct control of reactivity would be excellent as the third control input since it is a mode of disturbance very different from the other two.

35. The use of boron in the moderator for all reactivity control variations is not feasible on account of the rates required. Granted continuous adjustment of the long-term value of moderator height, it is acceptable to use moderator height itself as the means of reactivity control in the short-term, and this is the process adopted on current designs of enriched SGHWRs. Controlled draining of the moderator provides the basis for power set-back in appropriate fault conditions. The rapid insertion of large negative reactivity at a reactor trip is achieved by injecting concentrated boron poison into special shutdown tubes.

Available system alternatives

36. The requirement to regulate system power, system pressure and drum water level using control inputs on reactivity, steam flow valve and feed-water flow leads to only a finite number of possible arrangements.

37. Drum water level and feed-water flow are an immediately obvious pair, leaving only the relation between outputs:

system power and system pressure;

and the controls:

reactivity and steam flow valve

to be decided. The two basic alternatives are known as the:

coupled system in which pressure is controlled by altering reactivity and power demand is set by the steam valve position without the need for a power controller;

and the

decoupled system in which pressure is controlled by the steam valve and power output error is corrected by reactivity adjustment via a controller.

38. They are so called because, with pressure held constant, a turbine governor valve movement necessarily causes a corresponding change in reactor power in the coupled system, but not in the decoupled system since the turbine valve is brought back to its original position by the pressure control.

39. For zero or slightly negative void coefficients (as in enriched SGHWRs) pressure control is more rapid in the decoupled system; this is because the coupled system control loop includes the lag due to fuel conductivity in addition to the drum time constant, and matters discussed in paras 7 to 9, accentuate the difference for negative void coefficients.

40. When load following from changes in grid frequency, both systems start to increase reactor power after an initial valve opening as pressure and delivered steam rate begin to fall. With identical reactivity controls available for each system and zero void coefficient the rises in reactor power will be virtually identical. The decoupled system, whose pressure control starts to reclose the steam valve, will, therefore, have the smaller pressure drop but its delivered power will droop slightly more than the coupled system whose steam valve remains open.

41. In following a change in demanded station load, the decoupled system is at an advantage because the steam valve is initially stationary and the comparison between steam demand and delivery gives an immediate full error signal from the controller to raise moderator and increase reactor power. For the basic coupled system the increased load demand is made by opening the valve and there is no call for positive reactivity until drum pressure has started to fall. A power demand rate signal can be added to the pressure demand to provide a starting error.

42. There is little to choose between these systems for load following and the slightly better pressure control of the decoupled system at the void coefficient expected on Winfrith SGHWR, led to choice of the decoupled system for the auto-control of this reactor.

Pressure control loops

43. The pressure controls are shown diagrammatically in Fig. 2.

44. When the turbine is operating normally, the rate of steam delivery is altered by moving the turbine throttle via the governor speeder gear. The actual position of the throttle is a summation of a signal representing the grid frequency error and the position of the speeder gear. The position of the latter is also adjustable manually and, in effect, corresponds to the system loading. Under auto-pressure control, this receives a signal representing pressure error via a phase advance, and

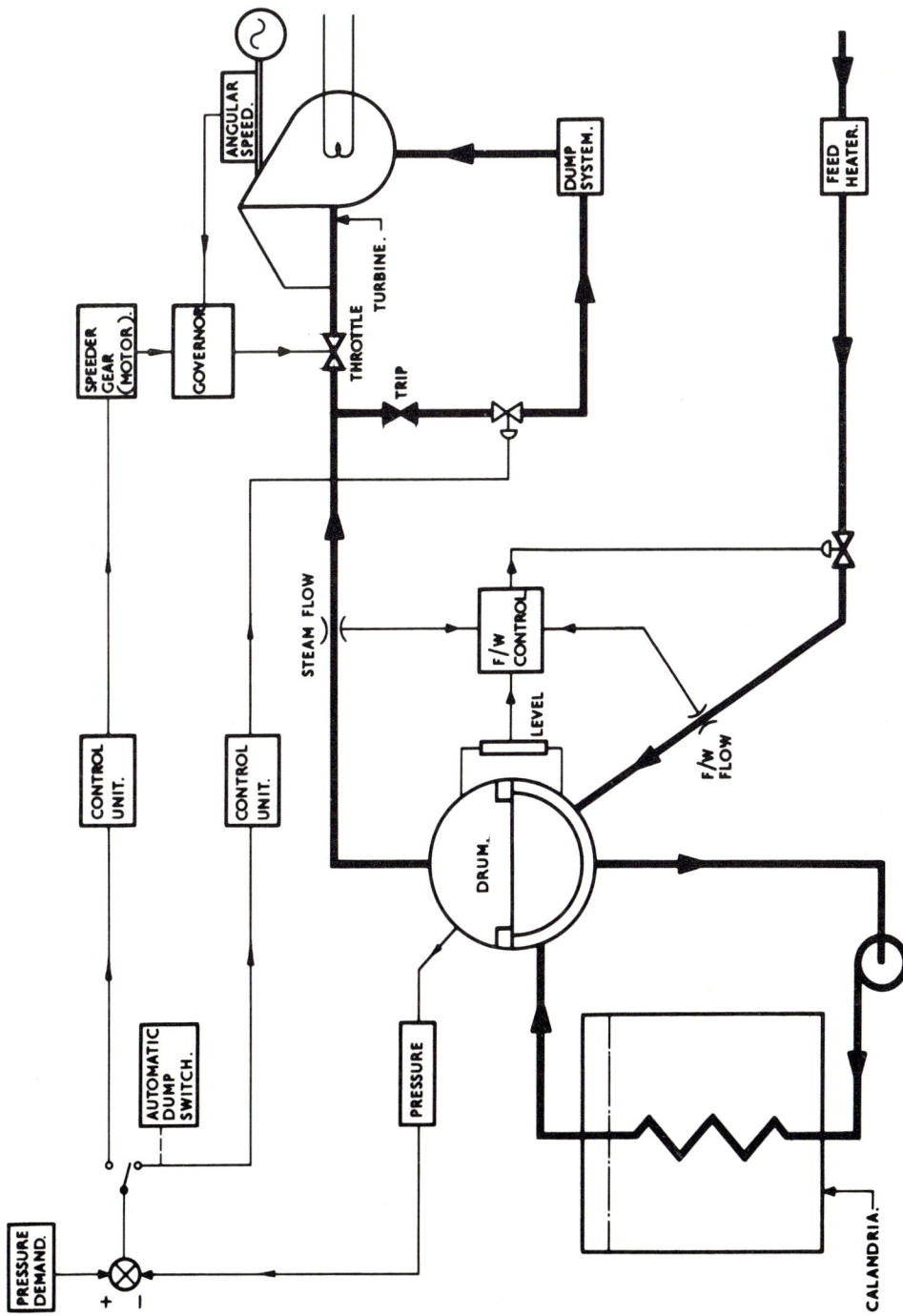

Fig. 2: Simplified schematic of pressure control systems

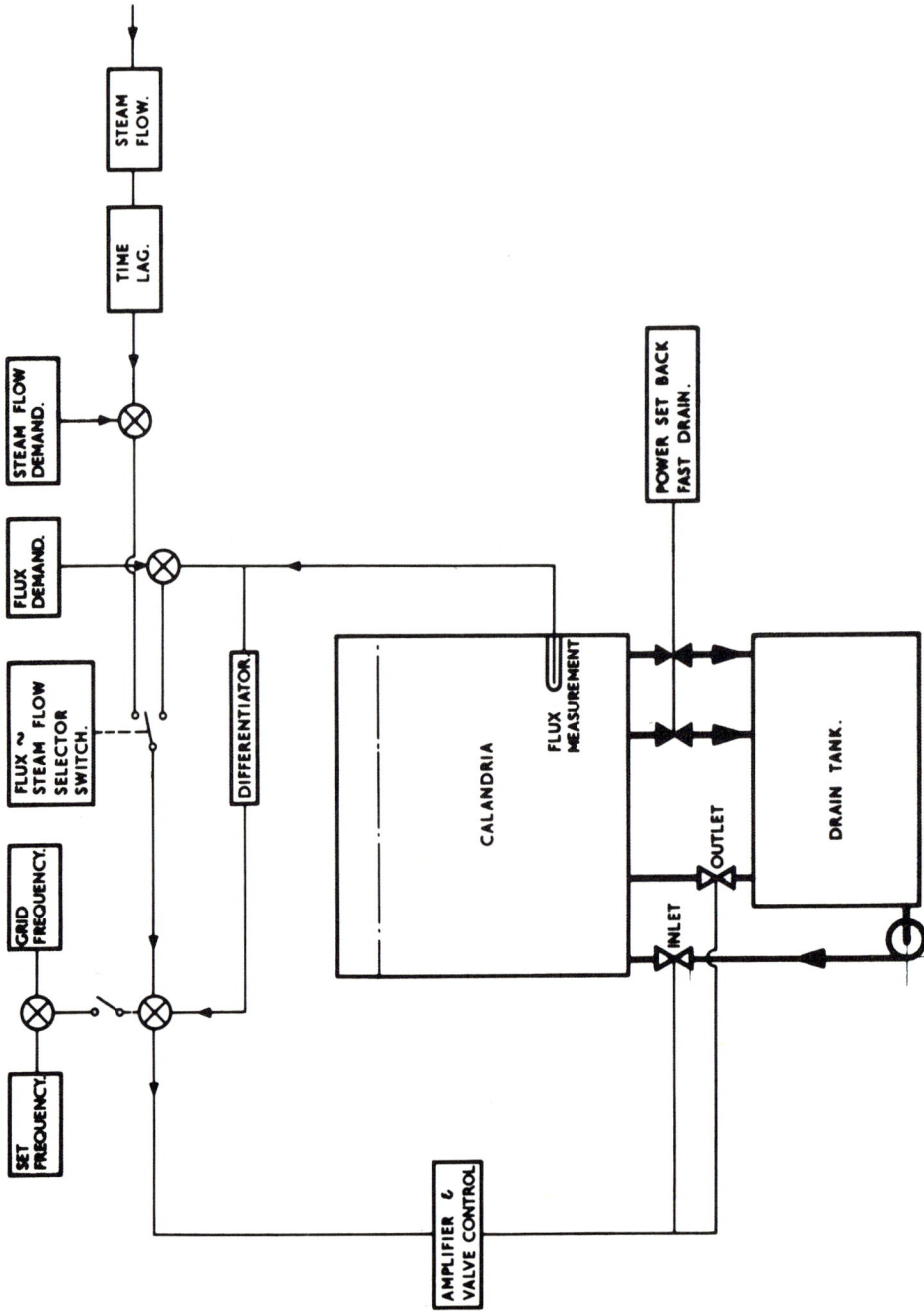

Fig. 3: Simplified schematic of reactor and power control systems

moves at a proportional rate. It, therefore, constitutes an integral term in the control loop thus ensuring that the pressure error is finally brought to zero, overriding the governor component of the throttle position.

45. When a fault arises disconnecting the turbo-alternator from the grid, the turbine stop valve is closed rapidly and at the same time a valve opens the dump system, which by-passes the turbine, to the condenser. This dump line includes a control valve similar to the turbine control valve which can also be ganged electrically to the speeder gear or pre-set manually to any position, say 100% open. When the turbine stop valve shuts, the pressure error signal is switched to control the dump control valve so that excessive change in pressure is avoided and pressure control maintained.

46. During start-up, before the turbine is synchronized, pressure is controlled by the same dump system either automatically or manually. As steam is passed to the turbine by opening its valve manually the dump valve must start to close to maintain pressure. Auto-control of pressure is switched onto the turbine valve as soon as possible and the dump valve closed manually, which causes the turbine valve to open and increase its loading.

Power control loops

47. For short-term reactivity control the moderator level is either lowered by draining D_2O under gravity into a drain tank or raised by pumping into the calandria. The inlet and outlet valves controlling the flow rates can be controlled either manually or by the auto-control system, the pump capacity and valve sizes being chosen to give a rate of change of moderator height corresponding to the required rate of station loading.

48. At low powers and for start-up, control neutron flux is measured at a beam hole facility in the side of the calandria. However, the errors due to spatial distributions become too large for adequate control to be based on such a measurement at or near full power. Consequently above 50% power, steam flow is used as a measure of reactor power, although a rate of change of flux signal is still retained for stabilizing the control.

49. Power shaping is maintained purely by fuel management; several schemes have been devised to keep the radial form factor within acceptable limits.

50. Normal auto-reactor control is shown diagrammatically in Fig. 3. It uses the difference between the manually set demanded power loading and that measured from the flux or steam supplied to the turbine to alter the moderator height. A step change in grid frequency alters the turbine valve position. After initial movements in power and pressure the result-

ing transients end with reactor power unchanged and the turbine valve returned to its original position by the pressure control. There is only a limited amount of load following when the governor initially moves the valve and before the pressure alters.

51. By measuring frequency change and adding a corresponding power demand to the manually set loading demand signal, the transient will end with the appropriately altered power on the reactor and the same demanded pressure. By adjusting the gain of the amplifier providing the change in demanded reactor power from grid frequency error, any degree of long-term load following from grid frequency can be provided.

Feed-water control of drum level

52. This control is illustrated in Fig. 4; it is based on a signal representing demanded feed rate which is derived from a combination of steam flow to the turbine and drum level error. This demanded feed rate is then met by a conventional three-term controller operating on the feed valve and using flow measurement in the feed pipe.

Emergency shutdown and power set-back

53. The emergency shutdown system is explained in detail in Paper 2 to this conference. Explained briefly, negative reactivity is injected in the form of lithium borate solution which is blown by stored helium pressure into shutdown tubes which pass through the core; in addition, the moderator is drained from the calandria. The moderator draining does not act as quickly as the liquid tube shutdown but provides additional shutdown.

54. The reactivity worth of the fast system is estimated to be a little over 3% Δk_{eff}. The reactivity worth of draining the moderator is sufficient to overcome any long-term effects, so that the liquid tube system can be reset once moderator drainage is complete.

55. Fracture of the primary circuit is detected by measurements of pressure and rate of rise of pressure within the primary containment. On receipt of such a signal, the protective system automatically initiates the following actions (called an 'X trip'):

(a) trips the emergency shutdown system, which makes the reactor sub-critical;

(b) closes all the containment isolation valves and commissions the clean-up plant;

(c) initiates the injection of emergency cooling water into the centre of each fuel cluster from a pressurized storage tank overhead;

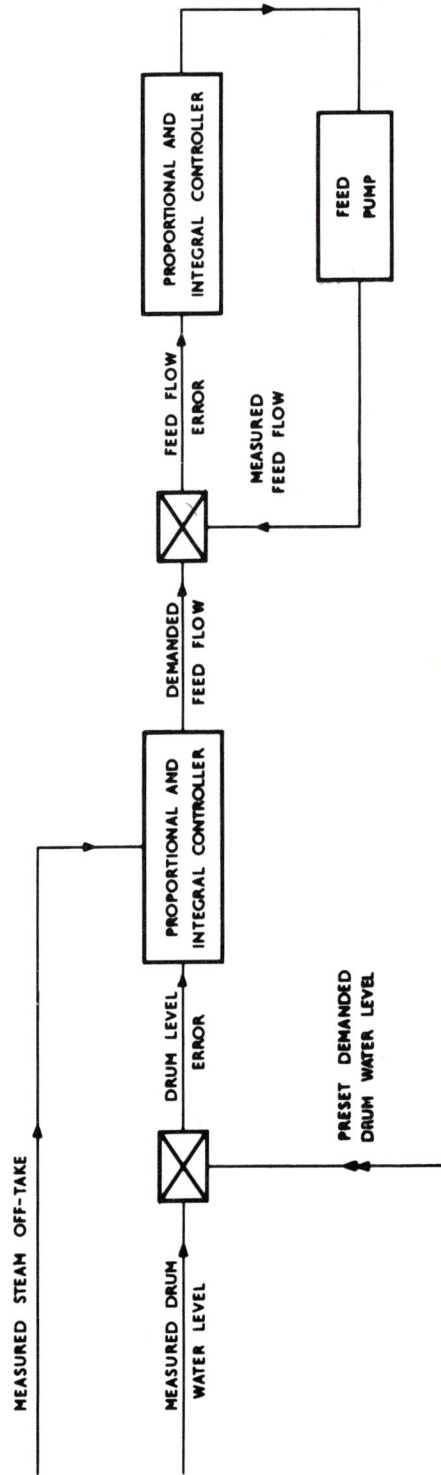

Fig. 4: Diagram of Winfrith SGHWR drum level and feed control system

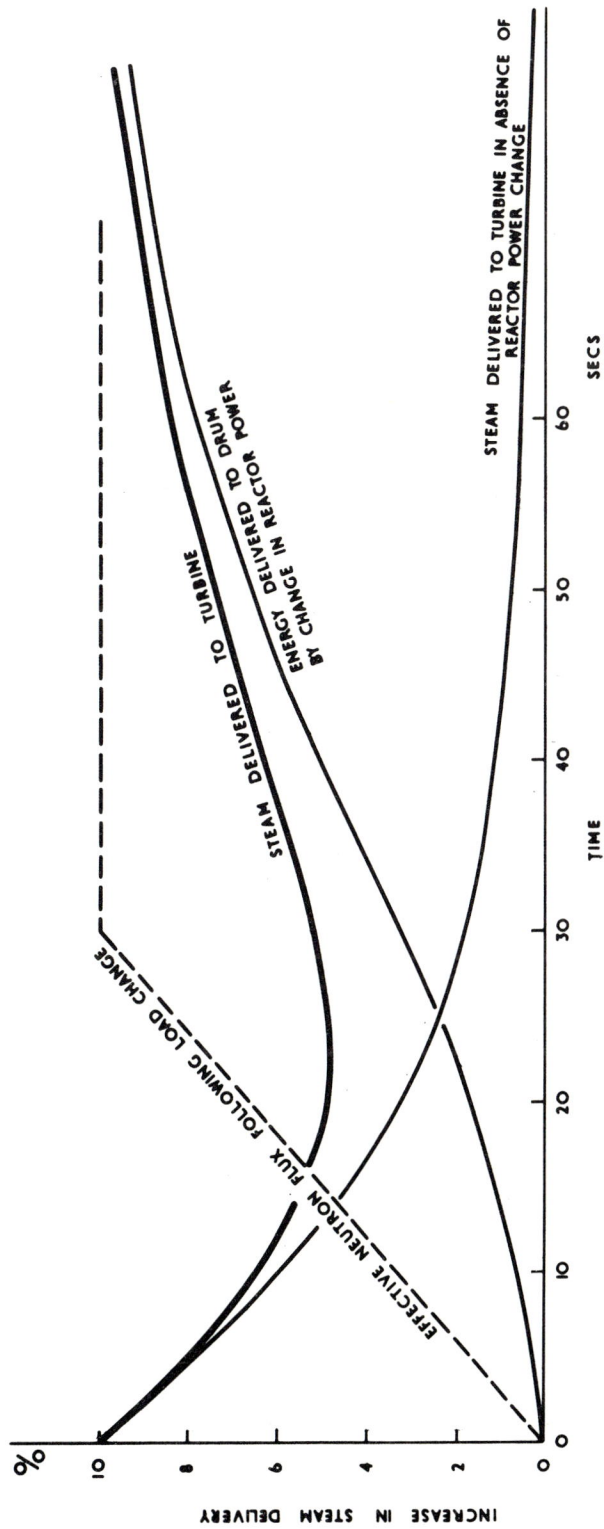

Fig. 5: Form of response of SGHWR system to step increase of 10% from governor movement

(d) initiates a fast depressurization of the primary circuit so that by the time the pressurized emergency cooling tank has emptied, the system pressure is so low that emergency cooling can be continued from the large, low pressure, demineralized water supply.

56. For incidents following which there is a risk of fuel dryout but where the primary circuit is intact, it is only necessary for the protective system to shut down the reactor (Y-trip). The incidents involving uncontrolled increase of power are detected by the nucleonic instrumentation which initiates a trip at 10% excess neutron flux. Loss-of-coolant flow is detected by the fall in pressure drop across the pumps or change in electrical power going to the pumps when they fail. Since a rapid reduction in circuit pressure is likely to cause cavitation in the pumps, this is detected by a differentiating filter with drum pressure input which trips at conditions including 1 psi/s fall lasting 40 s.

57. Power set-back following, for example, a turbine being disconnected from the grid (Z-trip) is carried out by draining moderator and opening the steam dump. The object is to continue controlling both pressure (with the dump valve) and drum water level so that no reactor trip is initiated. When the turbine is shut off, feed heating ceases and, if the reactor power is not brought down sufficiently, the increased sub-cooling at channel inlet will reduce voidage; a negative void co-efficient may then lead to an excess neutron flux trip.

COMMERCIAL DESIGNS

Enriched fuel SGHWRs

58. A range of enriched fuel SGHWRs, based on development of the 100 MW(e) Winfrith SGHWR, is now being considered for commercial power generation. Commercial requirements are expected to be for larger units; it is therefore important to study the effect of increasing size on control. Also the duties expected of the reactor will vary according to customer requirements and it is particularly important to examine load following capabilities.

59. Dynamic properties and control of larger SGHWRs. Since larger systems are achieved by increasing the number of channels, which individually are themselves not significantly altered, the boiling process and associated primary loop characteristics can be identical. Larger enriched SGHWRs are also expected to have void coefficients very near to zero. Hence, the overall dynamic properties remain as described.

60. The increased core size of commercial reactors can lead to xenon driven slow spatial modes of oscillation. This problem is very similar to that already met in Magnox reactors and can be treated in the same way by dividing the core into sectors. In one design for a 500 MW(e) SGHWR, four sectors are made in the calandria by partitions extending part way down into the moderator. The moderator height in each sector is controlled by altering the pressure of the inert gas over the moderator from a measurement of sector power. These instabilities have a very long period and manual control is perfectly feasible, but auto-control could be provided if required.

61. Load following. The rate at which the moderator can be raised on the Winfrith SGHWR corresponds to a reactivity rate of nearly 3×10^{-5} K/s at the slowest condition (when the moderator is near full height) giving an increase of power, relative to full power, of nearly 20% per min, i.e., approximately twice that specified. This is normally an acceptable rate for daily variations and anticipated load changes. At lower powers in particular, it is likely that the rate limiting feature will be on the turbine.

62. Load following of grid frequency is normally initiated by the turbine speed sensitive governor which opens or closes the steam valve from the speeder setting depending on the frequency error. This movement is nominally proportional to the frequency error with 100% valve movement corresponding to approximately 2 c/s frequency variation; power changes demanded thus are usually within 10%. If the steam valve is stepped open in response to a step change in frequency, then the steam delivery to the turbine is raised immediately, but it starts to fall off as pressure reduces and heat is taken from the drum storage. As the reactor power rises and replaces the heat taken from storage, the pressure re-establishes and delivered power returns to the total demand. A typical form of transient is shown in Fig. 5. The response could be improved by increasing the drum and circuit water-heat storage, and also by increasing the maximum moderator pumping rates.

63. The initial immediate response in steam flow to a change in grid frequency is not normally essential but it cannot be avoided when governors with a rapid response are used. By shaping the transient response of the governor so that it opens exponentially the dip in the load transient of Fig. 5 can be avoided. Detailed simulation shows that a 500 MW(e) SGHWR could provide a grid load following characteristic in the form of a clean exponential with time constant 15 s. For this, a reactivity rate of 3 mN/s is assumed and the drum size is proportionally similar to the Winfrith SGHWR. Following step changes in grid frequency which correspond to an additional power demand of 10% the system pressure variation is less than 10 lb/in². Fig. 6 shows the basic principles of the system, including the shaping of the governor response; it features a power demand signal sent to

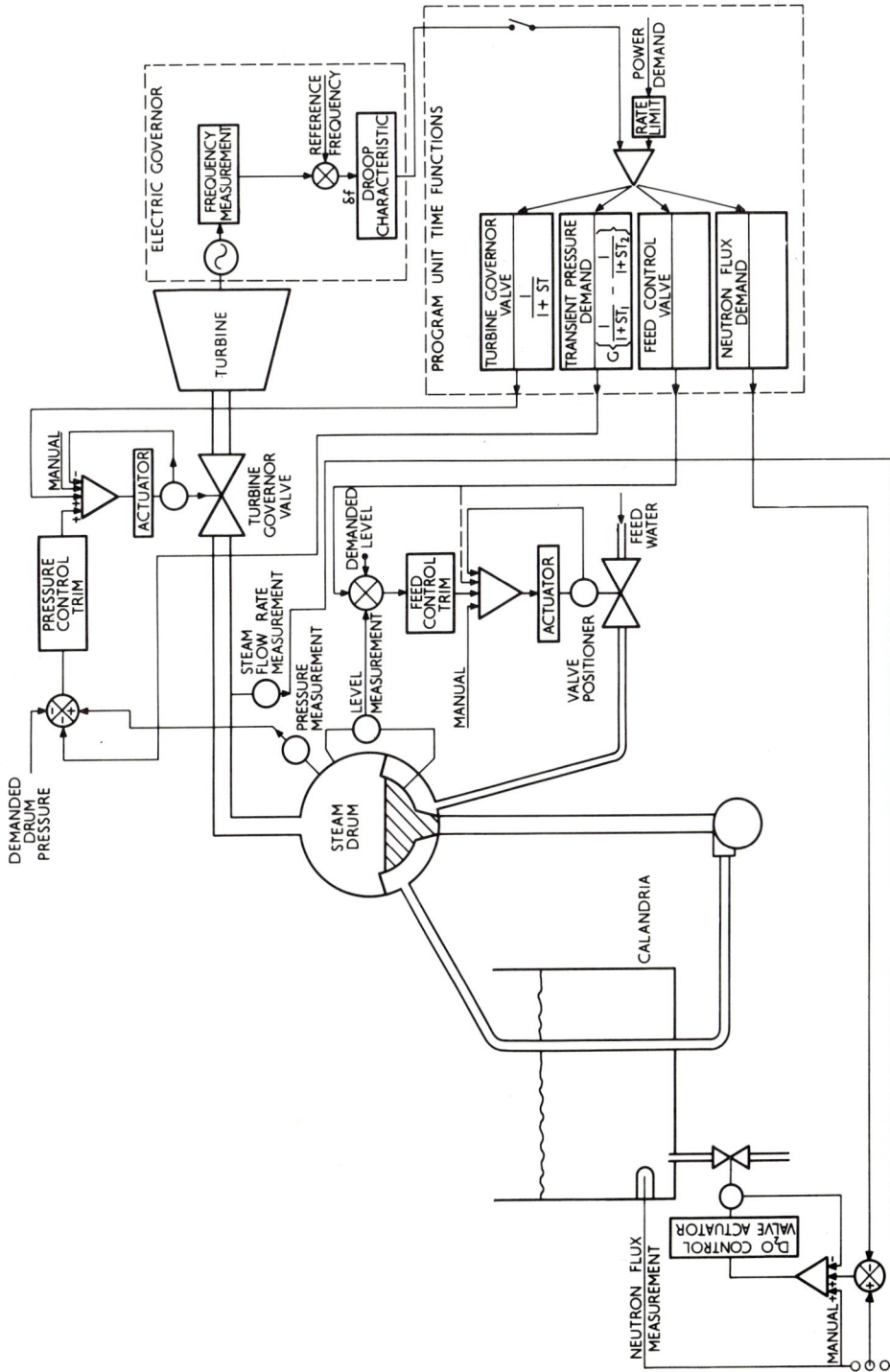

Fig. 6: System control and load following

93

the reactor power control derived from frequency error, and a similar programmed demand to the feed-water control valve.

Natural fuel SGHWRs

64. Design studies are also being made of a commercial SGHWR, using non-enriched fuel. From the point of view of station control the most important differences from enriched fuel SGHWRs lie in the significant positive void coefficient and the comparative lack of reactivity for start-up.

65. The large positive void coefficient is valuable as a means for providing reactivity. For this purpose the reduction of primary circulation flow at low power is being considered so that approximately constant voidage conditions are maintained. At start-up, either steam or pressurized hot water would be injected at channel entry to create the voidage from which start-up reactivity is achieved.

66. To ensure reactor stability with the large positive void coefficient, a rapid mechanism for control of reactivity is required. The principal methods being studied include variation of primary circuit flow and absorber rods. Primary circuit flow control was briefly mentioned as a possible degree of freedom for control in paras 16 to 18; the range of void coefficient expected on the natural fuel SGHWR makes it potentially more useful than on the enriched fuel SGHWRs.

67. Considerations of spatial stability are similar to the enriched, there being two azimuthal modes of instability in this case and control design is in terms of six sectors with independent reactivity control.

Use of control computers

68. While an on-line computer is not an essential feature of the SGHWR system, it is worth mentioning briefly some of the control functions that it could perform and the following are a few examples:

1. Routine operational sequences such as start-up and shutdown could be pre-programmed and controlled with checks at each step.

2. The computer could be used for the automatic control of moderator boron concentration from measurements of neutron flux and moderator height. This would assist in overriding xenon transients and minimize the amount of boron addition and removal.

3. Channel power measurement from quality meters, coupled with a knowledge of fuel loading pattern and appropriate physics constants, could provide a complete map of the power distribution over the core and hence values for irradia-

tion burn-up for each channel.

4. Finally, there are several obvious computational facilities such as heat balances and thermal efficiency calculations which could be of value in optimizing station efficiency under rapidly changing operating conditions.

CONCLUSION

69. Power reactors of the SGHWR type, operating with a direct cycle steam drum system, have many closely interacting dynamic properties. Their degree of coupling is greater than on corresponding conventional power plant mainly because of the important influence of coolant conditions on the nuclear reactivity and hence on the power of the thermal energy source.

70. Current SGHWR designs provide a flexible system for generation of electricity and there is considerable potential for development of this flexibility with the same basic design. This development could result from using more advanced turbine governors and associated controls which would act in sympathy with the dynamic properties of SGHWRs and from further refinement or extension of reactivity controls.

ACKNOWLEDGEMENTS

71. This paper is published by kind permission of the Managing Director, The Reactor Group, UKAEA, Risley. Thanks are due to the many colleagues at Risley and Winfrith responsible for the work reported.

Fuel management in SGHWRs

F. P. O'DELL, BSc, UKAEA, Risley

D. R. HOPKINS, BSc, UKAEA, Winfrith

F. R. ALLEN, BSc, PhD, UKAEA, Winfrith

SYNOPSIS   The considerations governing the choice of fuel management schemes in SGHWRs are reviewed. Since the pressure tube construction permits ready access to individual channels, a wide range of schemes are possible and these can be adjusted to suit the requirements of particular installations. As examples the fuel management schemes evolved for the 100 MWe Winfrith reactor, a 350 MWe low enrichment design, and a natural uranium version are described.

INTRODUCTION

1.   In the context of this paper the term 'fuel management' refers to the strategies followed in loading, unloading and re-arranging the fuel elements in a reactor core. This topic is of great operational importance since small changes in the efficiency of fuel utilization inherent in alternative fuel management schemes may integrate to sizable capital sums over reactor life. There are also implications on design, since the fuel management scheme influences the power distribution in the reactor and hence the core size needed to achieve a particular output. Again different fuel management schemes may require significantly different fuel handling equipment.

2.   The pressure tube construction of SGHWRs permits easy access to individual channels and simplifies refuelling operations. In principle, it is possible to design the system for either on-load or off-load refuelling. A particularly wide range of fuel management schemes are, therefore, possible and this flexibility makes it feasible and indeed worthwhile to design the schemes to suit individual applications. There is, in fact, no general optimum fuel management scheme for SGHWRs, each application must be looked at in the light of the appropriate economic ground rules and system operating requirements. This paper will, therefore, indicate some of the more general trends and important specific results which have emerged from the studies so far made.

SGHWR FUEL MANAGEMENT PRINCIPLES

Requirements

3.   A satisfactory fuel management scheme should meet the following requirements:

(1)   fuel costs should be minimized by extracting the maximum of heat from the fuel during irradiation;

(2)   the power distribution must permit full reactor power to be attained without violating thermal performance limitations on individual channel output. Since present SGHWRs are controlled by soluble moderator poison rather than by variable arrays of solid absorbers, particular attention must be given to this aspect;

(3)   the reactor availability requirements must be met, e.g., an off-load fuelling scheme must be designed so that the frequency and duration of refuelling outages are compatible with the electrical grid requirements;

(4)   the irradiation history of individual fuel elements must lie within acceptable design limits, for example, those set by the build-up of fission gas pressure, etc.

Selection of cycle order

4.   In the design of schemes to satisfy these requirements, one of the key decisions which has to be taken at an early stage is the choice of the cycle order, i.e., the reciprocal of the fraction of the core removed at each refuelling shutdown. An on-load fuelling scheme represents the limiting case in which the number of re-fuelling batches has become equal to the number of fuel elements in the core. The following simple relationship imposes some practical restrictions on the choice of schemes:

$$I_m = m \, Rd \qquad\qquad (1)$$

where I_m = mean discharge irradiation for an m cycle scheme m = cycle order

R = reactor mean rating

d = time interval between refuellings.

5. In general, as the cycle order increases the refuelling interval decreases and it is clearly possible to operate the reactor with progressively smaller margins of excess reactivity and fuel inventory. It is thus possible to obtain progressively higher irradiation levels for a given feed enrichment. A general relationship derived from a large number of detailed 2- and 3-dimensional fuel management calculations is that for a given feed enrichment

$$I_m = C \left(\frac{m}{m+1}\right) I_\infty \qquad (2)$$

where I_∞ is the limiting irradiation attainable with on-load fuelling

C is a numerical coefficient ~0.8.

6. Equation 2 shows that there are strong pressures to increase the cycle order and so increase the efficiency of the fuel cycle and lower fuel costs. On the other hand, an increase of cycle order leads to more frequent refuelling shutdowns (equation 1) and hence tends to incur greater outage penalties. In the limiting case of on-load refuelling, the planned outage penalties may be reduced at the expense of more elaborate fuel handling equipment. The interplay of these factors will be illustrated in a later section devoted to a specific reactor design since the subject is too complex to pursue further in general terms.

Axial fuel management

7. Once the cycle order has been selected, it becomes necessary to consider the actual features of the fuel management scheme. It is convenient to consider the question of axial fuel management first since this is relatively independent of core size and power output.

8. In the early days of the SGHWR project, the merits of sub-dividing the length of the fuel element and adopting some form of axial fuel management were extensively debated. It was recognized that an axially undivided fuel element would be somewhat inefficient from the reactor physics point of view since the burn-up would be non-uniform. Calculations showed that the adoption of an undivided fuel element would lead to a loss of 1400 MWd/TeU in burn-up compared with shuffled sub-divided fuel. In an enriched reactor operating with a discharge irradiation of about 20,000 MWd/TeU, this could be corrected by an increase of enrichment level of about 0.1% U-235 and would involve a corresponding fuel inventory penalty. However, there are other considerations which have to be taken into

account, i.e.:

(a) full length fuel elements are simpler, involve less end fittings and are, therefore, cheaper to fabricate;

(b) large fission gas plena may be provided at each end of the assembly and design for large gas releases at high irradiation levels is, therefore, simplified;

(c) perturbations to the heat generation or coolant flow associated with the joints in a sub-divided fuel element are absent and possible deleterious effects on performance avoided;

(d) fuel handling equipment is greatly simplified;

(e) the axial neutron flux distribution becomes progressively flattened by burn-up. The peak ratings of individual fuel assemblies loaded at fuel cycle equilibrium are reduced by this effect.

9. These considerations were felt to outweigh the fuel inventory penalty and the Winfrith SGHWR and present commercial designs are based on a standard type of full-length, undivided fuel cluster. The only practical disadvantage is that the resulting assembly constitutes a comparatively large unit to use as a basis for fuel management and the change in channel power output with irradiation is rather large (30-40%). At some stage in the future, it might prove profitable to move to a bisegmented fuel element which could still retain large fission product plena at each end. The implications on heat transfer performance and fuel handling are currently being evaluated. Even with this type of fuel element, there would be no question of adopting an elaborate axial fuel management scheme; there would simply be the possibility of replacing the two halves at different times and so reducing the variations in channel power output.

10. In a reactor designed for operation with natural uranium, the arguments presented above do not apply, since the loss of 1400 MWd/TeU in burn-up associated with the full-length fuel element is too large a fraction of the attainable burn-up to be tolerated. This topic will be discussed in a later section devoted to the natural uranium design.

Radial fuel management

11. Since present designs of enriched SGHWR use full-length fuel elements, the fuel management strategy is essentially a question of choosing a suitable radial pattern. The simplest choice of all would be to divide the channels into a number of groups equal to the cycle order and scatter the members of each group uniformly over

the core. However, except under rather special circumstances to be discussed later, this would not lead to an acceptable degree of power flattening. The latter must be achieved by establishing a higher local reactivity in the outer region of the reactor. In principle the following methods can be identified:

(1) feeding the outer channels of the reactor with a higher fuel enrichment;

(2) moving partially irradiated fuel from the outer zone inwards;

(3) adjusting the discharge rates of fuel so that the discharge irradiation level for the outer zone is lower and the mean reactivity correspondingly higher;

(4) using control absorbers.

12. The first two solutions have been adopted for enriched SGHWR designs. The third solution is appropriate to the natural fuelled version. The fourth solution was felt to be basically incompatible with the objective of obtaining high efficiency fuel management schemes since it relies on parasitic absorptions. In the sections which follow, it will be shown how these general approaches have been adapted to the needs of particular situations.

THE 100 MWe WINFRITH SGHWR

General considerations

13. The 100 MWe Winfrith SGHWR raises some special questions in fuel management. In addition to its primary function as a demonstration power producer, the reactor also serves as a vehicle for irradiating more advanced types of fuel elements. It was decided that, in these circumstances, it would be best to operate initially with a single annual major refuelling shutdown. This pattern of operation provides a convenient framework for the irradiation of relatively large batches of fuel. An on-load charge-discharge machine has, however, been provided so that more advanced fuel management schemes may be used in future and so that individual fuel assemblies may eventually be loaded or un-loaded without the necessity for a reactor shutdown.

Selection of a 3-cycle scheme

14. The choice of annual refuelling implies that the Winfrith SGHWR must operate with a higher mean excess reac-tivity (and hence fuel inventory) than the later commercial designs where purely economic considerations are paramount. Moreover the reactor carries a reactivity load in the form of experimental facilities and suffers a higher neutron leakage than commercial reactors due to its smaller size. All these factors conspire to raise the necessary levels of enrichment. Bearing in mind the relationships expressed in equation 1, it appeared that the objec-tive of annual refuelling could best be attained with a 3-cycle scheme operating with a mean discharge irradiation of 15,000 MWd/TeU. This scheme requires a feed enrichment of 2.28% at fuel cycle equi-librium which is considerably higher than that needed in the commercial reactors to achieve more than 20,000 MWd/TeU. Basic mean irradiation levels of about 18,000 MWd/TeU would be attainable in the Winfrith reactor without increase in the level of feed enrichment by adopting more efficient fuel management schemes of higher cycle order. As will be shown, special provision has also been made to irradiate demonstration batches of fuel to beyond 20,000 MWd/TeU.

15. The most effective 3-cycle scheme is the so-called 'roundelay' which achieves power flattening by means of an inward radial fuel move. Once equilibrium is attained, the scheme is operated in the following manner. At each shutdown, a batch of fuel is discharged from (say) the 'white' squares of the inner chessboard zone. The batch of partly irradiated fuel occupying the outer buffer zone is transfer-red inwards to refill the 'white' squares and the buffer zone is recharged with fresh fuel. At the next refuelling, the 'black' squares of the chessboard are discharged, etc. Each fuel element, therefore, spends three cycles of operation in the core, one in the buffer and two in the chessboard. In the 100 MWe reactor size, this cycle gives a total radial form factor of 1.33 or better.

16. In the 3-cycle roundelay scheme, the flattening is produced by the fuel moves which concentrate the more highly irradiated fuel in the inner chessboard zone. Special measures are needed to start the cycle. The simple expedient of using two fuel batches of lower enrichment for the initial loading of the chessboard has been adopted in the Winfrith SGHWR. A 3-batch basic core loading using fuels of 1.24%, 1.56% and 2.28% U-235 has, therefore, been adopted.

Initial core loading of the Winfrith SGHWR

17. The basic simplicity of the 3-cycle roundelay fuel management scheme is complicated by some of the special features of the Winfrith reactor. These are:

(a) 8 experimental channels are provided for superheat fuel elements which because of their quite different design cannot become involved in a fuel move scheme;

(b) 4 channels are connected to a special booster pump and are reserved for highly-rated fuel elements;

(c) one channel can be operated on a special coolant loop;

(d) a batch of fuel elements is provided with extra enrichment to cover irradiation to beyond 20,000 MWd/TeU.

18. These considerations remove a number of channels from the scheme and the final core loading which arises is shown in Fig. 1. The channels marked 'through' do not participate in the fuel moves. The positions marked E are occupied by minor variations of the basic fuel design. The variations are in enrichment level, clad thickness, grid design, vibro-compacted instead of pelletized fuel, etc. These channels will give valuable information on potential cost savings. As has been shown in another paper to this conference, the power distribution and reactivity level of this complex loading have turned out to be close to predictions and the irradiations are proceeding according to plan (ref. 1).

FUEL MANAGEMENT IN LOW ENRICHMENT COMMERCIAL REACTORS

General

19. It is now appropriate to pick up some of the arguments of paras 3-12 and develop them in the context of present commercial designs. Since these are based on full-length fuel elements, the question at issue is the choice of a suitable radial strategy. In addition to satisfying economic criteria, it is necessary to ensure that at no stage during the life of a fuel element is its power output greater than that allowed by thermal performance limits. Further, it is necessary to check that the expected build-up of fission gas pressure is less than the design limit. These two requirements mean that the methods of calculation used must allow the explicit representation of each channel in the reactor, so that the rating history of individual fuel elements can be followed through all stages of the fuel cycle. The PATRIARCH scheme of computer codes for design purposes provides various alternative methods for such calculations, and the core representation models associated with these are discussed in the companion paper presented to this conference (ref. 2). Three of the codes are of particular importance in fuel management, i.e., ZADOC which provides a 2-dimensional XY model of neutron diffusion and burn-up, MAGOG which performs a similar function in 3-dimensions and JOSHUA, a 3-dimensional coupled nuclear-thermal-hydraulic model. The results quoted here have been obtained with these codes.

Selection of cycle order

20. The main factors bearing on the choice may be summarized as follows.

(i) For current commercial designs of SGHWR, the plant layout with a refuelling pond located above the core enables a relatively simple off-load fuel handling system to be used.

(ii) Enrichment and hence fuel costs decrease with increasing cycle order, the lowest cost being obtained with continuous on-load refuelling.

(iii) The refuelling shutdown time in any year increases with increasing number of batches, and this may involve a cost penalty on grounds of reactor availability, although for any scheme that has been considered the loss in availability is much less than 2%.

(iv) The channel form factor (maximum/mean channel power) depends on the scheme adopted. The channel form factor is made up from a macroscopic factor and a local peaking factor.

21. Varying the cycle order has two important and opposing effects. First, the refuelling peaking factor, which expresses the ratio by which the power from a freshly fuelled channel exceeds the general level, increases with increasing cycle order. Secondly, high cycle order schemes have less excess reactivity built into the core since refuelling operations are more frequent for a constant fuel discharge burn-up. On present designs of SGHWR, this excess reactivity is taken up by boron dissolved in the combined heavy water moderator and reflector, and a large change in boron content between refuellings has a deleterious effect on the macroscopic peaking factor due to changes in reflector effectiveness.

22. Obviously the balance of the above factors depends on a customer's requirements and the financial ground rules which are used in any economic assessment. As an illustration, a typical evaluation is given below for a 500 MWe reactor. Four fuel management schemes are considered; 4, 9 and 16-cycle off-load and continuous channel charge-discharge on-load. The ground rules adopted are:

interest rate	8%
reactor life	20 years
load factor	75%.

It is arguable whether outage penalties for off-load refuelling should be included since their effect on the reactor overall availability is small, and for any of these schemes would not affect any guarantee on this parameter. However, for the purposes of this paper, a present worth penalty of £0.46/kW is assumed for each day of refuelling outage time per year (ref. 3). It is further assumed that one of the refuelling shutdowns is coincident with the annual

Table 1
Cost comparison of alternative fuel management schemes

Scheme	4-cycle	9-cycle	16-cycle	Continuous
Feed enrichment (% U-235)	2.16	2.0	1.95	1.88
Initial enrichment (% U-235)	1.46	1.20	1.11	0.995
Reject U-235 (%)	0.548	0.458	0.429	0.396
Reject fissile plutonium (kg/TeU)	4.0	3.98	3.97	3.97
Number of refuellings/year	1	2	4	-
Refuelling outage to be debited (days)	0	2	6	4
Capital cost change (d/kWh)	-0.0017	0	+0.0010	+0.0018
Fuel cost change (d/kWh)	+0.0144	0	-0.0041	-0.0097
Outage penalty (d/kWh)	-0.0034	0	+0.0068	+0.0034
Net cost change ignoring extra cost of on-load equipment (d/kWh)	+0.0093	0	+0.0037	-0.0045

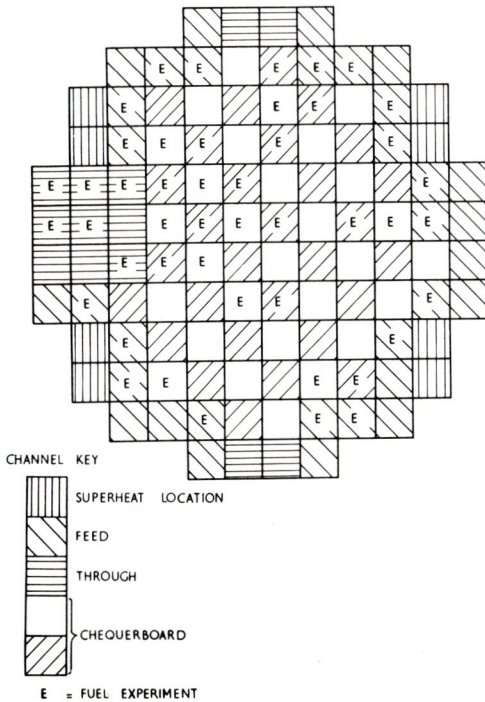

CHANNEL KEY

SUPERHEAT LOCATION

FEED

THROUGH

CHEQUERBOARD

E = FUEL EXPERIMENT

Fig.1. Winfrith 100 MW(e) SGHWR core arrangement: 3-cycle roundelay

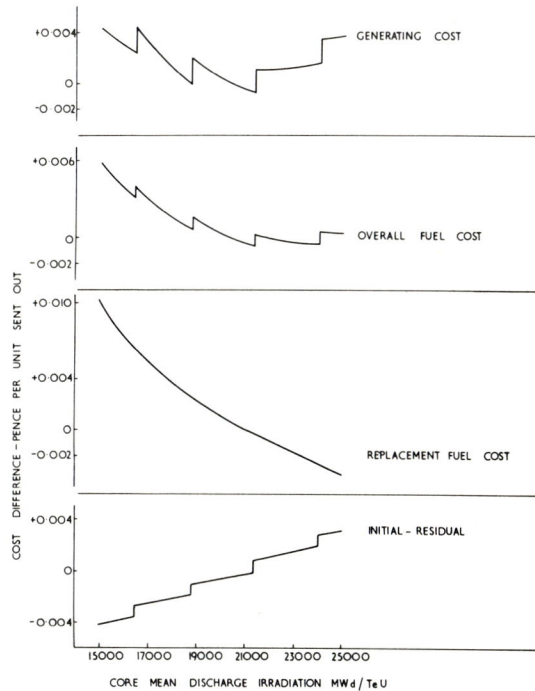

GENERATING COST

OVERALL FUEL COST

REPLACEMENT FUEL COST

INITIAL – RESIDUAL

COST DIFFERENCE – PENCE PER UNIT SENT OUT

CORE MEAN DISCHARGE IRRADIATION MWd/TeU

Fig.2. Fuel cost trends with irradiation level: 9-cycle fuel management scheme

maintenance period and thus excluded from the total outage penalty. For the continuous charge/discharge case, an outage penalty of 4 days per year is assumed for machine breakdown due to the complexity of the remote handling equipment. The cost differentials are shown in Table 1 for a 500 MWe reactor, taking the 9-cycle scheme as a datum, and a constant fuel discharge burn-up of 21,000 MWd/TeU.

23. In Table 1, the capital cost change item is related to changes in core size stemming from changes in channel form factor. The extra capital cost of the on-load refuelling machine is not included. In the case shown, this would need to be less than £600,000 to be economically justified. This figure is near the lower end of the estimated cost range for the additional equipment cost and thus on-load refuelling is unlikely to be attractive in reactors of 500 MWe or less. The off-load schemes seem to show optimum behaviour in the vicinity of 9-cycles.

Selection of discharge irradiation

24. The other important parameter besides cycle order is the selection of discharge burn-up. An increase in the discharge burn-up has the following consequences.

(a) The enrichments required for both the first charge and subsequent refuellings are increased. The cost of this is partially off-set by a rise in fissile plutonium content of the discharged fuel. In the range of economic interest, despite the increase in enrichment, the replacement fuel cost decreases as a result of the reduction in fuel throughput.

(b) The irradiation of the batches become more widespread and the mean core irradiation upon refuelling is increased. This causes the local peaking factor to increase, with a consequent rise in form factor for the whole core.

25. The form factor affects both fuel and capital costs since there is a limitation on maximum channel power output; thus the number of channels in the core varies with the form factor. In assessing the optimum discharge irradiation, this effect must be included. To do this, it is assumed that the electrical power output is fixed and the core size is adjusted in proportion to the form factor variation. The difficulty with this approach is that, for the practical situation to retain core symmetry, channels must, in general, be added in groups of 8 so that the plot of generating cost versus discharge irradiation has discontinuities.

26. Calculations have been made for a 9-cycle fuel management scheme, described in detail below, for the range of fuel discharge irradiations from 15,000 MWd/TeU

to 25,000 MWd/TeU. The results are summarized on Fig. 2. It can be seen that the generating cost variation is very flat between about 18,000 and 23,000 MWd/TeU. The ground rules used for the curve shown assume an interest rate of 8%, load factor 75%, and 20 years life. Similar calculations for other ground rules, e.g., interest rates between 6% and 8%, load factors between 60% and 75% yield similar conclusions.

A 9-cycle dual feed enrichment scheme

27. The currently preferred method for achieving a 9-cycle mode of operation is to group the channels into 3x3 supercell arrays repeated over the reactor core. Power flattening is achieved by dividing the reactor into two zones and feeding the outer zone with a higher feed enrichment. At each refuelling shutdown, one channel in each supercell is charged with fresh fuel.

28. The local peaking in a supercell of channels containing fuel at different irradiations is sensitive to the arrangement of the fuel irradiations. It is, therefore, important to choose an order of discharge which gives rise to no local peaks at any stage of the fuel management scheme. Several arrangements have been studied and that shown on Fig. 3 is preferred.

29. An important part of the development of a fuel management scheme is to identify an initial core loading and approach to equilibrium which satisfies the requirements set out at the beginning of the paper. A large number of possibilities exist. One method that has been examined in detail is to simulate the equilibrium conditions with regard to the distribution of relative channel reactivities by using a number of different enrichments in the initial core loading. In principle, for the dual feed enrichment nine cycle scheme, eighteen different enrichments are required for the initial core loading, these being selected to maintain a roughly constant interval between refuelling shutdowns as in the equilibrium conditions. In practice, these can be reduced by grouping into broader bands. This may still involve some fabrication cost penalty associated with the production of relatively small batches of fuel, but the attraction is that the fuel handling procedures follow a fixed pattern throughout the reactor life.

30. The METHUSELAH-ZADOC method has been used to study the performance of this fuel management scheme for the 350 MWe reactor core shown on Fig. 4 (ref. 2). In this design the average initial enrichments were 1.08% and 1.42%, and the feed enrichments were 1.86% and 2.30% for the inner and outer regions, respectively. The performance of this scheme is shown by the variation in channel form factor with time on Fig. 4. The mean discharge irradiation of the fuel at equilibrium is 21,500 MWd/TeU and 20,800 MWd/TeU for the inner and outer regions, respectively.

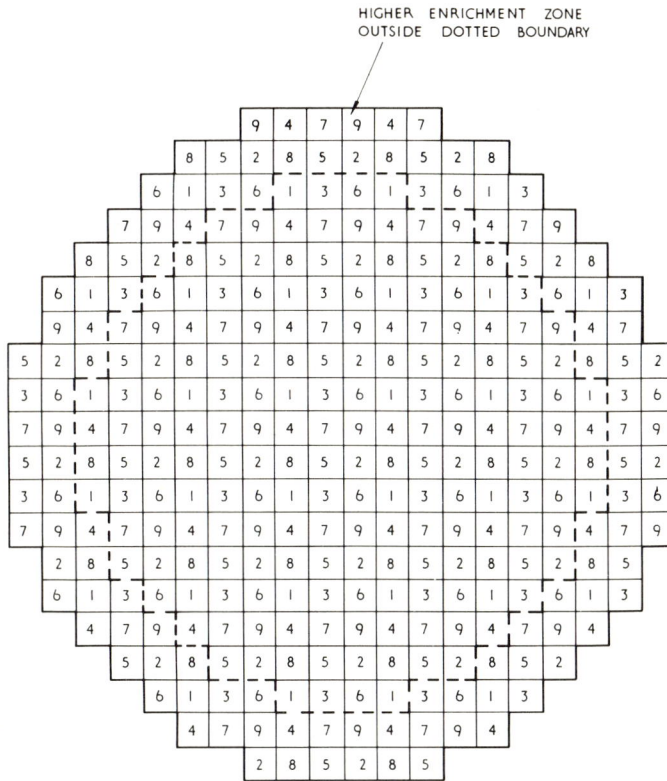

HIGHER ENRICHMENT ZONE
OUTSIDE DOTTED BOUNDARY

Fig.3. 9-cycle dual feed enrichment scheme for 308 channel core

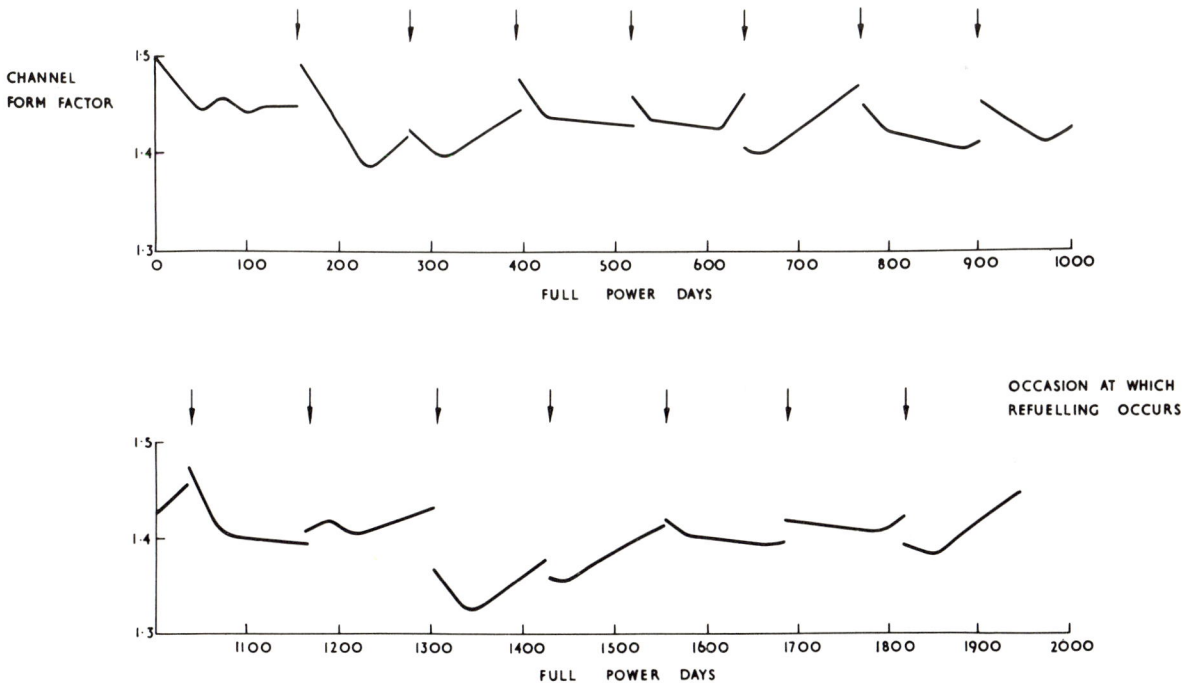

Fig.4. Performance of the 9-cycle dual feed enrichment fuel management scheme

101

NATURAL URANIUM SGHWRs

General considerations

31. In a natural uranium oxide fuelled SGHWR, reactivity is of prime importance to enable satisfactory fuel burn-up to be obtained, so that some form of axial fuel management is essential. This involves the use of segmented fuel and axial fuel movement during irradiation. However, the lower discharge burn-up of this reactor means that fission gas pressure build-up is not limiting and plenums to accommodate the fission gases are unnecessary.

32. The relatively large positive void coefficient results in a tendency for the axial flux distribution to peak towards the coolant outlet end of the core since this is the region of highest steam quality. This is undesirable from the thermal performance aspects and the axial fuel management scheme must be designed to counteract the tendency.

33. As for the enriched designs, off-load refuelling is both simpler and cheaper, but the lower discharge burn-up of the fuel means that shutdowns for refuelling must take place at more frequent intervals. This could lead to capitalized penalties on availability which are greater than the saving on plant cost. The choice is again on financial ground rules and customer choice. Similar considerations apply to the selection of number of fuel segments. Increasing the number allows a small increase in fuel discharge burn-up but the fuel handling is increased for both on- and off-load systems, and an economic balance must be made. In general, our studies show that the choice lies between 2 and 4 segments.

Axial fuel management

34. In studying axial fuel management, account must be taken of the interaction between the flux distribution and the steam void distribution due to the positive void reactivity coefficient. This requires the use of sophisticated methods of calculation. Suitable methods have been developed for both 1-dimensional TIRAZ and 3-dimensional JOSHUA studies. In selecting an axial fuel management scheme, some bias must be introduced to counteract the tendency for the neutron flux peaking towards the coolant outlet end. This can be done by arranging for the least irradiated fuel to be concentrated in the lower half of the channel. With two axial fuel segments this can only be achieved by adopting a bottom feed, push-through scheme. For some of the reactor designs studied, this procedure over-compensates for the void effect. The use of a greater number of segments permits more flexibility at the cost of extra handling and fabrication price.

Radial fuel management

35. In a natural SGHWR, the reactivity differences between radial zones required to achieve a flattened power shape cannot be achieved by differential enrichment as for the enriched design. Absorber flattening is not attractive due to the adverse effect on neutron economy, and thus the creation of mean irradiation level differences is the most attractive scheme. Because the flux tends to peak towards the middle of the reactor, there is a strong tendency for the reactor to be self-flattening when a constant dwell time is used since higher fuel irradiations are established in the middle of the core. This type of scheme results in a radial form factor of about 1.25 for a 600 MWe reactor, when the core flow distribution is gagged to give a constant steam exit quality in all channels. For reactors of other sizes, some changes in fuel dwell time with radius may be necessary. For the initial core loading, both axial and radial power shaping must be introduced by using depleted uranium.

CONCLUSIONS

36. This paper has shown relatively high order multicycle fuelling schemes are most appropriate for the next generation of low enrichment SGHWRs. These reactors are based on full-length, undivided fuel elements. Near optimum behaviour is exhibited by a simple 9-cycle scheme which, in the equilibrium state, is fed with two enrichments of fuel. This requires refuelling shutdowns at approximately 6 monthly intervals, but the ready access to channels in the SGHWR combined with a refuelling pond above the core permits this operation to be carried out in a long weekend.

37. The dual role of the Winfrith SGHWR as a demonstration power producer and irradiation facility for more advanced fuel designs, has led to the adoption of a special fuel management scheme. This involves initial 3-cycle operation with annual major refuelling shutdowns and so will provide large batches of irradiated fuel elements for post-irradiation analysis. An on-load machine has, however, been provided and more advanced fuel management schemes will be demonstrated in the future.

38. SGHWRs fuelled with natural uranium will require radically different fuel management schemes. In order to maximize burn-up and correct the distorting influence of the positive void coefficient on the axial power profile, axially sub-divided fuel elements are required. There is a much stronger incentive to use an on-load charge machine than in the enriched design.

ACKNOWLEDGEMENTS

39. This paper is published by kind permission of the Managing Director, The Reactor Group, UKAEA, Risley. Thanks are due to the many colleagues at Risley and Winfrith responsible for the work reported.

REFERENCES

1.   McCRICKARD J, SMITH D. and ENGLISH D.
Commissioning and operating experience with
the Winfrith SGHWR. Paper 11 to this
conference.

2.   HICKS D. JOHNSTONE I. and O'DELL F.P.
Nuclear design of SGHWRs. Paper 4 to this
conference.

3.   An appraisal of the technical and
economic aspects of Dungeness B Nuclear
Power Station. CEGB, 1965.

Session B: Discussion

Mr E.C.W. Perryman, Atomic Energy of Canada Ltd

1.   Dr Hicks mentioned that the inter-lattice tubes in the SGHWR have not been used. Does this mean that the calculations of void coefficient were unduly pessimistic or that control was easier than envisaged?

2.   Could Dr Hicks give an opinion on the ability to control SGHWR with a fuel such as uranium metal having a considerably higher thermal diffusivity and hence a shorter time constant than UO_2?

3.   Could Mr O'Dell give more justification for his belief that long fuel elements are preferable to short? I cannot agree with the first few points he lists in favour of long elements. Some delegates may have experience of fuel failure produced by fission product gas pressure.

Mr R.G. Naudet, CEA, France

4.   I should like to ask what is the $D_2O:UO_2$ ratio contemplated for the natural uranium versions and what would be the void coefficient in terms of ΔK_V, and/or reactivity release by total voidage of the channels?

Prof G. Casini, Euratom, Ispra, Italy

5.   Does the fuel temperature coefficient of the SGHWR at Winfrith remain negative at the end of the fuel life? What is the order of magnitude of this variation for the prototype and in the case of commercial and natural uranium types? Have any experiments been made to check this point?

Mr A. Forbes Gower, Central Electricity Generating Board

6.   Two small bore pipes are taken from a Venturi in every channel to a transducer. Why should not one of these be used for BCD sampling? Is BCD sampling in every channel really necessary?

7.   Since refuelling can only be carried out in a depressurized state it is very expensive. Can the reactor be operated with failed fuel in the same way as an AGR may be? How much refuelling would be done if a pin failed? Could not failed

channels be more easily detected once the lid is off for refuelling?

Authors' reply: Paper 4

8.   In response to Mr Perryman's questions, interlattice tubes have not been used because the void coefficient calculations were correct. The tubes were included to ensure that the coefficient could be brought to a negative value if the calculations were in error. In fact this has not proved necessary.

9.   A reduced fuel element time constant will speed up the change in steam generation in the reactor following a neutron flux change. In the case of a reactor with a negative void coefficient of reactivity around -0.02 in magnitude, this would not introduce any control difficulties. In fact, it would be of benefit to the control system designer in obtaining fast load-following behaviour. However, for a reactor with a significant positive void coefficient of reactivity, which would normally require a rapid means of varying reactivity for control purposes, a reduction of fuel element time constant would directly increase the difficulties of reactor control. A reduction of fuel element time constant also increases the possibility of a fast void-reactivity driven instability occurring with a negative void coefficient, but the magnitude of void coefficient at which this is likely to occur is very much greater than has been encountered in SGHWR designs.

10. On his final point it must be pointed out that for the same basic design of fuel element (i.e., the same number of pins, can thickness, etc.), segmented fuel requires more end fittings. These both cost more and involve more operations in fabrication as well as increasing the parasitic absorption of the fuel. With regard to the point about fission gas pressure, we have no knowledge of fuel failure due to this phenomena; nevertheless, it is standard practice for all fuel element designers to put a limit on the internal gas pressure within the can. This is not an important limitation on the low burn-up natural design but for the enriched design with fuel burn-up at 21,000 MWd/tU, fission gas build-up is of greater significance. The avoidance of high gas pressure is also beneficial in the case of a circuit pressure

transient as can strain is thereby reduced. It is, therefore, advantageous to be able to use a fission gas plenum to control the gas pressure at the desired value.

11. In the natural uranium SGHWR, the D_2O/UO_2 ratio requested by Mr Naudet is determined by optimization, balancing the lower fuel cost with increase in the ratio against the extra cost of D_2O. Therefore the choice of this parameter depends on the particular ground rules for any application. Our current design is being optimized to Australian conditions and for this we have adopted a ratio of moderator to fuel of 11.4.

12. The operating void coefficient for this design varies with the particular reactor conditions. For unirradiated core we anticipate a value of +0.06 reducing to +0.04 at fuel cycle equilibrium.

13. The last part of Mr Naudet's question referred to the reactivity change on depressurization. The reactivity change on complete core voidage from the hot, pressurized zero power condition, is about 3.5% and from the operating full power condition is rather less, about 2%. The safety consequences of these large reactivity changes are reduced in the reactor design by using a number of independent coolant circuits.

14. On the question raised by Prof Casini, the point of fuel power coefficient on the Winfrith reactor is estimated to change from $-1.9 \times 10^{-5} \Delta K_{eff}$ per $^{\circ}$C to $-0.9 \times 10^{-5} \Delta K_{eff}$ per $^{\circ}$C. Since the actual reactor will contain fuel with a variety of irradiation levels, the actual swing during a burn-up cycle will be considerably less. The effective coefficient will, therefore, always be negative. In a natural fuelled reactor the rethermalization effects are much more important. For a particular design we estimate that the point of fuel coefficient would change from an initial value of $-1.23 \times 10^{-5} \Delta K_{eff}/^{\circ}$C to $-0.37 \times 10^{-5} \Delta K_{eff}/^{\circ}$C at 6000 MWd/t. The average effective value is still, therefore, negative.

15. We have based our estimates on free gas thermalization models. It is difficult to see what could be done in the way of experimental checks. On the Winfrith reactor we are planning to install a reactivity oscillator which should enable us 'to make an analysis of the power co-efficient into its components of void and fuel temperature effects. This will enable us to check our calculations under actual reactor operating conditions.

16. Mr A. Forbes Gower raised a question on the BCD samples. It would not be feasible to use the Venturi tappings to withdraw a BCD sample as the flow through the impulse line would introduce a pressure imbalance and invalidate the instrument reading. It is essential to vent the impulse lines to remove the gases and even occasional use for sampling would lead to unacceptable errors due to the introduction of gases into the line. The use of the connections to the quality meters in a dual role in the BCD system is related to the prototype reactor where a quality meter is used on every channel. In our later designs, quality meters are used on only one in every four or even eight channels, so the incentive does not appear so strongly in these designs. The BCD system provided in the later design takes samples from the headers in the steam risers and so enables a burst to be located as being within the channels (eight or nine) feeding that header. A more detailed examination of these channels would then be made at shut-down.

17. The SGHWR has been operated at full power with a failed fuel pin. The cluster in question was removed at the recent planned shutdown in order to provide an early opportunity for metallurgical examination. This has demonstrated that the SGHWR can operate with a failed pin and that absence of on-load refuelling facilities is not a serious handicap in this respect. At the early stages of irradiation the failed fuel can be replaced by a cluster of the same enrichment without involving fuel shuffling, but towards the end of the irradiation cycle the replacement might need to have a lower enrichment to avoid a local peaking in the core power distribution.

PAPER 5

Messrs J.G. Collier and A. Wharf, Atomic Power Constructions Ltd

18. One of the features of the experimental programme carried out by the AEA in support of the thermal design of the SGHWR fuel element has been the use of the 9 MW heat transfer loop installed at Winfrith. In this loop electrically heated full-scale models of the fuel element have been tested for burn-out and pressure drop.

19. Such tests are time-consuming and expensive in the power they require and consideration has been given to techniques for modelling or scaling the thermal performance of a boiling fuel element. The team at Winfrith have pioneered the use of Freon 12 for this purpose. The advantages of using Freon for the initial optimisation of the design result from the considerable reductions of pressure, temperature and power needed to achieve conditions comparable with water at 1000 lb/in^2.

20. Scaling laws and empirical scaling factors developed at Winfrith have satisfactorily related information on burn-out in simple geometries such as round tubes and annuli. More recently APC have been engaged in a programme of work to extend the knowledge of these scaling factors to the more complex geometries of rod clusters. This work, carried out under contract to the UKAEA, has been undertaken in a large Freon loop installed at the company's Heston laboratory.

21. This loop is capable of testing full-scale SGHWR type fuel elements under boiling conditions, having a flow in excess of 60 lb/s and a channel power up to 900 kW (9 MW water equivalent) (Fig. B1). Fig. B2 shows a typical SGHWR type, half-scale, 36-rod cluster, not necessarily identical to the prototype fuel design tested in the APC Freon loop. Fig. B3 shows channel power at burn-out plotted against channel length for various flow rates and sub-coolings. It will be seen that the effects of flow rate, sub-cooling and channel length on the burn-out power are qualitatively similar to similar measurements taken using water.

22. These results are being compared to similar results taken in water from the 9 MW rig to extend our knowledge of the Freon scaling laws. The present experimental programme on the APC loop is aimed at narrowing down some of the uncertainties in the HAMBO code concerning turbulent mixing between the sub-channels of the fuel element. This work is also being carried out under contract to the UKAEA.

23. The APC laboratory also carried out vibration tests in Freon on a full-sized fuel element freely supported in a simulated reactor channel and electrically heated to give the appropriate boiling conditions. To overcome the problem of preserving the mechanical freedom of the element in the channel in a water rig at 1000 lb/in^2 with a power input of 4 MW, the steam and water has to be pre-mixed at channel inlet to simulate the channel outlet conditions required and the element is unheated electrically. Because of the thermal properties of Freon it is possible to simulate the correct channel fluid conditions with an electrical power input to the fuel element of only about 300 kW, and this can be supplied without any additional constraint to the vibrating system.

24. At four positions along the length of the test section gross movement of the fuel element was monitored by stirrup type pick-ups. Twelve of the fuel pins carried strain gauges internally at intervals along the length. The strain gauge leads are taken from the bottom of the element and out of the rig through glands in the inlet plenum chamber. This arrangement can be seen in Fig. B4, which also illustrates the amplification, recording and local analysis equipment. The electrical supply arrangements to the fuel element at the triple top grid system can be seen in Fig. B5. The brazed joint seen towards the top of the element between the Zircaloy pins and the copper end pieces was made by inserting a stainless steel distance piece. The grids were electrically insulated from the Zircaloy pins by coating with nylon, which can be used at the low temperature of 45°C in Freon.

25. No vibration above 50 c/s was detected and during all the tests the fuel element was very stable. The maximum signal detected on the strain gauged pins was only about one quarter of a microstrain, but the good correlation with the displacement

transducer signals demonstrated that the signals were, in fact, real. The frequency at which vibration was most marked was 17-20 c/s, which corresponds to a wavelength of six grid pitches, giving two complete cycles in the cluster length. The amplitude was always very small and in no case more than 0.005 in.

Mr F. Gretz, Euratom, Ispra, Italy

26. Have the Authors any opinion on the future strategy of increasing steam exit quality? In addition to technical considerations, have they any data on steam exit quality as it affects capital and other costs?

Mr M. Muysken, Reactor Centrum, Nederland

27. I would like to put a question concerning the heat transport from the fuel channels to the moderator. Could the Authors mention what percentage of the total heat produced is dissipated in the moderator, and perhaps elaborate on the method of insulating the calandria tube from the pressure tube?

Mr P Cohen, Westinghouse Advanced Reactors Division

28. What considerations have been given to the potential effects of surface deposits on (a) friction, (b) reactivity, and (c) heat transfer in design and future development programmes, in the light of the experience of other laboratories?

Mr G.L. Duffet, Atomic Power Construction Ltd

29. There are references in the paper to the use of current UK ground rules. These bias the optimization towards minimum generation cost. If the emphasis is on low capital cost, would this lead to a very different design? In particular, would the channel diameter be different?

30. For reactors fuelled with natural uranium it is said that a uniform exit quality across the core is obtained. How is this achieved and maintained during operation? Would such a system be beneficial in the enriched design?

Dr R.A. Bonalumi, CISE, Italy

31. It appears from Paper 5 that the inner diameter of the pressure tube is kept constant in both enriched and natural uranium reactors. Is this due to technological difficulties involved in changing the dimensions?

32. On another point, in our studies on the natural uranium fuelled CIRENE reactor, where we only consider continuous axial refuelling, we also found that a unidirectional scheme tends to over-compensate for the roof-topped flux distribution. A reasonable scheme seems to be one with two bottom feed channels and one top feed channel. Following your studies, what would be a reasonable scheme in the case of multi-segmented fuel?

Fig.B1

Fig.B2

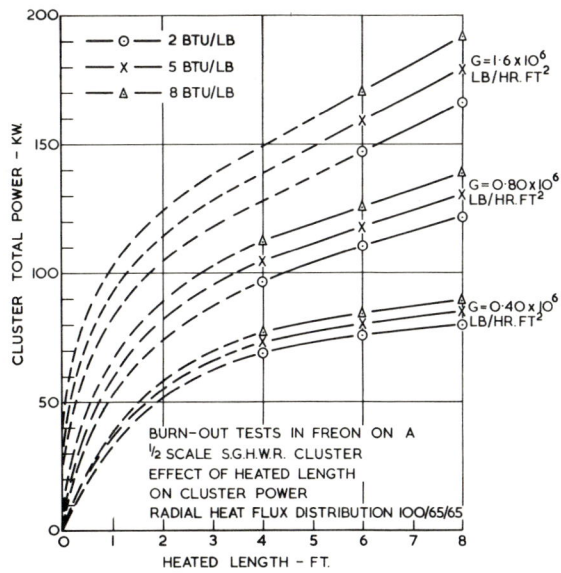

Fig.B3. Burn-out tests in Freon on half-scale SGHWR cluster

Fig.B5

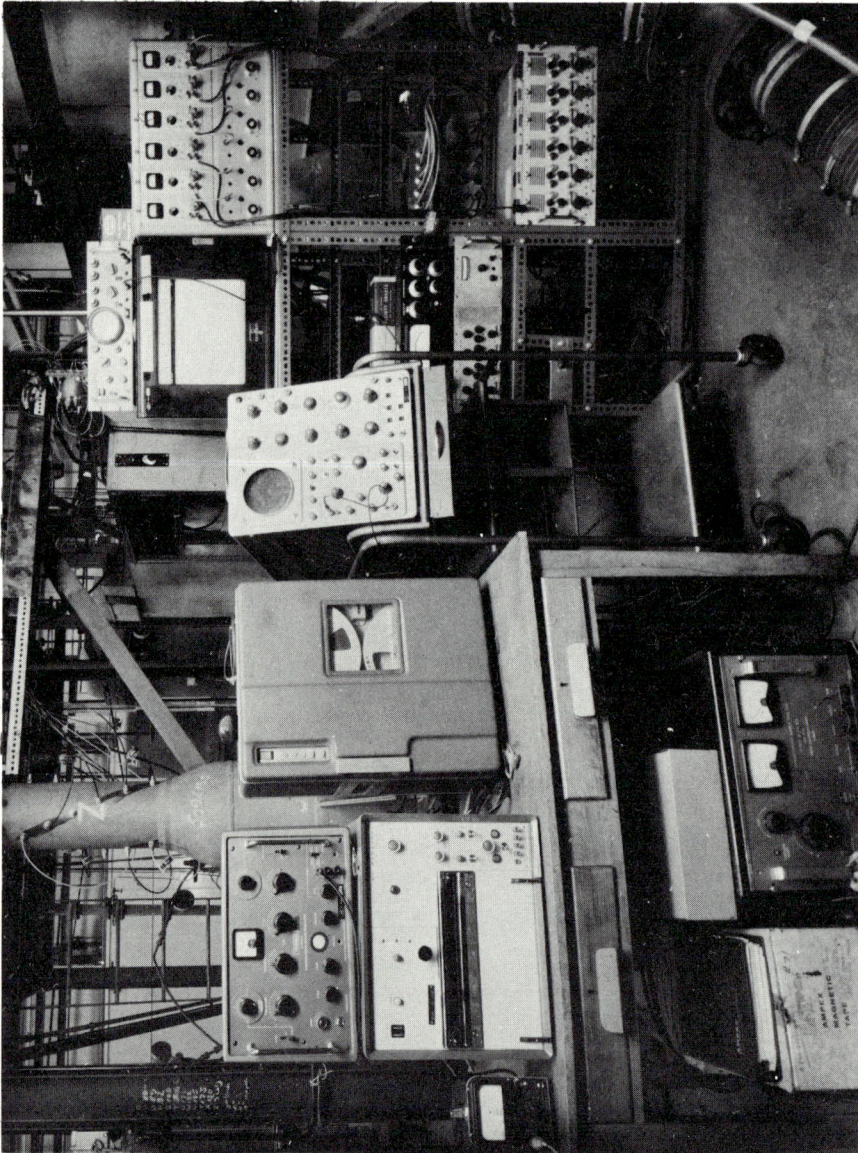

Fig.B4

108

33. We would agree that the contribution from Freon experimental rigs, both at Winfrith and at the APC laboratories at Heston, assists greatly in examining the effect of design geometry variables. This applies to the hydrodynamic and dry-out behaviour in the relatively complex fuel flow passages. From the experiments and comparative tests carried out to date it is demonstrably clear that the Freon representation holds considerable promise in these areas and relieves somewhat the work load in the large 9 MW rig. However, since our understanding of the appropriate scaling laws is not yet complete some caution is necessary in interpreting Freon data quantitatively. For this reason, the present thermal design support programme includes full-scale tests in the 9 MW rig using design replicas of the fuel assemblies with relevant coolant conditions and power distributions.

34. The ability to increase exit quality on which Mr Gretz raises a query is dependent on improving the heat transfer performance of the fuel design. It is anticipated that when the full heat transfer data from the 9 MW rig are available it will be possible to obtain greater increase in exit quality. As an example of the effect on generation cost, if the performance and hence exit quality were increased by 15%, i.e., from about 11% to about 12.6%, generation cost could be reduced to 0.006 d/USO in the enriched design. In the case of the natural reactor, in which fuel cost is strongly dependent on exit quality, a much higher exit quality of 24% has been adopted.

35. In reply to Mr Muysken, of the total fission produced in the core approximately 4% is generated directly in the moderator, and 1% is lost by conduction from the pressure tube because of the temperature difference between the channels and calandria. The only insulation between the calandria and the pressure tube is the stagnant gas gap existing between them; this is fully adequate to limit the heat loss to the above value.

36. Mr Cohen raises a number of points, so far no allowances for crud absorption have been made in the reactor physics calculations. Since the water chemistry in SGHWRs is significantly different from the PWR references cited it is difficult to see how far this experience can be carried over. The operation of the Winfrith reactor will soon show us if we have problems.

37. In our view it would take a very thick crud layer on the fuel pins to make a really significant difference to flow. This arises because the pressure drop over the fuel is only a fraction of the total circuit pressure drop. For example, in the Winfrith reactor a 30% increase in pressure drop over the fuel leads to a 5% loss of flow, which in turn corresponds to a 2½% shift in dry-out margin. There seems to be plenty of scope for crud to form

before we should get too worried on this account. Special experiments are being loaded into the Winfrith reactor to examine crud formation at high heat fluxes. These experiments will attempt to follow the temperature changes in the clad and should improve our knowledge of crud formation in SGHWRs*.

38. In response to Mr G.L. Duffett's questions it has been found from optimization studies that the effect of increased bias towards lower generation cost would be to increase the value of peak channel power at which increased capital cost is obtained. The optimum peak channel power is, however, unlikely to be greater than about 5.5 MW, which would not necessitate any major design change. Studies have shown that costs tend to increase if channel diameter is increased. This is because the flux depression across the cluster increases with channel diameter, and causes average fuel rating to be decreased for the limiting value of peak rating. The resulting increase in power output from the larger channel is less than proportional to the increased fuel contained in the channel, resulting in an overall cost increase. Nevertheless, the optimization of channel size is fairly flat in the region of the selected design.

39. Coolant flow through the core of the natural reactor design is controlled by multi-port valves, each valve covering a group of channels. These valves are controlled during the fuel cycle, from flow and quality measurements. It will be possible to maintain approximately either a uniform exit quality, or a uniform dry-out margin across the core. In the case of the enriched reactor, fuel cost is insensitive to coolant quality, and the only incentive is to save on the cost of coolant circulation. Because the power in any individual channel varies considerably during the lifetime of the fuel it would be necessary to use a control valve in each channel operated from measurements of flow and quality. It is considered that the cost of such a control system would not be justified by the saving in cost of coolant circulation.

40. In response to the points raised by Dr Bonalumi, optimization studies of the natural reactor have shown that cost variation with pressure tube diameter is very flat, with a tendency to a very slight, negligible reduction at a smaller diameter than the reference. There is however a strong incentive to maintain the reference diameter of the prototype design in order

---

*At this point Mr Forbes Gower asked Mr Cohen what comments he had on the results from Yankee where it had been found that there was a release of reactivity rather than a loss? Mr Cohen replied that in the US PWRs it was found that, at any particular reactor condition, the reactivity was greatest and closest to a priori estimates when the pH (or alkalinity of the coolant) was in the neighbourhood of 10×10^{-4} mol, based on room temperature measurements.

that the fuel and channel designs which will be used in natural reactors may be fully demonstrated in the prototype. In view of this it is not considered worthwhile to change the channel diameter for the very small cost reduction which may be obtained.

41. We have found that the particular choice of axial fuel management scheme for a natural uranium SGHWR design depends to some extent on the design parameters, particularly the ratio of moderator to fuel and the discharge burn-up. I would agree with Dr Bonalumi that whilst some preferential loading of the fresh fuel towards the bottom of the channel is required, a unidirectional scheme in general tends to overcompensate for the positive void effect. We are currently evaluating a number of alternative schemes in some detail and have not yet made a firm decision.

PAPER 6

Major L. Cave, Atomic Power Construction Ltd

42. From the information given in Paper 6, it is difficult to judge the suitability of the SGHWR for use as spinning reserve. Are the curves of Fig. 5 based on calculation or tests? What was the power level prior to the transient? Have the Authors calculated the total heat stored in the steam mains and drum of the SGHWR at, say, 75% power? What increase in drum size do they think would be needed to maintain a 10% increase in power output for 20 s without reliance on increased power from the reactor, at 75% load?

43. It is stated that, in the natural uranium version, large positive void co-efficients are to be expected. Has any estimate been made of the likely effect on the maximum rates of absorber insertion required in reactor trip conditions?

Dr G. Peterlongo, CISE, Milan, Italy

44. Attainment of maximum efficiency in SGHWRs requires that feed-water heating should be as high as possible. Has the use of live steam from the drum in a last pre-heater been considered? This could have the additional advantage of not being influenced by a turbine trip.

45. Two possible control schemes for the station, the 'coupled' and 'decoupled' have been presented. During the study of a general control of the CIRENE reactor, we have found that a 'co-ordinated' scheme of the forcing type, in which a load demand signal is fed to both the reactivity control and to the turbine valve, allows a considerably better dynamic behaviour, with time constants of the turbine power of the order of 1-2 s. Is this type of scheme being studied?

46. Would moderator level control be an attractive proposition for sector control

of large natural uranium reactors, considering the difficulty of designing a sufficiently fast system?

Mr A. Mihaila, Institute of Atom Physics, Bucharest, Rumania

47. Taking into account the positive void coefficient in natural uranium fuelled SGHWRs, what are the problems with the dynamic behaviour of this type of reactor, especially in the case of hydrodynamic instability?

Mr P.J. Cameron, TNPG

48. The SGHWR control system comprises power control by moderator level, sector control by differential moderator level, scram by liquid rods, and long-term reactivity by boron injection. This is complex and furthermore does not provide a facility for local power shaping. On this basis, TNPG have advocated the use of solid rods on future large SGHWRs, because local flux control is then possible and all the other control requirements except long-term reactivity control can then be covered by the solid rods. Will the Authors please say whether or not recent work confirms the advantages of solid rods, and if so, why they are not being used?

Mr A. Forbes Gower, Central Electricity Generating Board

49. Increase in gas pressure above the hot sector leads to a fall in the moderator level power in this sector, but would apparently be accompanied by a rise in the moderator level and power in the other sectors (probably the greatest rise occurring in the sector with the currently largest gas pocket). Is this desirable and is it fail-safe? What would happen if there were a failure in the gas pressure above one sector? Does an immediate drop in moderator level and flux in other sectors hold down the transient in the sector in which the gas pressure has fallen?

50. The CEGB grid system is the largest in the world and the rate of change of frequency is fairly small; the percentage rate of increase in demand is also not very great. Therefore, the load-following requirements of a reactor for use within the Board's grid is much more similar to the response required of a lorry or oil tanker, rather than that of a racing car, destroyer, or fighter plane. Why, therefore, have the designers worked for such large rates of power change and gone to such lengths to be able to change power with frequency so quickly?

Authors' reply: Paper 6

51. In reply to Major Cave, the curves of Fig. 5 are based on calculation but are supported by responses obtained on the simulator which is described briefly in Paper 6. Comprehensive comparison between dynamic performance of the simulator and the Winfrith SGHWR has not been completed

yet; however, the limited dynamic tests on the plant carried out so far have shown an encouraging level of agreement with the simulator. The curves apply to operation of the Winfrith SGHWR at near full power, but are representative for operation at 75% of maximum continuous rating (MCR). At lower powers, the time constants of both components of steam delivery to the turbine increase, but the form of the curves is similar. The primary circuit heat storage varies only slightly over the full power range since steam pressure is held constant and the steam temperature is at the corresponding level for saturation. Variations in channel voidage with power level provide one varying contribution.

52. The rate of change of drum pressure at any time is, to a first approximation, proportional to the difference between the rate at which steam is being carried away and the rate at which heat is being delivered from the reactor core, and the constant of proportionality is itself approximately inversely proportional to the thermal storage. When the turbine control valve (TCV) is opened while reactor power is held constant, drum pressure falls and the delivery of steam to the turbine is represented in Fig. 5 by the curve which asymptotically approaches the time axis. The rate of fall of this curve is, from the consideration above, approximately inversely proportional to the thermal storage, and if the associated steam delivery is permitted to fall to only 8% from an initial 10% increase over the first 20 s while operating near full power it is necessary to increase the thermal storage by a factor of nearly 3.5.

53. It should be noted that the maximum dip in the delivery curve when reactor power is also raised is not reduced by the same factor, since when the thermal storage is greater, a longer time must be allowed for the increased reactor power to build up pressure in the drum to increase the steam delivery.

54. On the question of using SGHWRs for spinning reserve duty, when it is required typically to proceed from 75% to 90% MCR in $2\frac{1}{2}$ s in order to help make up for the loss of a larger set elsewhere in the grid, the following results from a simulator study should be of interest. If the occurrence of this situation can be recognized from, say, grid frequency changes and the resulting action used to limit additional opening of the TCV to 15% and introduce 200 milliniles of reactivity, then a 'step' increase of 15% in delivered steam power is achieved and maintained. Furthermore, the normal power control is still available to raise power further. Means of introducing this reactivity are being considered in terms of engineering design, and plant tests are being proposed to verify these simulator predictions.

55. In reply to Major Cave's last point, in the natural fuelled SGHWR the burst circuit accident determines the fastest reactivity insertion rates required from the emergency shutdown system. Unless specifically restricted, the circuit could depressurize at such a rate that a very fast shutdown system indeed would be required. For this reason the circuit has been designed in conjunction with special auxiliary accumulators. The rate of potential depressurization is by these means reduced so that reactivity insertion rates similar to those achieved in the prototype SGHWR are adequate.

56. The use of live steam taken from the drum as suggested by Dr Peterlongo has been considered for feed-water heating, but this has some undesirable features as far as the steam cycle is concerned. To put the problem into perspective, the events following a turbine trip should be considered. The feed temperature drops by some 150°F when the feed heating is lost, but due to transportation delays the effect of this is not felt in the reactor core until some 35-45 s later. The subsequent reduction in core voidage produces a neutron flux increase of only about 10% with a void coefficient of reactivity of -0.02. Thus if the reactor power is reduced by 20% per min from the time of the trip, the neutron flux rise due to the loss of feed heat will not exceed the initial flux level. Reducing reactor power at 20% per min following a turbine trip presents no difficulties and is therefore preferable to the use of live steam feed heating. It is in any case desirable to reduce the reactor power at some time to reduce unnecessary dumping of steam.

57. The description of the coupled and decoupled control systems is largely historical as these were the two systems considered for the Winfrith SGHWR. In more recent work on control systems for load-following we are considering systems in which the load demand signal is applied directly both to the reactor power control and to the turbine throttle valve. We agree that this type of control system has advantages in producing fast response to changes in load. Fig. 6 does in fact show such a system which has been designed to produce a turbine power variation with a 15 s time constant in response to a step change in demand. With this type of control considerable flexibility is available to provide the type and speed of response which any particular customer may require to match the characteristics of the electrical supply network.

58. For natural uranium SGHWRs we are not considering the use of moderator height variations for control. One method for the control of total power which is being considered is to vary the channel flow and hence voidage, and utilize the positive void coefficient of reactivity for reactivity control. This has advantages in a natural fuelled design in that extra reactivity at low power can be obtained by reducing the channel flow. With this method of control, it is convenient to control the flow in groups of channels in a sector, and this then forms a means of controlling spatial instabilities.

59. The hydrodynamic instability mentioned by Mr Mihaila is something which will not occur in either natural or enriched fuel designs of SGHWRs. If it could occur it would be difficult to control, and hence the circuit will be so designed that there is an adequate margin against hydrodynamic instability under all reactor operating conditions. In the flow control system for the natural reactor, referred to in the reply to Dr Peterlongo, the means of controlling channel flow will be arranged to provide sufficient pressure drop in the channel inlet feeder pipes to ensure hydrodynamic stability under all conditions of power and flow.

60. The case for using solid rods as proposed by Mr Cameron depends somewhat on the use made of them. For example if used for emergency shutdown, it would mean locating control mechanisms in the difficult environmental conditions either above or below the core. The temperature conditions would necessitate a guaranteed cooling system to ensure reliable operation. A further problem arises in the arresting of a solid rod from the initial high velocities required for protection which, coupled with the retrieval problem and the very confined space available, considerably complicates the design problems. In comparison, the liquid rod has only one moving part of fairly conventional design located in a relatively cool environment and of easy access.

61. For control purposes there appears to be some economic incentive in the larger cores in providing some form of power shaping. This could be provided by solid rods but with most of the attendant problems already mentioned. Alternative methods using tubes containing a gaseous absorber, such as krypton or xenon, under a variable pressure are being studied at the moment. These tubes could provide the dual purpose of power shaping and sector control but would not be used for emergency shutdown.

62. Summarizing, although there does not appear to be a case for discrete absorbers in the small cores, this may not be so for larger cores. In these cases solid rods do offer an alternative solution but they must be considered on their merits and in comparison with other alternative methods.

63. Mr Forbes Gower raises a number of points. On sector control, while it is true that increasing the pressure in one sector would force the level up in the other sectors, since each is independently controlled no resultant change in level in those sectors should arise. However, the whole of the sector control system is designed to be very slow in its response, so that in the event of a fault developing in one sector, the resultant excursion in flux should be very slow. While the control systems in the healthy sectors should be capable of controlling the excursion, full nucleonic protection is provided in each sector.

64. The load following requirements of SGHWRs were not specifically related to CEGB requirements, but were written round the requirements common to many possible customers. However, the CEGB have stated requirements for SGHW reactors operating in the mid-1970s in a power-following role similar to that described in the Paper. In addition they would be required to increase load very quickly to offset the effect of a large nuclear station tripping off the grid. The provision of fast load-following characteristics does not really complicate the design, but rather utilizes the natural capability of the reactor system to its fullest extent.

PAPER 7

65. Mr O'Dell pointed out in his presentation that the dual enrichment scatter-loaded fuel management scheme had also been evaluated for a 500 MWe reactor. It had been found that a satisfactory approach to equilibrium could be obtained from an initial core loading of eight different enrichment levels, and that the form factor could be kept below the target value of 1.45. In this larger reactor, the mean enrichment of the initial core was 1.2% leading to an average burn-up of the first core of about 11,000 MWd/tU. At equilibrium, the mean feed enrichment of 2.0% resulted in a fuel average discharge burn-up of 21,000 MWd/tU.

Mr J. Scott, TNPG

66. I would like to ask the Authors whether they consider that the best lattice parameters have been chosen for a civil SGHWR? Paper 4 gives two criteria for the choice of prototype lattice parameters: (a) a slightly negative void coefficient, and (b) a balanced D_2O:U-235 cost. Of necessity this decision on the ratio of fuel to moderator was taken relatively early in the prototype construction programme, and new factors have emerged. Paper 4 shows that the errors on the void coefficient are now ±0.003 rather than ±0.01. Paper 7 emphasizes the importance of the radial form factor in the choice of fuel management scheme. The radial form factors obtained during the fuel cycle are $V_{D_2O}:V_{UO_2}$ dependent. In this case the moderator:fuel ratio will influence the choice of fuel management scheme. In the future, reactors built in the UK will be required to be load-following and the cost of this is $V_{D_2O}:V_{UO_2}$ dependent. The optimization studies carried out in support of the natural uranium fuelled SGHWR indicate that a higher $V_{D_2O}:V_{UO_2}$ ratio is necessary for an economic reactor.

67. Some of these factors oppose one another, and the balance of costs should now be examined even if the search only shows that the original choice was best, it would prove that the most competitive reactor has been chosen.

Mr K.R. Brennan, UKAEA, Risley

68. Why is radial shuffling of fuel, as adopted for the Winfrith fuel management scheme, not apparently being considered for larger low enriched reactors?

Mr R.J. Burton, Atomic Power Constructions Ltd

69. In discussing the initial loading of the nine cycle dual feed enrichment scheme, the Authors note that ideally it might be desirable to have eighteen different enrichment levels, but that in practice this number can be reduced. It would be interesting to know what they would consider to be a realistic number of initial enrichments for this case?

70. The results illustrated in Fig. 4 show fairly significant variations of channel form factor during each burn-up stage. Are these variations caused by macroscopic flux perturbation as suggested by the results, where it appears that the core oscillates between an under- and an over-flattened condition? To what extent are they a consequence of changes in radial reflector worth with changing boron concentration?

Mr T. Currie, Atomic Power Constructions Ltd

71. Have the Authors considered plutonium spiking of natural versions as proposed in Duret's paper to the Vienna symposium? Could they comment on his view that besides allowing higher irradiations (15.2 MWd/kgU against 8.5 MWd/kgU for natural oxide), substantial benefit in terms of control should accrue from the lower void coefficient?

Mr J. Panossian, GAAA, France

72. What is the gain on the form factor to be expected with the type of control described as against control rods? Is this not strongly dependent on the disposition of control rods and lattice characteristics?

Authors' reply: Paper 7

73. Mr Scott makes a plea that the design parameters of the enriched SGHWR should be carefully re-examined in the light of experience gained from our development programme and the early operation of the Winfrith reactor. Of course it is important to do that and we do review the main parameters for each new application. Relatively simple optimization studies have shown only a limited dependence of generating cost on $V_{D_2O}:V_{UO_2}$ over the range 6-8, with a minimum at a ratio of about 7. In view of this it does mean that the sort of consideration suggested by Mr Scott has much more significance in the selection of the design point. The text referred to optimization under present-day ground rules. They still are very similar to those obtaining at the time of the selection of the Winfrith reactor parameters and we see no reason for large changes. The text referred to the performance of a particular fuel element, i.e., the standard enriched design with $V_{H_2O}:V_{UO_2} \simeq 1$. This is unsuitable for natural uranium reactors since there is too much parasitic absorption. If $V_{H_2O}:V_{UO_2}$ is reduced, more D_2O must be added to restore reactivity. The optimum $V_{D_2O}:V_{UO_2}$ ratio then moves to higher values in the vicinity of 12.

74. With regard to Mr Scott's particular points, the accuracy of void coefficient prediction is now so good that no constraint to the design need be made to cover uncertainties in its value. Secondly we have not noticed any strong dependence of the local peaking contribution to the form factor on $V_{D_2O}:V_{UO_2}$, and a positive coefficient would assist the load-following response of the plant. On the other hand, a negative coefficient could be attractive from the safety point of view, since, for example, following a loss of circulating pumps, the reactor would tend to shut itself down with a negative coefficient, without relying on the protective system.

75. In response to Mr Brennan, radial fuel move schemes have been considered for the larger low enriched reactors, and indeed studies have been completed for the two sizes, 300 MWe and 500 MWe, from first reactor start-up through to equilibrium. The schemes adopted for these two sizes were respectively a 10-cycle scheme and a 9-cycle scheme, in which the centre zone in each case formed an 8-cycle chequer-board pattern. Fuel was therefore being moved once from the outer to the inner zone. Since the use of a radial fuel move introduces great flexibility with a very wide range of choice, the studies were limited to those states which maintained four-fold symmetry in the reactor. Special fuel moves had to be arranged to produce these states. The real point about the radial fuel move is that it involves extra fuel handling and therefore introduces an outage penalty. As explained in Paper 2, when this fact is introduced into the overall optimization one has to accept that this means that individual components involved in the design, e.g., fuel management, are not always themselves at the optimum.

76. In answer to Mr Burton's first question, we have demonstrated a satisfactory approach to equilibrium using an initial core loading of eight different enrichments. We have also studied schemes starting with only two different enrichments in the initial core. However, we found in these cases that a satisfactory form factor performance could only be obtained by increasing the fuel throughput during the approach to equilibrium. This resulted in an unacceptably large penalty on fuel cost.

77. Mr Burton has drawn attention to the characteristic form of the form factor variation with time for the dual enrichment fuel management scheme. As he supposes, this is largely due to macroscopic power variations associated with changing boron concentration. In the enriched design as

currently conceived, excess reactivity is
taken up by boron dissolved in the combined
moderator and reflector. As irradiation
proceeds, the reduced fuel reactivity is
compensated by reduction in the boron concentration, and thus the reflector effectiveness gradually increases between refuellings. As a result of this the balance
of enrichments between the zones is
arranged so that roughly equal power peaks
are obtained at the beginning and end of
each irradiation interval when the flux
peaks are in the core centre and core outer
region, respectively. An unpoisoned
reflector would enable us to design for a
lower form factor, and this is currently
being studied for possible application to
our commercial designs.

78. Mr Currie raises the question of
plutonium spiking. We have not considered
plutonium spiking of the natural SGHWR
design as proposed by the Canadians, but
we have carried out some preliminary investigations of plutonium recycle. In this
case the plutonium from reject fuel is
extracted and converted to PuO_2, mixed with
UO_2 of natural enrichment, and used as a
feed to the reactor. For our current
design of natural reactor, this would
enable the fuel burn-up to be approximately
doubled, and as Mr Currie suggests, there
would be a small reduction in the void coefficient. The predicted and initial reactivity available and the reduction in the
void coefficient with plutonium fuel have
been confirmed by zero energy experiments
in the JUNO reactor. However, it must be
pointed out that plutonium recycle in the
current design optimized for a once-through
fuel cycle still results in a positive void
coefficient. We have carried out some
limited optimization studies for the
natural uranium fuel design which indicate
that by reducing the $V_{D_2O}:V_{UO_2}$ ratio we
could design a reactor using plutonium recycle with a zero void coefficient, which
would have an economic fuel burn-up, and
operate with make-up of natural uranium.

79. It may help in answering
Mr Panossian's question if it is turned
the other way round. Is there any potential for improving radial form factor by
the use of discrete absorbers? We are
currently investigating the use of
discrete absorbers for power shaping and a
reduction in form factor from our present
design point of 1.45 to about 1.35 is
anticipated. However, as suggested by
Mr Panossian, this does depend on the disposition of the absorbers. The form of
absorber system we are evaluating is one
with a number of tubes in which the pressure of neutron absorbing gas can be
varied. We consider that this scheme is
preferable to one using partly inserted
solid rods since the engineering is simpler
and no axial flux perturbations arise.

Pressure tube materials for SGHWRs

R. W. NICHOLS, BMet, FIM, UKAEA, Culcheth
B. WATKINS, MSc, FIM, UKAEA, Culcheth

SYNOPSIS   The properties achieved in the Zircaloy-2 pressure tubes manufactured for the SGHWR are described. It has been found that corrosion in-pile is higher than out of the reactor, leading to increased hydrogen absorption in the metal. However, extensive tests, including tests on full size tube have demonstrated that this hydrogen absorption, even in the presence of irradiation embrittlement, will not limit the life of the pressure tubes. Neutron irradiation has also been found to increase the creep rate of a zirconium alloy under given conditions of stress and temperature. However, the present evidence indicates that this will not cause a problem with cold-worked Zircaloy-2 tubes in present designs. Some results on heat-treated zirconium-2½% niobium alloy tubes are also described.

INTRODUCTION

1.   Whilst the concept of individual pressure tubes avoids the difficulties which can arise in the design and manufacture of a large pressure vessel, it introduces other problems which must be solved to achieve a safe and economic design. Most of these problems arise from the need to minimize parasitic neutron absorption in the pressure tubes. As well as limiting directly the choice of alloy systems of interest in this application, it also makes it desirable that the material shows a high strength and is able to tolerate the chemical, irradiation and thermal environments without the need for large corrosion allowances, shielding or insulation. It is such considerations which have led to the use of zirconium alloys for pressure tubes in water reactors.

2.   It is also essential that the pressure tubes are demonstrably of high integrity, and that a particular design can be validated by examination of the various possible modes of failure. To some extent this is made easier than the pressure vessel case by the fact that the pressure tubes are of simple cylindrical geometry without the complication of nozzles and support structures.

3.   An obvious requirement for a pressure tube is that it must be able to withstand the required internal pressure without any risk of fracture or of undue deformation. Possible modes of failure to be considered are tensile yield or bursting, fast fracture from local defects after embrittlement by hydriding or irradiation, excessive deformation or fracture by creep.

4.   With regard to tensile bursting, it is conventional to define the thickness of the tubes so that the hoop stress in the metal does not exceed one-third of its tensile strength at temperature. Thinner pressure tubes and better neutron economy can thus result from the use of materials which are stronger than the annealed Zircaloy-2 alloy which had been used in previous pressure tube reactors. One possibility is to strengthen by cold work and by this means the design thickness for the Winfrith SGHWR pressure tubes was reduced from 0.29 in to 0.185 in. Another possibility is to develop an heat-treatable alloy, and here most attention has been given to a Zr-2½% Nb alloy which has sufficient strength to permit the tube thickness to be reduced to about 0.1 in. The subsequent discussion is in the main concerned with the properties of these two alloys, namely cold-worked Zircaloy-2 and heat-treated Zr-2½% Nb, typical compositions being given in Table 1.

TENSILE PROPERTIES

5.   The development and assessment of the cold-worked Zircaloy-2 used for the Winfrith SGHWR has been described previously (ref. 1). This work indicated that a transverse tensile strength of 50,000 lb/in^2 at 300°C on the autoclaved condition could be achieved by applying a cold drawing process in the final stages of manufacture so that the tube goes into service in the 30% cold-worked condition. The ability to achieve this strength has been confirmed by the results of tensile tests taken from each end of every SGHWR production tube. Other tests have demonstrated that the hoop stress in an actual length of tube is somewhat higher than the conventional tensile strength, typical results being given in Table 2. In all such tests on cold-worked Zircaloy-2, it was found that appreciable bulging occurred before failure, giving circumferential strains of the order of 20% with a maximum reduction in thickness of about 18%. The

Table 1
Representative compositions of pressure tube alloys

	Zircaloy-2	Zr-2½% Nb
Sn	1.20-1.70%	200 ppm max
Fe	0.07-0.20%	800 ppm max
Cr	0.05-0.15%	200 ppm max
Ni	0.03-0.08%	70 ppm max
(Fe+Cr+Ni)	0.18-0.38%	-
O	1000-1400 ppm	1100-1500 ppm
N	80 ppm max	80 ppm max
H	25 ppm max	25 ppm max
Hf	100 ppm max	100 ppm max
Nb	-	2.50-2.90%

Composition by weight in all cases.

Table 2
300°C tube burst properties

Material condition	Hoop stress at failure lb/in²x10⁻³	Circumferential strain at burst %	Maximum reduction of wall thickness %	Ratio burst stress/ UTS (T)
20% cold-worked Zircaloy-2 tube (autoclaved)	59	18-25	15-20	1.3
30% cold-worked Zircaloy-2 tube (autoclaved)	67	~20	~20	1.34
20% cold-worked Zr-2½ Nb alloy tube (autoclaved)	82	1-1.5	16-18	1.09
Heat treated Zr-2½ Nb tube (Q.880, T.550)	97	1.3-1.5	14-16	1.04

failure pressure was 4200 lb/in²(g) compared with a reactor working pressure of 950 lb/in²(g).

6.   The higher tensile strength of the heat-treated Zr-2½% Nb alloy results from the stronger metallurgical structure which is produced by a martensitic transformation on quenching from a temperature above 800°C, and from subsequent ageing changes which occur in this alloy during tempering at temperatures of about 500°C. A considerable amount of work was done to optimize the composition and heat treatment and six heat-treated Zr-2½% Nb tubes were installed in the Winfrith SGHWR to gain operating experience (ref. 1). Burst tests on this material at 300°C show a consider-

able increase in strength over the cold-worked Zircaloy-2, as indicated in Table 2. In these tests, the alloy showed low values of circumferential strain to fracture but the local reduction in wall thickness at the point of failure was similar to that observed for Zircaloy-2.

CORROSION BEHAVIOUR

7.   Whilst this aspect is discussed in more detail in another paper to this conference, the interplay of corrosion effects with other properties makes a short discussion necessary here (ref. 2). There is considerable evidence that the rate of corrosion of Zircaloy-2 in pressurized,

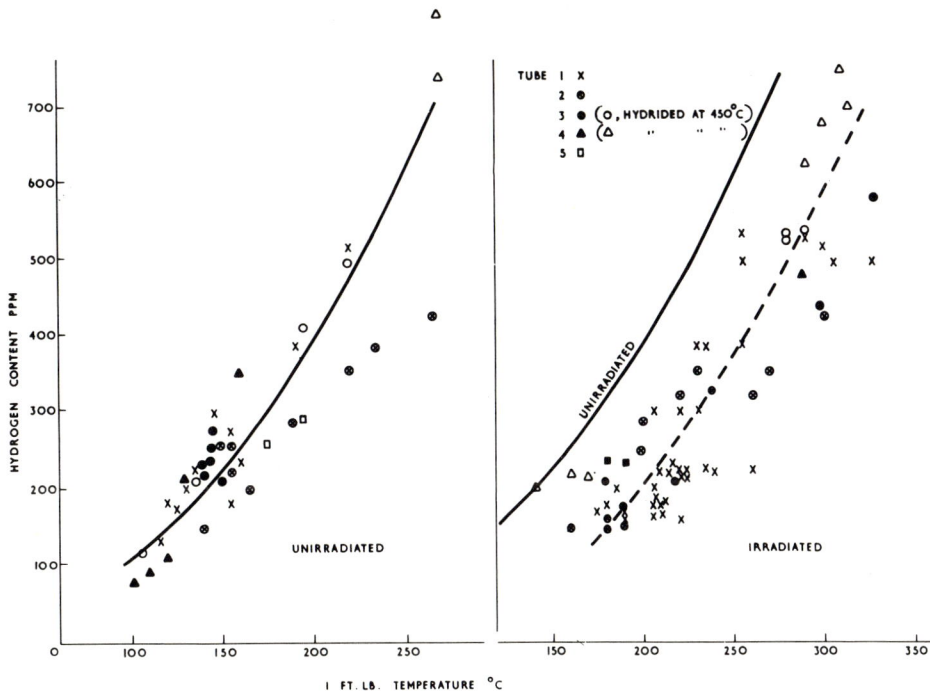

Fig. 1: Effect of hydrogen and irradiation on the sub-size, V-notch impact transition temperature for Zircaloy-2

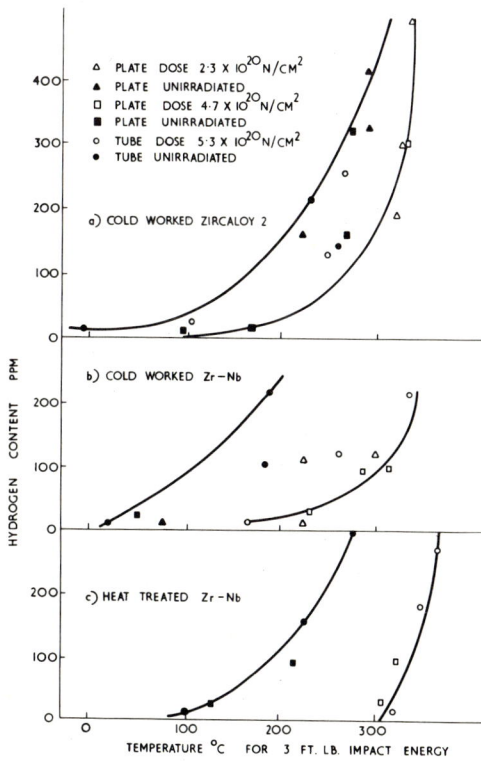

Fig. 2: Summary graph showing combined effect of hydrogen and irradiation on impact properties of zirconium alloys.

boiling water is increased by neutron irradiation and that the in-pile rate is also dependent on the detailed environmental conditions and water chemistry (refs 3, 4). This evidence indicates that even with pessimistic assumptions the weight loss and loss of section from the SGHWR pressure tubes will not be an embarrassment during operation nor a limitation on reactor life. However, the corrosion processes lead to hydrogen evolution, some of which is absorbed in the metal. Dawson et al. considered that the conditions in the Winfrith reactor could lead after twenty years continuous operation to a level of about 350 ppm hydrogen in the 0.2 in thick tubes and more recent assessments give broadly similar values (refs 3, 2).

8. With regard to the zirconium-niobium alloy, it appears that its corrosion rate is not much affected by irradiation, but it is very dependent on the local chemistry and can be accelerated by oxidizing conditions. The corrosion rate is also dependent on heat treatment condition, and good resistance is shown by material aged for 72 hours at 500°C. With such material and with suitable chemical control, it is expected that, as with Zircaloy-2, there will be no problem due to loss of section and the important consideration is that of hydrogen absorption and its consequent effect on mechanical properties.

EFFECT OF HYDROGEN AND IRRADIATION ON MECHANICAL PROPERTIES

9. Tests have shown that randomly distributed hydrogen contents up to 600 ppm have little effect on either the tensile strength or ductility of Zircaloy-2. However, the hydride platelets may show some degree of preferred orientation dependent on the method of manufacture and on the subsequent applied stress, especially that existing whilst the hydrogen is being absorbed into the metal (ref. 5). On hydriding of SGHWR pressure tube material, the hydride orientation is mainly circumferential with some 45° elements. Samples cut transversely from pressure tubes and cooled from 300°C at a stress of 20,000 lb/in² showed no tendency to produce radial hydrides; there is no decrease in room temperature tensile ductility even when the specimens are cooled from 400°C with an applied stress of 35,000 lb/in². Specimens concurrently hydrided at 400°C with an applied stress up to 16,000 lb/in² showed some reorientated hydrides, and the amount of radial hydride produced increased with stress level. However, even in the extreme case with a stress of 33,000 lb/in² which gave 80-95% radial hydrides, the room temperature tensile elongation was in the range 4-10%, with no reduction in tensile strength. The major effect of hydrogen embrittlement is found to be that of reduction in fracture toughness as reflected in the reduction of strength in the presence of a notch or stress concentration.

10. Turning to the effects of neutron irradiation, the tensile properties at 20 and 300°C have been measured after doses of up to 2×10^{21} n/cm² (>1 MeV), and it has been found that there is a small increase in yield and tensile strength with reductions in elongation, especially in the elongation before necking occurs (Ref. 6). Again the effect of greatest engineering significance is that of reduction of fracture toughness and this effect is additional to the embrittlement produced by hydrogen. This is demonstrated by the results of notch impact tests (Fig. 1) in which the transition temperature is increased by both hydrogen and irradiation, although the latter effect appears to saturate at a dose between 10^{19} and 10^{20} n/cm² (>1 MeV).

11. Assessment of the engineering significance of these changes in fracture toughness can be made by measuring the defect size needed to produce failure at a given stress level (ref. 7). Tests were made on samples of cold-worked Zircaloy-2 tube from the Winfrith SGHWR production route, the failure stress in the presence of an artificial defect being measured over a range of temperatures and hydrogen levels. These tests showed that at 16,000 lb/in² stress and 300°C even with 900 ppm of hydrogen, the critical defect size is of the order of a 4-in long, sharp-ended defect through the full thickness of the pressure tube wall. In the SGHWR design, this turns out to be the most severe condition because the pressure applied to the pressure tube decreases with decrease of temperature in accordance with the saturation vapour pressure/temperature relationship.

12. Other tests have shown that similar critical sizes apply to fatigue-cracked specimens as to artificial machined defects, and that through-thickness defects represent the most severe condition (ref. 8). The effect of radial hydrides has been studied in tubes in which this orientation was favoured by a prior cold-sinking treatment. In tests on this tube at 300°C, it was found that there was no change in critical defect size (about 4-in at 16,000 lb/in²) on hydriding from 25 to 200 ppm hydrogen. Recent tests at 300°C on 3.25 in dia. cold-worked Zircaloy-2 tube containing 200 ppm hydrogen somewhat surprisingly showed a slight increase in critical defect size on irradiating to a dose of 2×10^{20} n/cm² (>1 MeV) at 300°C, presumably because increase of hardness outweighed the decrease of fracture toughness (ref. 9).

13. These results indicate that it would need a sharp-ended defect of about 4-in length to produce failure in an SGHWR pressure tube, even with pessimistic assumptions on hydrogen level, hydride orientation and irradiation dose. Such a defect size is several orders of magnitude greater than that which could be detected by the inspection techniques applied prior to commissioning or that which can be applied intermittently throughout its service. Moreover this length of defect is significantly greater than the lengths which have been shown in laboratory tests

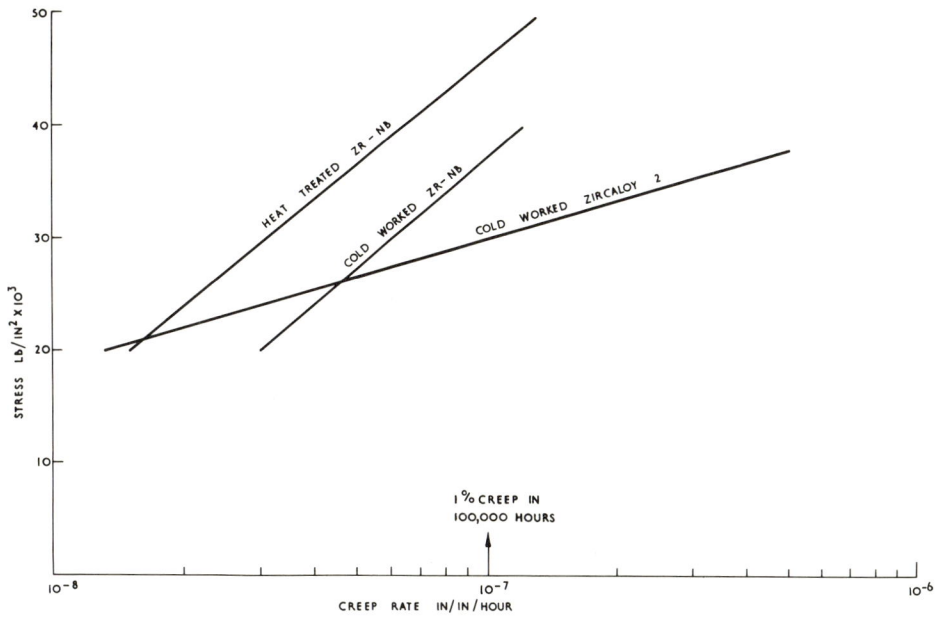

Fig. 3: Out-of-pile creep behaviour of Zr-2½% Nb alloy and Zircaloy-2 at 300°C

Table 3
Typical design values for Zircaloy-2 and Zr-2½% Nb alloys

Design criteria	Cold-worked Zr-2	Cold-worked Zr/Nb	Heat-treated Zr/Nb
1/3 UTS at temperature	16,000	21,000	29,000
2/3 Y stress (0.2% off set)	28,000	34,000	44,000
Stress for 1% creep in 10^5 hours	30,000	27,000	46,000
80% stress for rupture in 100,000 hours	29,000	40,000	50,000

to show leakage rather than catastrophic failure (ref. 10). It is concluded that hydrogen and irradiation embrittlement will not limit the useful life of a cold-worked Zircaloy-2 pressure tube in an SGHWR.

14. Irradiation and hydrogen absorption have the same general effect on heat-treated Zr/Nb as on cold-worked Zr-2. Thus, irradiation to a dose of 6×10^{20} n/cm^2 (greater than 1 MeV) results in an increase of about 30% in the 0.2% proof stress and ultimate tensile stress at 300°C with a decrease in elongation of about 30%. Wood et al. have shown that the effect of irradiation is to move the transition curve to higher temperatures and to reduce the maximum energy in the ductile region (ref. 11). At low hydrogen contents, the impact properties of Zr-2 are better in both the unirradiated and irradiated condition than Zr-2½% Nb alloy. Compared with Zr-2 there is a tendency for Zr-Nb to have a lower transition temperature at higher hydrogen levels, but the effect of irradiation is greater. However, both materials show that after irradiation, the transition temperature of material containing greater than 200 ppm of hydrogen is in the range 300-350°C (Fig. 2).

15. Only limited critical crack length tests have been done in Zr-Nb alloy, but these show that at 20°C Zr-Nb is more susceptible to embrittlement compared with Zircaloy-2. At 300°C, the embrittlement is reduced and at a stress level of 20,000-25,000 lb/in^2, the defect length is of the order of 1½-2½ in with 500 ppm of hydrogen. Again, such defect sizes are much greater than the detection limit of the inspection methods, and could be expected to result in leakage rather than catastrophic failure. Unless the combined effects of irradiation and hydriding are more severe than in the Zircaloy-2 case, it is not expected that embrittlement would limit the life of the heat-treated Zr-2½% Nb tubes.

CREEP AND CREEP-RUPTURE ASPECTS

16. Information available when the Winfrith SGHWR was being designed indicated that the design stress in the absence of irradiation should be based on tensile strength rather than creep strength. Subsequently, confirmatory tests extending to 10,000 hours have been made on material cut from the cold-worked and autoclaved Zircaloy-2 tubing from the Winfrith SGHWR production. It was found that, at temperatures of 300°C and even with a stress as high as 25,000 lb/in^2, primary creep strain forms a large component of the total strain. At stresses of both 16,000 lb/in^2 and 20,000 lb/in^2, secondary creep rates are $\sim 1 \times 10^{-8}$ in/in per hour and even a pessimistic extrapolation of the data would indicate that in 100,000 hours under the operating stress the total creep strain will only be of the order of 0.2%.

17. Creep rupture data on uniaxial specimens are available at 300°C for testing times up to 15,000 hours; failure occurs at a stress corresponding to about 80-85% of the tensile strength. Extrapolating by means of a Larsen-Miller time/temperature parameter indicates that at 300°C the rupture strength for a 30 year life is about 34,000 lb/in^2 which is over twice the design stress and nearly three times the working stress of 12,400 lb/in^2. The values of elongation to failure (based on a gauge length of $10\sqrt{A}$) are in the range 7-12% and there is no indication of a decrease in ductility at long times to rupture. The results obtained from tests on tubular specimens show agreement with the uniaxial creep-rate tests and the failure stress in tubular rupture tests can be predicted with reasonable accuracy from the uniaxial data assuming that failure follows an octahedral shear stress criterion. Additionally, the circumferential strain at rupture is in the range 10-20%.

18. Turning to out-of-pile tests on the heat-treatment Zr-2½% Nb alloy, the results of a series of uniaxial tests are summarized in Fig. 3. On this basis, a stress of 46,000 lb/in^2 would be required to give a creep strain of 1% in 100,000 hours at 300°C, as compared with 30,000 lb/in^2 for cold-worked Zircaloy-2. Similarly, the stress for rupture in 30 years at 300°C is over 65,000 lb/in^2 for the heat-treated Zr-2½% Nb alloy, against 37,000 lb/in^2 for cold-worked Zircaloy-2. These values emphasize that for a design based in a conventional way on the properties in the absence of irradiation, the thickness of a pressure tube is controlled by its tensile strength (Table 3).

19. However, it is now well established that zirconium alloys under stress at temperatures around 300°C will creep more rapidly in a neutron flux than in out-of-reactor tests (refs 12, 13). A typical result from UKAEA work which indicates the magnitude of this difference between in-pile and out-of-pile creep rates under conditions approaching those relevant to SGHWR pressure tubes is given in Fig. 4, and over recent months considerable amounts of experimental work in Canada, the UK and the US have been devoted to obtaining such curves. It has been found that the irradiation enhancement increases with increase of neutron flux level.

20. To interpret such data in terms of the permissible stresses for a pressure tube material, it is necessary to decide how much strain can be tolerated in the particular design of pressure tube. For a vertical tube reactor such as the SGHWR, this question becomes one of how much increase of diameter (and associated wall thinning) is acceptable. Considerations such as the effect of pressure tube diameter on coolant flow, on fuel element support or on calandria tube gap do not provide a strain limit of less than 3%.

21. One aspect to be considered is that of the strain permitted in comparable components in conventional practice. In only very few engineering situations is the

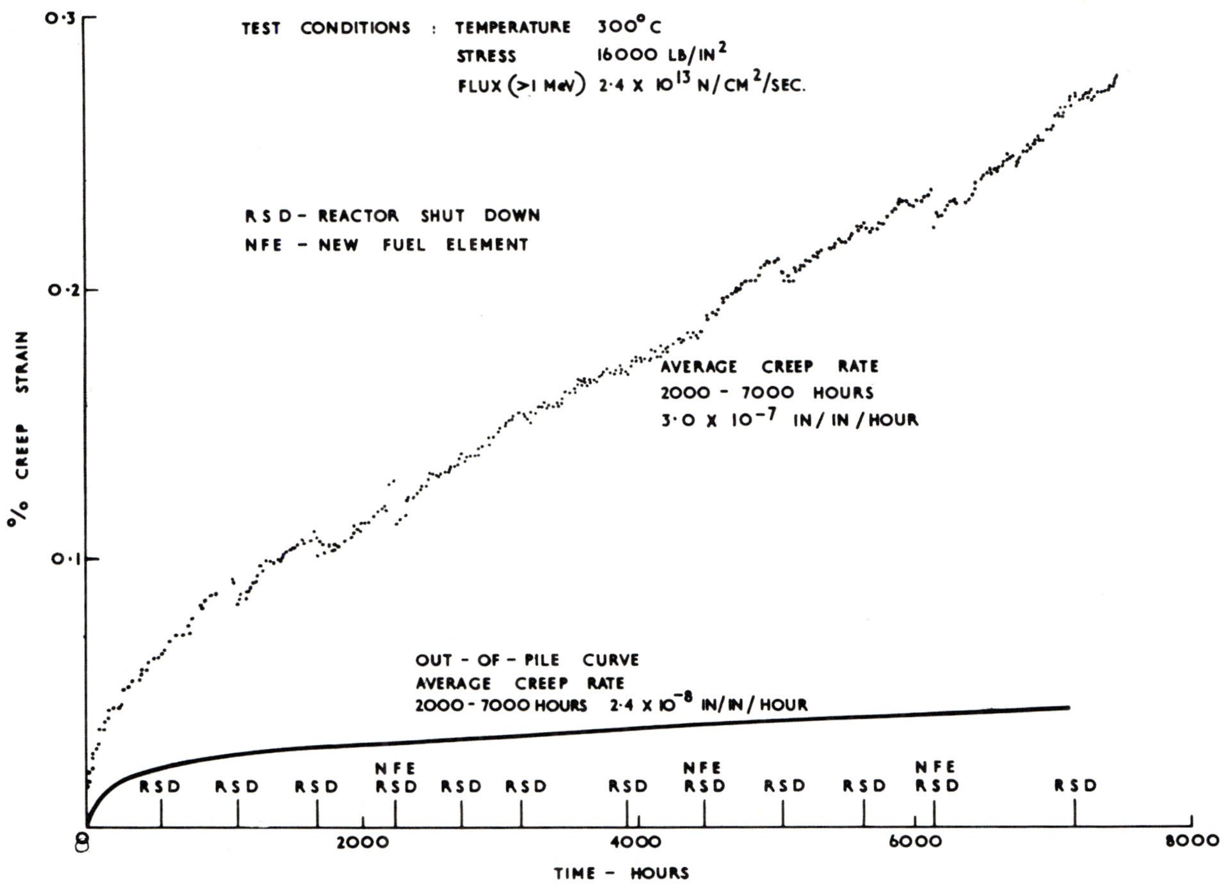

TEST CONDITIONS : TEMPERATURE 300°C
STRESS 16000 LB/IN²
FLUX (>1 MeV) 2·4 X 10¹³ N/CM²/SEC.
RSD - REACTOR SHUT DOWN
NFE - NEW FUEL ELEMENT
AVERAGE CREEP RATE
2000 - 7000 HOURS
3·0 X 10⁻⁷ IN/IN/HOUR
OUT - OF - PILE CURVE
AVERAGE CREEP RATE
2000 - 7000 HOURS 2·4 X 10⁻⁸ IN/IN/HOUR
RSD
NFE
% CREEP STRAIN
0·3
0·2
0·1
0
2000
4000
6000
8000
TIME - HOURS

Fig. 4: Typical example of the uniaxial creep behaviour of cold-worked Zircaloy-2 under irradiation

design such that small amounts of strain are of themselves limiting. In other cases, a more general limitation is that of ensuring that creep-rupture failure does not occur at points of stress concentration. For example, for steel pressure vessels, the present design codes indicate that the design stress shall not exceed the stress that will produce 1% creep in 100,000 hours (11½ years) although the value of this requirement has recently been questioned. Since this requirement is applied to components which may be in use for more than 20 years, it does not actually define the acceptable strain and indeed it permits values to exceed 2 or 3%. Moreover, this value is applied to the membrane stress level in structures containing significant stress concentrations. Thus, a structure built to such a specification could show local strains considerably greater than 2 or 3% after 30 years service. Accordingly, this criterion is not relevent to the design stress applied to a reactor pressure tube since, in the regions of high flux where creep has to be considered, the tube is of a simple cylindrical shape and free from significant strain concentration.

22. The conventional component most comparable to a pressure tube is a steam pipe although even this is, in general, of a more complex geometry. In the appropriate specification for steam pipes (BS 806.1967), the permitted design stress to be used for up to 250,000 hours operation at temperatures in the creep range is based on the stress to give rupture in 100,000 hours divided by a design factor of 1.8. At the present time, this approach cannot be used for zirconium alloy pressure tubes as there are no in-pile stress rupture data on which it could be based. Whilst there are such tests now in progress in UKAEA reactors, the difficulties of in-pile testing make it desirable to make a different approach to the problem.

23. A possible approach is to determine from the in-pile creep tests the conditions under which the strain rate is less than 10^{-7} per hour, since this should only lead to a strain of about 2% in 30 years operation. This assumes that the creep rate remains constant with time, which is a reasonable assumption on the present evidence. In other aspects, this approach errs in the direction of caution. The results of out-of-pile tests on tube specimens, some of which are shown in Table 4, indicate that the time taken to reach 2% strain is only about half the time taken to produce a stress rupture failure. Results of tests on both tubular and uniaxial specimens suggest that this safety margin between the time to reach 2% strain and the time to failure actually increases as one approaches the long times of interest in the practical case.

24. The limited in-pile data suggest that the safety margin in using this approach is even greater than the out-of-pile tests suggest. An example is given in Fig. 5 which shows the in-pile creep curve for a uniaxial test at a temperature of 325°C and

a stress of 34,000 lb/in^2 in a flux of 3×10^{13} n/cm^2/s. Under these conditions, the specimen has exceeded 9% strain without any indication of tertiary creep or of fracture. Out-of-reactor specimens at the same creep rate have shown the onset of tertiary creep at about 2-3% strain. This indicates that the difference between the time for 2% strain and the time for fracture will be even greater under in-pile conditions.

25. Using this cautious criterion, the present information for cold-worked Zircaloy-2 would permit an operating stress of about 12,000 lb/in^2 at 290°C in a neutron flux of 2×10^{13} n/cm^2/s. A major programme of in-pile tests is now in progress to establish the effect of variations in stress, temperature and flux level on in-pile creep rate and stress-rupture behaviour and additional information will be obtained from accurate diameter measurements which will be made at shutdown on several of the tubes in the Winfrith SGHWR. These experiments will also provide information on the in-pile creep behaviour of the heat-treated Zr-2½% Nb alloy for which the present data are insufficient to define the stress for an in-pile creep rate of 10^{-7} per hour.

OTHER ASPECTS

26. In some circumstances, it is desirable to be able to weld the pressure tube material. For example, in the Winfrith SGHWR reduced diameter sections are welded on to the lower end of the pressure tube to facilitate assembly of the channel. Techniques for welding Zircaloy-2 are well established, but obviously the thermal effects associated with welding will partially anneal and reduce the strength of the cold-worked material near to a weld. Tests have been made in which tensile strength surveys have been made across joints in cold-worked Zircaloy-2 of pressure tube thickness, welded by the tungsten-arc process. These indicated that the tensile strength at 300°C was reduced to about 70% of that of the cold-worked material, the softened zone extending to about 0.8 in. each side of the centre line of the weld. Similar tests with electron beam welds made by 150 kV, 3 kW equipment showed a drop to about 84% of the cold-worked strength at 300°C together with a very much narrower zone of softened material extending only to 0.3 in. from the weld centre line.

27. In the case of the circumferential welds needed to join a length of tube to an end fitting, it was argued that this softened region would be supported against diametral strain by the material surrounding it so that the softened region should not significantly reduce the failure strength. This has been confirmed by internal pressure burst tests which have been made on a number of tubes with welded end fittings of different types. The results shown in Table 5 refer to samples using argon-arc welds with Zircaloy-2 filler metal, and in all these cases

Table 4
Some results of internal pressure creep rupture tests on SGHW Zircaloy-2 tube samples
at 300°C

Stress 10³ lb/in²	Time to rupture h	Circ. strain at rupture %	Ratio of time to reach 2% strain ÷ time to rupture
60	160	10.6	0.46
56	762	25.0	0.69
55	2439	14.3	0.38
54.5	1929	11.2	0.31
54.5	1960	9.5	0.61
54.5	3278	7.0	0.28

Table 5
Results of tube burst tests at 300°C

Materials	Weld	Burst stress lb/in²
30% cold-worked Zircaloy-2	Unwelded	67,000
30% cold-worked Zr-2/Zr-2 fabricated reducer	Argon arc	66,500
20% cold-worked Zr-2½% Nb	Unwelded	81,000
20% cold-worked Zr-Nb/Zr-Nb reducer	Argon arc	81,000
Heat-treated Zr-2½% Nb	Unwelded	97,900
Heat-treated Zr-Nb/Zr-Nb reducer	Argon arc	115,000

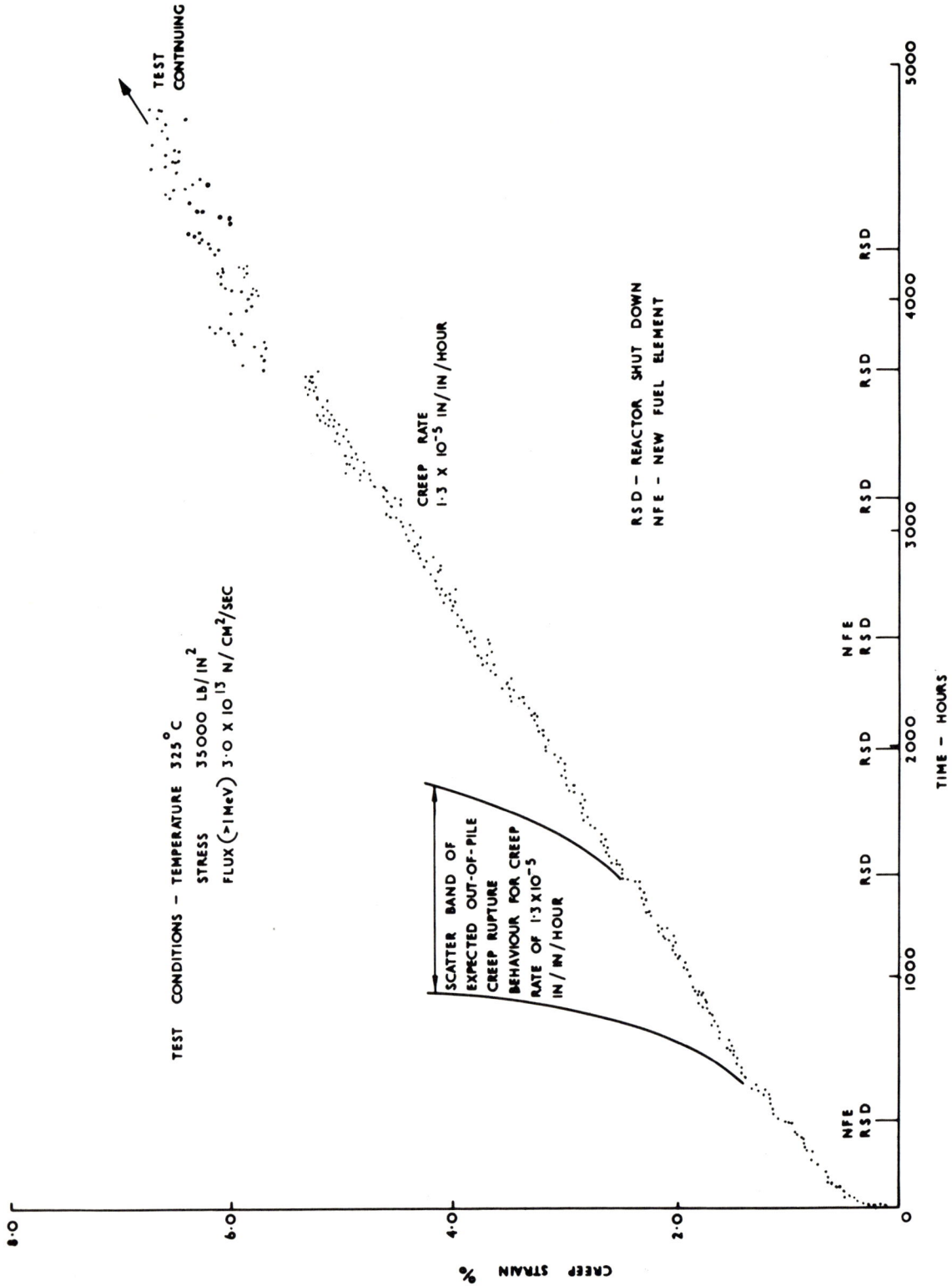

Fig. 5: High strain creep behaviour of cold-worked Zircaloy-2 under irradiation

124

failure occurred in the tube at a stress very similar to that of the similar un-welded tube. It is considered that such welded connections can be made in either cold-worked or heat-treated zirconium alloy tubes using the same design stresses as for unwelded tube.

CLOSURE

28. This paper has summarized some of the work related to the development of zirconium alloys as pressure tube materials. It however covers only a part of the total development which has been carried out towards providing satisfactory reactor channel units for the SGHWR. For example, detailed development and assessment of fabrication routes has ensured the practicability of using in future constructions either the Zircaloy-2 or the zirconium-2½% niobium alloys, in the cold-worked or heat-treated conditions. Other work has been done on establishing satisfactory methods for making rolled-joints and on establishing suitable quality control procedures. The work described in this paper has provided evidence that the embrittlement resulting from corrosion processes, and from irradiation effects, will not limit the economic use of these materials.

29. Attention has been drawn to the accelerating effect of neutron irradiation on the creep of zirconium alloys. The present evidence indicates that this will not cause a problem with cold-worked Zircaloy-2 pressure tubes in SGHWR designs. Considerably more information on this aspect of Zircaloy-2 and heat-treated Zr-2½% Nb alloy behaviour will arise from current experimental work in research reactors and in the operation of the Winfrith SGHWR.

ACKNOWLEDGEMENT

30. This paper is published by kind permission of the Managing Director, The Reactor Group, UKAEA, Risley. Thanks are due to the many colleagues at Culcheth, Harwell and Risley associated with the work reported.

REFERENCES

1. WATKINS B. and COCKADAY R. Development of zirconium alloy pressure tubes for the Winfrith Heath Steam Generating Heavy Water Reactor. Inst. of Mech. Eng. Conf. on New Engineering Mats., 13th-14th October, 1965.

2. TYZACK C, BERRY R and CAMPBELL C.S. Paper 9 of this conference.

3. DAWSON J.K., ASHER R.C., WATKINS B., BOULTON J. and WANKLYN J.N. The properties of zirconium alloys for use in water cooled reactors. Proc. 2nd Int. Conf. on Peaceful Uses of Atomic Energy, 1964, Paper P/158.

4. JOHNSON A.B. and IRVINE J.E. BNWL-463, July 1967.

5. LOUTHAN M.R. and MARSHALL R.P. J. Nuc. Mats. 9 170 (1963).

6. HOWE L.M. and THOMAS W.R. Effect of neutron irradiation on the tensile properties of Zr-2. AECL 809, March 1959.

7. NICHOLS R.W. and WATKINS B. Implications of embrittlement during the life of a zirconium pressure tube reactor. Paper presented to 69th Annual Meeting ASTM, Atlantic City, 27th June-1st July, 1966.

8. COWAN A. and COWBURN K. Critical crack length measurements in hydrided Zr-2 pressure tubes. J. Inst. Metals 95 (10) 302-307 (1967).

9. COWAN A. and LANGFORD W.J. Effect of irradiation on the critical crack length of Zr-2 pressure tubes. J. Nuc. Mats. - submitted for publication.

10. PANKASKIE P.J. Crack propagation characteristics of Zr-2.5% Nb alloy tubing BNWL-560, October 1967.

11. WOOD D.S., WINTON J. and WATKINS B. Effect of irradiation on the impact properties of hydrided Zr-2 and Zr-Nb alloy. Electrochemical Technology 4 No. 5-6, May-June 1966.

12. FIDLERIS V. and WILLIAMS C.D. Influence of neutron irradiation on the creep of Zircaloy-2 at 300°C. Electrochemical Technology 4 No. 5-6, May-June 1966.

13. ROSS-ROSS P.A. The in-reactor creep of cold-worked Zr-2 and Zr-2.5% Nb. Trans. Amer. Nuc. Soc. 10 No. 1, June 1967.

Some material compatibility aspects of SGHWRs

C. TYZACK, BSc, PhD, UKAEA, Culcheth.

R. BERRY, BSc, ARIC, UKAEA, Culcheth.

C. S. CAMPBELL, MA, UKAEA, Culcheth.

SYNOPSIS   The paper reviews the major areas where compatibility aspects are of importance in a SGHW reactor system. These include the closely related aspects of selection of materials for primary and secondary circuits and choice of water chemistry regime. There is some discussion of subsequent work which has been carried out in support of the mild steel primary circuit concept.

The in-pile and out-of-pile aqueous corrosion and hydrogen pick-up of zirconium alloys used as reactor pressure tube materials is discussed particularly in relation to differing behaviour under oxidizing (neutral) and comparatively reducing environments (ammonia). The materials selection and chemical aspects of the moderator circuit are outlined.

INTRODUCTION

1.   The Steam Generating Heavy Water Reactor is the first in a new line of development as far as the UKAEA is concerned, and while it has certain factors in common with other water-cooled reactors such as the American BWRs and the Canadian NPD-CANDU series, some aspects of its technology represent a departure from previous practice.

2.   The present paper briefly surveys the current situation on the compatibility of materials used in the Winfrith SGHWR and possible future versions, and discusses how this may be affected by the choice of water chemistry for the system. Broadly this entails operating the reactor neutral, under oxidizing conditions due to radiolysis, or with an ammonia addition which must be at a sufficient level to produce reducing conditions, i.e., supress oxygen formation and hence nitric acid formation.

3.   It is not proposed to deal with each item used in the reactor but to discuss the factors affecting the choice of materials in a broader perspective as the choice of the major items, and of the water chemistry regime interact upon one another, and a decision to fix on one may limit the freedom of choice for the others.

PRIMARY CIRCUIT - SELECTION OF STEEL

4.   The first major materials decision which had to be made was whether to construct the out-of-core primary circuit in a silicon-killed boiler steel or in an austenitic stainless steel. Factors in favour of mild steel were reduced costs, greater fabrication experience with mild steel vessels and piping, a diminution in activity levels from activated corrosion products such as Co-58 and Co-60, and lower thermal expansion. Carbon steel is the standard material of construction for conventional steam plant, and it was known that mild steel had been selected to be used in the Canadian pressurized heavy water reactors, NPD and CANDU, and also in the American NPR at Hanford. In conventional steam plant and the secondary side of nuclear plants, the feed water is de-aerated and chemically treated, while in the pressurized water reactor, a hydrogen overpressure is maintained the net result of which is to reduce the oxygen level in the water below the limit of detection by suppression of radiolysis. On the other hand, it was known that the Dresden BWR had a stainless steel primary circuit and operated without pH conditioning or hydrogen additions. Although most of the gases formed by radiolysis in the core were stripped into the steam the recirculating water was known to contain around 0.1 to 0.2 ppm oxygen with roughly the stoichiometric equivalent of hydrogen. This figure, while apparently perfectly satisfactory in stainless steel was grossly in excess of what would be considered acceptable in conventional practice for mild steel.

5.   In view of the lack of information available at the time, a decision was taken to use stainless steel for the primary circuit of the Winfrith SGHWR. Since that time, however, a number of new experimental facts have emerged from our programme which suggest that in future systems of SGHWR type mild steels can be used in the primary circuit. The findings of Vreeland and his co-workers at GE on the corrosion of mild and low alloy steels at 285°C in water, saturated steam and steam-water mixtures where deliberate additions of oxygen and hydrogen in stoichiometric ratio were made in an out-of-pile loop, has been independently investigated in the UK and their

Table 1
Corrosion of carbon steel in water at $30^\circ C$
Rates in mdd

Exposure days	Immersion in aerated water			Immersion in de-aerated water	
	Neutral Continuous purification Conductivity 0.1 μmho	Neutral Zero purification Conductivity <100 μmho	10 ppm NH_3 Continuous purification Conductivity 40 μmho	100 ppm NH_3 Continuous purification	100 ppm NH_3 Zero purification
10	0.1	70	-	0.2	6.4
21	-	-	2.6	-	-
27	-	-	-	0.1	16.3
43	0.1	-	0.9	-	-
84	0.1	-	0.8	-	-

Note: Aerated neutral water contained a minimum of 6 ml O_2/kg. In the de-aerated water tests the oxygen was reduced down to 0.01 ml/kg level by nitrogen purge.

results broadly confirmed (refs 1, 2). Corrosion tests on mild steel have been made in a recirculating pressurized water loop where oxygen and hydrogen have been introduced by electrolysis, and excessive hydrogen build-up prevented by blowing off steam from the pressurizer. The corrosion and release rates for mild steel exposed at $280^{\circ}C$ for 28 days in neutral coolant containing 0.1 ml O_2/kg (0.07 ppm) of 1.4 and 0.15 mdd are in good agreement with Vreeland's work (1.5 and 0.3 mdd) and earlier work in the UK by Babcock & Wilcox Limited (1.5 and 0.1 mdd) under similar conditions. No increase in corrosion rate was found in our work on increasing the oxygen level from 0.1 to 0.6 ml O_2/kg at this temperature, nor was pitting attack observed.

6. These results indicate that as far as high temperature operation of a ferritic circuit with oxygenated coolant is concerned no difficulties are to be expected, and it seems that choice of coolant chemistry to give acceptable corrosion and release rates may well be influenced to a greater extent by conditions prevailing at shutdown than by those when the reactor is on load. Tests are being conducted in the laboratory with mild steel immersed in a variety of solutions to assess the relative merits of chemically dosed and neutral water for conservation of ferritic circuits during shutdown.

7. Tests at $30^{\circ}C$ on mild steel coupons exposed to flowing neutral oxygenated water have demonstrated that by keeping the conductivity below 1 μmho serious metal wastage and pitting can be prevented (see Table 1). Other tests were conducted to determine whether the adverse effects arising from the presence of impurities responsible for the conductivity of water could be counteracted by ammonia additions. The table illustrates that to arrest corrosion of mild steel it is more effective to remove impurities and produce high resistance water than simply to increase the pH of the solution. Intensive localized attack was observed on specimens immersed in the ammonia dosed aerated water. Microscopic examination of these specimens revealed numerous cavities in the form of grooves running parallel to the direction of flow.

8. In the range of flow investigated to date (0.1 to 3.2 fps) it has been found that the velocity of aerated water over plain coupons has only a minor influence on the corrosion resistance, but that the incidence of pitting increases at the lower velocities. The presence of ammonia does not alter this trend but its presence does lead to higher corrosion rates at the respective velocities. In crevices both pitting and wastage is more pronounced. After six weeks immersion in aerated water the occasional pit of up to 0.003 in. depth has been found in crevice specimens. The addition of 10 ppm ammonia to the water did not materially alter the findings.

9. The above results would appear to be in line with the view that both oxygen and anion species are initially adsorbed at the oxide surface, and that oxygen molecules conserve or even repair the oxide film whereas anions tend to disrupt it (ref. 3). Thus in the presence of high concentrations of harmful anions, and low oxygen content, general weakening of the oxide film will occur, leading to complete breakdown in areas already weakened by damage, internal stresses, impurities, etc. In such circumstances the corrosion of mild steel will be controlled by the rate of the cathodic reduction of oxygen, and hence by the rate of transport of oxygen from the bulk of the solution to the corroding surface. Conversely at high oxygen-anion ratios, and where there is an ample and continuous supply of oxygen to the surface, the corrosion will be predominantly under anodic control where the magnitude of the corrosion current is determined by the degree of breakdown of the oxide which will be determined by the type and concentration of anions in solution. Both Brasher, and Resch and Odenthal have demonstrated using NaCl, Na_2SO_4 and $NaNO_3$ in the concentration range 10^{-2} to 10^{-5} mol/l that the nature of the anions is important, and doubtless this applies at lower levels where the effects of carbon dioxide, one of the main impurities in high quality water, cannot be neglected (refs 4, 5). Conductivity has been considered the best guide in determining the aggressive nature of a solution, particularly as under our test conditions CO_2 is the most likely impurity.

10. Our work to date therefore suggests that water quality during shutdown is of paramount importance, and that the removal of ionic matter is a far more effective way of arresting the corrosion of steel than raising the pH by ammonia additions. Operation of the power stations at Hamburg provide a large-scale practical demonstration of the efficiency of wet conservation of mild steel circuitry on aerated high purity water, as no additions are used during shutdown (ref. 6).

PRIMARY CIRCUIT - SELECTION OF PRESSURE TUBES

11. It was decided to use 30% cold-worked Zircaloy-2 as a pressure tube material for the Winfrith reactor because this was the only zirconium alloy on which fabrication technology was sufficiently advanced and about which extensive knowledge on physical, mechanical and corrosion properties was available, largely from North American sources. An undeveloped alternative was an alloy based on a zirconium composition containing 2.5% by weight niobium. In the solution treated, quenched and aged condition this alloy shows markedly superior mechanical properties to Zircaloy-2, and in the event it was possible to include a small number of heat treated pressure tubes in the Winfrith reactor.

12. It was generally agreed that in oxygen free water at 280°C the heat treated material in an optimized condition was not as good in corrosion resistance as the best Zircaloy-2, but only worse by a factor of about 2 to 3, and that this might be largely offset by a reduction in the percentage of corrosion hydrogen absorbed by the material, which was probably in the range 10-20%, against a percentage pick-up by Zircaloy-2 in low oxygen water of 50-90% hydrogen in post-transition, so that the total hydrogen content of the pressure tube at end of life might be somewhat in favour of the niobium alloy.

13. The corrosion behaviour of the niobium alloy was found to be sensitive to metallurgical condition, not only in the water phase but also in gas atmospheres simulating that to be expected in the reactor vault to which the outside of the tubes would be subjected. Work has been carried out on the out-of-pile corrosion evaluation of the $2\frac{1}{2}$ Nb-Zr alloy in pressurized water in the temperature range 280-330°C, in steam in the temperature range 350-500°C and in moist air, moist CO_2 and moist air-CO_2 mixture at 300°C. Materials in the cold-worked condition, in the annealed condition (5 h at 700°C) and in the solution treated condition ($\frac{1}{2}$ h at either 880 or 1000°C, followed by water quenching and tempering for various periods between 5 and 168 h at 500°C) have been examined. In moist air at 300°C corrosion rates were very high for cold-worked, annealed and quenched and tempered material which had been aged up to 48 h at 500°C in the range 1 to 4 mdd, which is sufficiently high to cause worry about loss of metal section in the pressure tube during a thirty-year life (0.019-0.076 in). Much more acceptable results were obtained on material quenched from 880°C and tempered at 500°C for periods of 72 and 168 h, giving extrapolated losses of 0.0027 and 0.0014 in. in 30 years. At this stage it was not possible to predict precisely the composition of the vault atmosphere in the reactor, but it is expected that moist carbon dioxide will not contain more than a few per cent of air in which case cold-worked material or 880°C quenched material tempered for 24 h or more should be adequate in corrosion resistance.

14. This marked sensitivity of the material to the oxygen content of the carbon dioxide environment is a feature peculiar to the niobium alloy, and one which is not apparent with Zircaloy-2 which corrodes at very similar rates in water, steam, CO_2 and air at 300°C in out-of-pile tests. These observations caused a re-examination to be made of the oxidation behaviour of the niobium alloy in water environments containing oxygen such as would be encountered in the Winfrith SGHWR operating neutral. Some increment in corrosion rates was observed in tests at 290°C in replenished autoclaves in which the oxygen level in the water was maintained at 7 ppm, compared with results in degassed water, suggesting that some improvement could be obtained by working under reducing conditions.

15. Short-term proof tests, i.e., 3 and 14 days exposure to 1500 lb/in^2 steam at 400°C, were carried out on material cut from preproduction and production Zircaloy-2 pressure tubes and these indicated in some cases particularly in the preproduction tubes somewhat higher weight gains than for sheet and fuel element material. The results were not particularly consistent but the high weight gains appear to be associated with coarse microstructures. It is not clear whether the association arises directly from the coarseness of the intermetallics, to their poor distribution or to areas being denuded of iron, chromium or nickel, but slow cooling from the β-field is known to give poor corrosion resistance in 400°C steam tests and it has been claimed that resolution followed by quenching can improve poor corrosion resistance (refs 7, 8, 9).

16. Somewhat more consistent results together with a better differentiation of coarse material was achieved by a reduction of the steam test pressure to 100 psi. Modification of the production route to include a high temperature heat treatment, followed by a water quench gave some improvement in corrosion resistance of the subsequent Zircaloy-2 tubes.

17. Long-term tests of material from a number of pressure tubes and sheet material in steam at 400°C and 1000 lb/in^2 which currently extend to 12,000 h where weight gains are of the order of 300-400 mg/dm^2 are, however, showing little if any difference in post-transition rates despite somewhat higher rates for the pressure tube materials in the early stages.

18. In long-term tests in more realistic operating conditions (pressurized water at 310°C) there was no marked increase in corrosion rates for pressure tube materials in the pretransition region, but the results indicate slightly higher rates in post-transition, e.g., Zircaloy-2 sheet 0.045 mdd, pressure tube 0.055 mdd after 26,000 h exposure. On balance it must be concluded that the 400°C steam proof test is not a particularly good guide to long-term behaviour in water at lower temperatures.

19. The foregoing refers to out-of-pile data, but in addition a considerable experimental programme has been mounted in the UK to study in-pile corrosion phenomena of zirconium alloys, and experiments have been mounted in wet helium, wet carbon dioxide, steam at atmospheric pressure, pressurized water (in refreshed autoclaves and in the boiling water loop in DMTR) and in boiling water in the Canadian X4 and X6 loops. Corrosion acceleration factors for Zircaloy-2 of the order of five or slightly greater have been found at 340°C in wet helium by RML and in atmospheric steam at 300 and 340°C by workers at AERE (ref. 10). The latter workers have order of magnitude accelerations in oxidation rate using oxygenated water at 340°C in a refreshed autoclave. Long-term results from the RML programme

in the boiling water loop (310°C) under neutral conditions will be available towards the middle of 1968. It is interesting to compare these figures with what is available on the subject from the rest of the world's reactors. Publications from Westinghouse have consistently maintained that there is no increase due to irradiation of Zircaloy-2 cladding in their PWRs, such as Saxton, and in the blanket fuel elements of Shippingport (refs 11, 12). If there is an effect the acceleration is certainly not greater than a factor of 2, unless some oxide dissolution phenomenon is masking a bigger in-pile effect. The Zircaloy-2 pressure tubes in the PRTR reactor operating at 260°C which have their outer surfaces exposed to wet helium, have shown an increase in oxide thickness corresponding to an acceleration factor of around 10, while the bores exposed to pressurized lithiated heavy water containing about 0.15 ppm oxygen have shown a somewhat greater and clearly flux dependent increase in oxide thickness corresponding to a factor possibly of the order of thirty (ref. 13). Similar in-pile enhancements are emerging from experiments under neutral boiling water reactor conditions in the loops at Chalk River (ref. 14). Factors of 30 have been observed on corrosion coupons, while examination of oxide thickness on fuel cladding indicates similar enhancements. Average oxide thicknesses corresponding to exposure out-of-pile at 360-400°C have also been reported from Dresden and other boiling water reactors operating with water temperatures of around 285°C, but in these cases it is not clear whether some of the enhancement in corrosion rate may be due to crud deposition raising the surface temperature of the cladding (ref. 15). In the G7 ETR loop at Idaho Falls specimens have been exposed at 280°C in lithiated pressurized water containing about 0.8 ppm oxygen. In one set of tests extending up to 125 days rates of around 1 mdd were observed representing an acceleration in time of about 35, and in another series extending up to 250 days metallographic examination suggested corrosion rates in excess of 2 mdd (ref. 16).

20. As was noted earlier, in out-of-pile tests the corrosion of Zircaloy-2 is little effected by oxidation potential, however it is notable that the most marked increases in oxidation rate under irradiation have been associated with oxidizing conditions. While there is no obvious reason to suppose that fast neutron damage to the oxide film could be increased in any way by oxidizing conditions it is possible that the highly oxidizing specimens that exist in-pile in the absence of adequate dissolved hydrogen levels might be responsible for some increase in the transport of oxygen beyond that to be expected by neutron damage, particularly if Bacarella and Sutton are correct in their postulate that oxide growth in Zircaloy-2 is controlled by a field dependent ionic transport of oxygen (ref. 17). A change in the cathodic depolarization process under irradiation could produce a change in the potential gradient across the film, while a cubic rate law would imply ionic transport proportional to the square of the gradient.

21. On the other hand most of the North American information has been obtained under conditions where defective fuel could have been present at some time during or preceding the in-pile exposures. Probably only traces of the order of 10^{-6} g uranium/cm^2 would be required near the metal surface to account for the highest rates observed. If some of the observed in-pile enhancement were due to fissile contamination, and this is not remote from the practical situation, then some of the effects of water chemistry may be simply a reflection of a dependence of fissile release rate and deposition on uranium or plutonium chemistry and variations in the enhancement observed, particularly local ones would be more easily explained.

22. A marked effect of water chemistry has appeared in further tests carried out in the ETR.G7 loop specifically to examine this point. Strongly reducing pressurized water conditions have been maintained by ammonia dosing, giving a high level of dissolved hydrogen ($\sim$45 ml H_2/kg). In the current tests non-preoxidized samples have shown enhancements after 77 days exposure at 280°C at fast fluxes around 10^{14} cm^2/s equivalent to 3-4 in time. This represents an order of magnitude reduction of the in-pile effect observed under oxidizing conditions. Corresponding reductions in absolute hydrogen pick-up have been observed between oxidizing and reducing conditions in-pile.

23. Relatively little information is available as yet on the in-pile oxidation behaviour of $2\frac{1}{2}$ Nb-Zr alloy, experiments carried out at RML in wet helium, at AERE in steam and at Chalk River in boiling water tend to suggest that the in-pile enhancement is small. In view of the out-of-pile susceptibility of the material to oxygen in the water (or CO_2) environment it might be expected that ammonia additions to the coolant would prove beneficial in a reactor environment. Some limited data from the loops at Chalk River suggest that this may well be the case, although much further work needs to be done to clarify the relative effects of oxidation damage and chemical environment.

CONDENSER - FEED-WATER SYSTEMS

24. The chemistry of the steam condensate-feed-water system of the Winfrith SGHWR (operating neutral) differs from that of conventional power plant mainly in respect of the significant concentrations of oxygen present in the steam supplied to the feed-water heaters in the nuclear system. Carry-out of corrosion products which may deposit on the fuel is particularly important but, nevertheless, conventional experience has been useful in the selection of materials.

25. Thus, in order to avoid the corrosion-exfoliation problems associated with cupro-nickel HP feed heaters, stainless steel was specified for the HP heaters in the SGHW reactor. Subsequently it was decided to use mild steel in No. 4 unit on an experimental basis to assess its potentialities for future systems. Dynamic tests conducted in mild steel loops with the appropriate temperature and chemistry indicated mild steel wastage rates of 2 mdd after 1000 h exposure with 30% release of corrosion products. While some pitting does occur it is by no means as serious as the exfoliation which could be expected if cupro-nickel tubes had been installed in the HP units.

26. On the low pressure side 90/10 cupro-nickel was used to tube Nos 1 and 2 LP heater, and the deaerator vent condenser, as at low temperatures of operation no serious corrosion was expected on the steam side even in the presence of oxygen. On the water side most of the released corrosion products will be removed by the full flow ion exchange treatment given by Powdex resin interposed beyond the second LP heater. Typical analysis for water which has been given this treatment are 5 ppb maximum for metals normally encountered in feed-water circuits. Unfortunately it is clear from power station experience that a significant pick-up of corrosion products on the water side takes place in the high pressure feed heaters downstream of the clean-up plant.

27. Originally it was specified that the main condenser should be tubed in Admiralty brass, with Naval brass endplates. However, as there was the possibility of operating the reactor at some future date with ammonia dosed coolant, at a concentration at least an order of magnitude greater than that used in conventional plant, it was deemed prudent to fabricate the inlet and gas extract regions of the condenser in 70/30 and 90/10 cupro-nickel respectively, which are resistant to stress corrosion cracking.

28. Experiments have been carried out on the copper-based materials of interest in ammoniated water at the temperatures and concentrations relevant to the condenser and feed line. A wastage rate of 0.6 mdd was observed with brass in water containing 20 ppm ammonia at $32^{o}C$, which is comparable with results observed in neutral water, so that no significant increase in the wastage of brass tubes or end plates is anticipated from the use of ammonia. In the region of the extract section of the main condenser, however, where concentrations of up to 1000 ppm ammonia would be encountered, wastage rates are higher and for the cupro-nickel a value of around 7 mdd is to be expected. Provided that corrosion is uniform this wastage rate is probably tolerable, but it does throw a large burden on the Powdex plant (influent ~50 ppb Cu). Use of cupro-nickel in the critical zones should ensure freedom from stress cracking of the condensor during reactor operation with ammonia, but it may be necessary to

prevent air ingress at shutdown under these conditions.

MODERATOR CIRCUIT

29. The moderator circuit comprises the aluminium alloy calandria and ancillary circuitry including a heat exchanger and ion exchange unit fabricated in stainless steel, in which the circulating heavy water is cooled and purified. In addition there is a moderator blanket gas circuit comprising a condenser to remove heavy water vapour and a catalytic recombination unit for deuterium and oxygen. The function of this circuit is to ensure that the deuterium content of the helium blanket gas produced by the radiolysis of heavy water does not exceed 1 per cent by volume, and to prevent access of air to the moderator. The latter is important as light water vapour would reduce the D_2/H_2 ratio of the heavy water, nitrogen would react with oxygen to form nitric acid under the influence of neutron flux and similarly the active isotope argon 41 would be formed. Control of the reactor involves the use of a soluble nuclear poison and additions of up to 10 ppm ^{10}B as boric acid are made for this purpose. There are in addition shutdown tubes which pass through the calandria which can be filled with more concentrated boron-containing solutions.

30. Aluminium alloys in which the matrix is strengthened by the presence of magnesium in solid solution have been developed commercially for applications where medium strength and high ductility are required, in combination with good corrosion resistance and welding properties. Additionally they have low neutron capture cross section for nuclear application. The selection of the alloy for the prototype calandria had essentially to be a compromise between obtaining satisfactory welding characteristics and adequate resistance to corrosion and stress corrosion. These are opposing requirements as, while higher magnesium contents are desirable to avoid hot cracking during welding, they also increase the susceptibility to stress corrosion cracking.

31. There have been a number of studies on the effect of magnesium content, cold work and ageing on susceptibility to stress cracking, and it is generally believed on the basis of the work of Dix et al. and Bowen that alloys with up to 5% are acceptable for room temperature applications, but that for higher temperature service under conditions of stress and corrosive environment the magnesium content should be restricted to below 3.5% to ensure freedom from stress corrosion (refs 18, 19). In view of this a modified N4 composition, average about 2.8% magnesium with N5 weld filler rod (3.6% magnesium), was chosen for the SGHWR calandria, which operates at about $80^{o}C$, in order to minimize stress corrosion hazards and to ease the welding difficulties as far as possible.

32. An experimental programme was initiated to confirm the correctness of these precepts. Aqueous corrosion tests of several thousand hours duration have been carried out on modified N4 specimens both with and without irradiation, and have indicated a wastage rate of not greater than 0.1 mil/year and an absence of significant pitting or crevice attack. The tests also confirmed the superior resistance of the magnesium-containing alloys to high alkalinity, which should allow greater flexibility in moderator chemistry and choice of solution composition for shutdown tubes. Whilst the oxide film on the metal surface is known to absorb approximately 0.5 μg B/cm^2 from solutions containing 10 ppm B as boric acid, no enhancement in corrosion can be attributed to the (n, α) reaction which occurs in the presence of a thermal neutron flux. Neither has the presence of galvanic couples formed between aluminium and stainless steel resulted in serious pitting attack in tests where ion exchange clean-up has been maintained.

33. Out-of-pile stress corrosion tests been mounted on plate and weld sections of N4 which had been previously exposed in HERALD reactor for periods up to 6 months in boric acid solutions. No failures have so far been observed.

34. Serious waterline pitting attack is possible with Al-Mg alloys under heat transfer conditions. Tests at heat transfer values comparable to the maximum expected in the reactor have shown pits of several mils depth in material exposed for several hundred hours, but only if an interface was present. In the reactor this problem at the moderator-blanket gas interface is overcome by wetting the tubes with returning cooled D$_2$O so that a continuous water film is maintained.

35. The ion exchange plant described in Paper 9B to the Symposium has a dual role as it is used for reactor physics control in addition to control of correct chemical environment (pH 5.5) to minimize aluminium corrosion. The system adopted is based on the use of resin beds of a strong base anion exchanger to remove nitrate, borate and other anionic impurities, and a cation exchanger to remove lithium ions which are formed by burn-up of ^{10}B, and metallic corrosion products. In order to have some selectivity with respect to boron removal as opposed to other anions it is necessary to include additional beds of either weak base anion exchanger or alternatively columns of the strong base material saturated with boric acid. Tests have shown that the latter approach is superior in controlling the nitrate level and removing objectionable ions such as chloride without removing borate ions. Whilst under normal running conditions the throughput for removal of nitrate and other anions can be expected to be small, the beds must be correctly sized to cater for the high flow operation necessary for clean-up of nitrate ions at start of reactor life, or after opening the calandria for any

reason, or in the event of a major inleak of air.

36. The region within the primary containment constitutes the reactor vault, and all spaces within it are filled with carbon dioxide at slight positive pressure during reactor operation which under normal conditions should give an atmosphere low in air and moisture content. Under start-up conditions air concentrations up to 10% might be expected and obviously under fault conditions involving circuit leaks higher moisture levels might be encountered although it is not possible to give precise figures. In the absence of radiation the corrosion of aluminium in moist carbon dioxide at temperatures up to 100°C is insignificant, nor is it influenced by the presence of air. However, fairly severe localized corrosion has been observed in some Canadian reactors utilizing aluminium alloy calandrias due to the presence of air and moisture in the vault forming nitric acid under irradiation. Landsman and Laing have determined G (NO$_3$) values for moist CO$_2$-air mixtures under irradiation at 80 and 300°C (ref. 20). Experiments were carried out both in the presence of N4 and in its absence, and in the former case a G(NO$_3$) value of 3.5 was estimated. Using this figure and assuming steady state levels of 10% and 1% air in the vault, and assuming that all the nitric acid formed reacts uniformly with the calandria tubes, penetrations of 12.5 and 1.25 mil in twenty years are estimated. These figures are realistic and tolerable provided leakages of moisture are not so great as to produce conditions where condensation can occur on the upper cooler parts of the calandria tube surfaces, i.e., a dew point of the gas greater than 55°C. Under these conditions attack by nitric acid and by organic acids such as formic or oxalic which might be formed by the irradiation of moist CO$_2$ is likely to lead to pitting of the calandria walls.

CONCLUSIONS

37. Examination of the compatibility of the Winfrith SGHWR system broadly confirms the original choice of materials. Out-of-pile corrosion rates for Zircaloy-2 pressure tubes are well established and extrapolations suggest a total hydrogen content of around 120 ppm at the end of life. In-pile experiments indicate that some acceleration in corrosion rate will undoubtedly occur under irradiation although it is difficult to put a precise factor on this, but one might reasonably expect a hydrogen content of several hundred parts per million in the pressure tubes at end of life. This accelerated pick-up of hydrogen could probably be reduced by operating under reducing conditions (ammonia) but not eliminated. No clear effect of irradiation has been demonstrated in the corrosion behaviour of the niobium-zirconium alloy, but the material is very sensitive to the oxygen content of the environment and the corrosion rates in-pile under oxidizing conditions may well be

comparable with those of Zircaloy-2, although the corrosion hydrogen pick-up may be less. In order to follow the corrosion history of the pressure tubes a large number of zirconium monitoring specimens has been included in the reactor fuel channels and vault.

38. No particular problems are foreseen arising from the selection of materials for the primary circuit or the moderator circuit, but the SGHWR system shares with other direct cycle boiling systems the characteristic that over long periods the feedtrain releases quantities of corrosion products into the primary circuits and these may tend to plate out on fuel cladding surfaces. This has been ameliorated as far as possible by selection of feedwater materials, and in the longer term the development of high temperature filtration or ion exchange techniques could be rewarding.

ACKNOWLEDGEMENTS

39. This paper is published by kind permission of the Managing Director, The Reactor Group, UKAEA, Risley. Thanks are due to the many colleagues at Culcheth associated with the work reported.

REFERENCES

1. VREELAND D.C., GAUL G.G. and PEARL W.L. Corrosion. June 1961, Vol. 17, No. 6, 169t-276t.

2. VREELAND D.C., GAUL G.G. and PEARL W.L. Corrosion. March 1962, Vol. 18, No. 3, 368t-376t.

3. LORKING K.F. and MAYNE J.E.O. J. Appl. Chem., 1960, Vol. 10, 262.

4. BRASHER D.M. British Corrosion Journal, May 1967, Vol. 2, No. 3, 95-103.

5. RESCH G. and ODENTHAL H. Mitteilungen der VGB, February 1962, Vol. 76, 4-11.

6. STRANGE E. and KIEKENBURG H. Mitteilungen der VGB, 1960, Vol. 69, 384-391.

7. KASS S., GROZIER J.D. and SHUBERT F.L. WAPD-283.

8. KASS S. Pleasanton Symposium, GEAP-4089, Vol. 1.

9. SCHEMEL J.H. Trans. Met. Soc. AIME, 1961 (221), 1129.

10. ASHER R.C. et al. Zirconium Symposium, Buffalo. Electrochemical Technology, October 1966, Vol. 4, 231-236.

11. McKLINTOCK D.R. ANS Transactions, November 1964, Vol. 7, No. 2, 457-458.

12. DRALEY J.E. et al. Geneva Conference, 1964, A/Conf/28/P.243.

13. MAFFEI H.P. HW-84281, September 1964, 5.26-5.27.

14. LE SURF J.E. and BRYANT P.E.C. Presentation to the High Purity Water Symposium of the NACE Annual Conference, March 1967.

15. NELSON R.C. Symposium on Zirconium Alloy Development, Pleasanton, GEAP 4089, Vol. 1, 17-0 to 17-19.

16. BURNS W.A. and MAFFEI H.P. Corrosion of Zirconium Alloys ASTM Special Technical Publication No. 368, November 1963, 101-117.

17. BACARELLA A.L. and SUTTON A.L. J. Electrochemical Soc., June 1965, Vol. 112, No. 6, 546-553.

18. DIX E.H. Jr. et al. Tech. Paper No. 14, 1958, Alcan Research Laboratories.

19. BOWEN A.M. IMI Report MD/RR/12/61, 1961.

20. LANDSMAN D.A. and LAING T.F. AERE-M 1589, 1965.

Chemical control in SGHWR circuits

G. K. DICKSON, BSc, FRIC, MIChemE UKAEA, Risley

W. R. BURTON, MA, PhD UKAEA, Risley

J. A. RILEY, BSc, MSc, AMIMechE UKAEA, Risley

SYNOPSIS   The choice of materials from which to construct a direct cycle nuclear reactor is limited by nuclear and engineering requirements and by the environment in which they are required to operate. Development of materials themselves are discussed in other papers presented at this symposium, whilst engineering requirements have been indicated elsewhere (ref. 1). This paper is concerned solely with the chemical control of reactor circuits. Although a number of fluid circuits which require such control exist in the Winfrith SGHWR, only two of the water circuits have been selected for discussion to illustrate how the present systems came to be adopted and how subsequent development work has led to substantial improvements which can now be incorporated with confidence in future reactors.

Data obtained from early operation of the two circuits will have become available by the time this paper is presented, to enable predictions to be compared with actual performance.

CHEMICAL CONTROL IN THE MODERATOR CIRCUITS

General considerations and process requirements

1.   In the earliest designs of the Winfrith SGHWR no poisoning of the heavy water moderator was specified. Consequently since the calandria was, for chemical purposes, an aluminium tank with stainless steel piping, the only water purification system required was a simple mixed cation-anion exchange resin column, as in many MTRs with similar chemical environments (ref. 2). A low flow through the ion exchanger was sufficient:

   (a)   to prevent build-up of aluminium and steel corrosion products;

   (b)   to control nitric acid formed by irradiation of air inleaks to a pD of about 5.5, which minimizes aluminium corrosion (ref. 3).

In addition, in the gas phase, a recombination unit similar to that in MTRs was included to cater for deuterium and oxygen arising from slight radiolysis of the moderator.

2.   At an early stage in the design of the reactor, it was also decided that it was preferable to control excess reactivity arising from the first fuel charge by adding soluble poison to the moderator, rather than by rods, either solid or gaseous (e.g., boron trifluoride or helium-3). Various poisons were reviewed, e.g., boron, cadmium, gadolinium, etc., but with the system conditions indicated above, boron, in the form of boric acid, was considered the most suitable. In the early stages of the fuel cycle, boron must be added continuously, since its burn-up rate is faster than the loss of fuel reactivity, but at a later part of the fuel cycle, reactivity compensation is met by removing boron from the moderator.

3.   Boron can readily be removed from solution by strong base anion ion exchange resin; nitrate ions would be removed simultaneously. Traces of corrosion products and lithium-7 from the nuclear burn-up of boron-10 can be removed by cation ion exchange resins, as also can corrosion products.

4.   Thus a system based on the use of ion exchange resins was put forward. It consisted of a cation exchange bed, replicated anion exchange beds, a column for deuterating and dedeuterating resins, means for injecting deuterated nitric and boric acids, and for regenerating spent resins. Equipment was provided also to prepare deuterated regenerants and to recover heavy water from spent regenerants. Transfer of resins between vessels was accomplished hydraulically.

5.   Because of the cost of heavy water, equipment, and especially 'dead' spaces, needed to be kept to minimum volume. A substantial advantage was obtained in this regard by using enriched boron (B_{10}), whereby the sizes of the anion exchange resin beds were reduced in volume considerably and boron solution injection volumes were reduced by 80%. (A further disadvantage in using natural boron would have been the embarrassing build-ups of boron-11 which, though innocuous nuclear-wise, would have to be removed at the same

time as boron-10.)

6.   Having now provided facilities for controlling boron concentrations in the moderator, considerable advantages could be obtained by controlling not only reactivity at start of life of the reactor but also:

   (i)   poison start-up with xenon-free fuel;

   (ii)   xenon compensation during load changes;

   (iii)   on-load refuelling reactivity compensation;

   (iv)   power changes (e.g., two-shift operation).

The Winfrith moderator process

7.   The above requirements were met by arranging plant as shown in Fig. 1 in which the ion exchange beds are numbered Items 1-5.

8.   Extensive laboratory investigations were carried out at the English Electric Co. laboratories for the UKAEA in order to determine the best cation exchange resin for lithium and corrosion product removal and the best strong base anion exchange resin for boron removal. The capacity of the latter resin decreases as the concentration of boron in the feed solution falls and hence beds will be operated in rotation when possible, first on weak feed and later on strong feed, until each is saturated at their highest capacity.

9.   Originally, a weak base anion exchange resin bed was proposed for removal of nitric acid without removal of boron, but later this was eliminated when it had been shown that, at the maximum possible nitric acid production rate, nitric acid removal could be achieved on boron-saturated strong base anion exchange resins without excessive displacement of boron.

10.   Since displacement of light hydrogen atoms from resins would cause isotopic degradation of the moderator, it was necessary to replace these labile atoms by deuterium atoms before introduction into the moderator circuit. This is done in a deuteration column (Item 6) in which a very slow flow of heavy water is fed upwards through a resin charge displacing the light water plugwise. This operation produces a narrow band of light and heavy water mixture, the volume of which represents about 10-20% of the resin volume and has a mean D_2O concentration of about 50%. The reverse operation, or de-deuteration, can be achieved by employing light water flow in a downward direction to recover heavy water from the resin when this is to be discharged from the system. Another route for the disposal of resin from the system is through the evaporator (Item 7) which is primarily intended for D_2O recovery from the spent regenerant used in the regeneration of the resins. Whereas this route

would incur no degradation of the recovered D_2O by light water, it would involve small losses and slight organic contamination of the recovered heavy water.

11.   The removal of impurities and boron from the heavy water moderator by ion exchange is a batch process and a point is reached where the separate resin beds no longer have any absorbing capacity. At this stage the resins can be regenerated for further use in a regeneration column (Item 8) by treatment with deuterated nitric acid (DNO_3 for the cation resin) or potassium deuteroxide (KOD for the anion resin) (Item 10).

12.   Deutero-nitric acid is prepared by entraining gaseous NO_2 in air or oxygen in D_2O in a packed tower (Item 10). Potassium deuteroxide is prepared by electrodialysis of potassium carbonate in a two-compartment cell separated by a cation exchange membrane, the potassium ion passing into the anode compartment to form KOD, without contamination by the carbonate ion (Item 10).

13.   Following regeneration, residual regenerants must be removed from the resins before they can be returned to the circuit, to prevent circuit contamination. Rinse water can come from either the clean D_2O tank (Item 9) or the distillate from the D_2O recovery evaporator (Item 7). Rinse effluent can be returned (to Item 7) and thus provide a continuous supply of distillate as rinse water from the minimum hold-up of heavy water.

14.   The preparation of deuterated orthoboric acid (D_3BO_3) for injection into the moderator relies on the dehydration of orthoboric acid (H_3BO_3) under conditions of controlled temperature and vacuum to yield boric acid (B_2O_3) which is then dissolved in heavy water to give a solution of D_3BO_3. H_3BO_3 will be supplied either by the recovery of the boron from the spent regenerants as potassium borate in the light water phase or the supply of fresh recrystallized H_3BO_3 to the dehydration evaporator. Cation exchange resin will be used in the deuterizing column to remove the potassium from the light water solution of potassium borate to yield a solution of H_3BO_3 in H_2O for feeding to the dehydration evaporator.

15.   The laboratory work associated with the development of these processes was carried out principally at Winfrith (K. Harding and co-workers). The same group has contributed to work on flow distribution in resin beds which has been centred on the Aldermaston laboratories (J.R. Nash and co-workers) with support from the British Hydromechanics Research Association.

Developments

16.   The above system was installed because the principles involved were simple and because the development required could

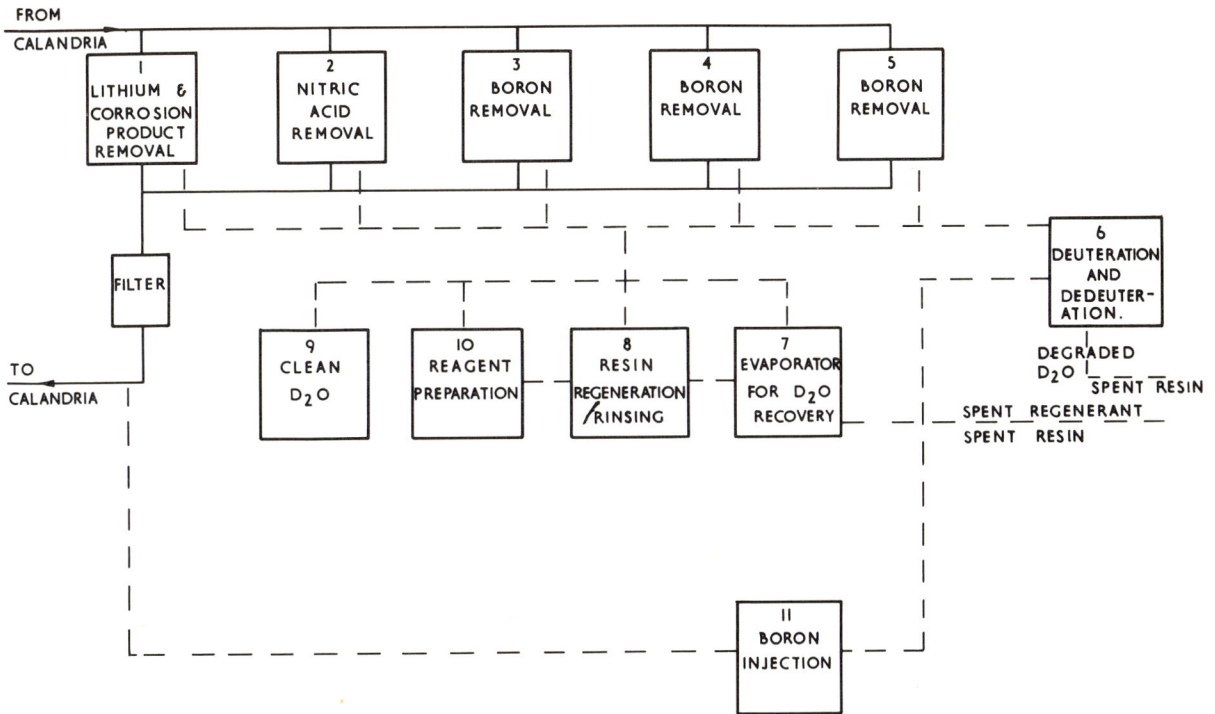

Fig. 1: Functional diagram of Winfrith SGHWR moderator
treatment plant

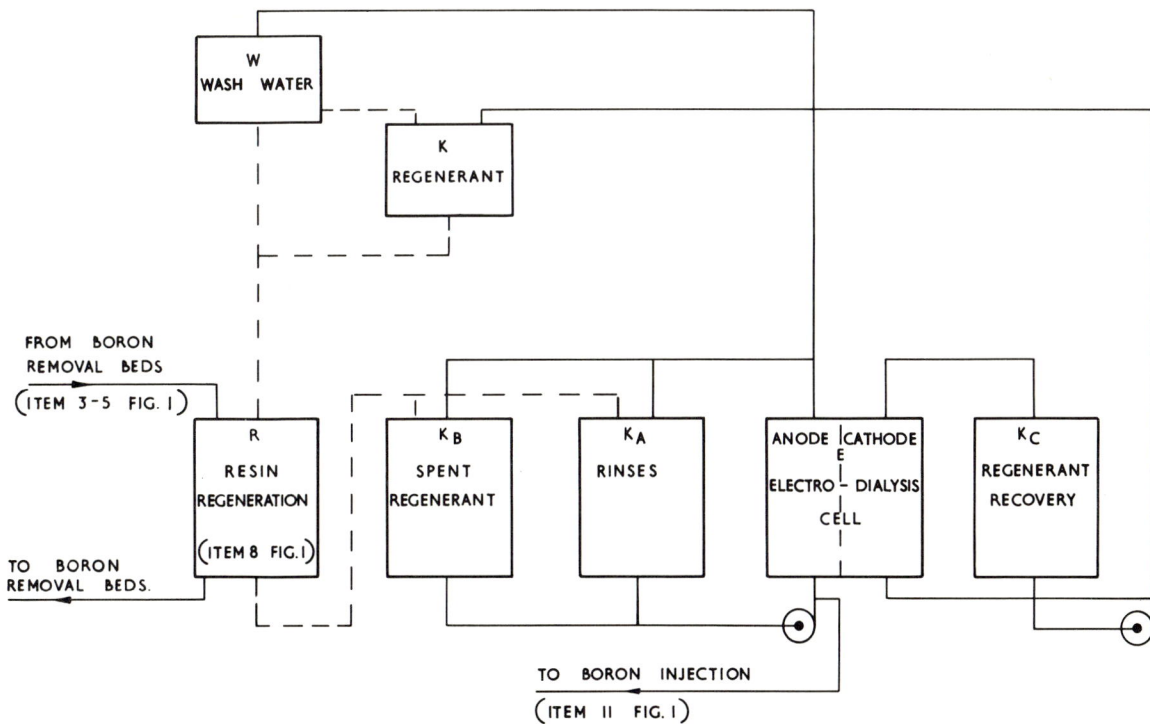

Fig. 2: Functional diagram of 'Brandy' system for SGHWR

be carried out after the main plant items had been specified and ordered. However, it is inelegant and requires a considerable number of auxiliary plant items.

17. Therefore, concurrently with work on the Winfrith SGHWR system, a more attractive system requiring less plant and a lower heavy water inventory has been developed, based on the principle of recycling the resin, regenerants and heavy water in closed circuits.

18. This system, which is based upon electrodialysis, has been designated 'Brandy' (boron regeneration and electrodialysis) and is shown in diagrammatic form in Fig. 2 (ref. 4).

19. Briefly, boron-saturated resin is transferred to the resin regeneration column R. Potassium deuteroxide regenerant (Item K) is introduced to remove boron to the spent regenerant tank (Item K_B). Subsequent heavy water rinses (from Item W) remove excess alkali to the vessel K_A. The resin is now ready for transfer back to the boron removal beds (Fig. 1). The spent regenerant is now circulated through the anode compartments (A) of the electrodialysis cell (E) which contains cation exchange membranes. On passing current through the cell, the potassium ions pass through the membranes into circuit K_C, leaving only boric acid in circuit K_B. The concentration of initial regenerant is chosen so that the final boric acid concentration in the circuit K_B is suitable for direct re-injection into the reactor moderator. In a similar manner the potassium ions in wash liquors (in K_A) can then be removed by recirculation through the anode compartment of the cell. The water in circuit K_A is then pumped back to the wash water tank (W) for re-use in the next cycle. The cathode compartment liquors recirculate through circuit K_C and recover potassium deuteroxide which is returned for further regenerations to tank K. Adjustment of regenerant concentration can be effected with heavy water from tank W.

20. Several variations of this scheme can be used. The early work on electrodialysis was carried out at AERE and subsequently the process was demonstrated on the full scale at AWRE. It is now incorporated in all civil reactor designs.

CONTROL OF PRIMARY CIRCUIT AND CONDENSATE WATER CONDITIONS

Background

21. Control of water quality in a direct cycle nuclear installation is essential to minimize corrosion of circuit materials themselves, both within and outside of the core regions, and to minimize:

    (a) deposition of corrosion products; particularly on fuel elements where heat transfer might be impaired, and in mechanisms whose reliability might be affected;

and (b) activation of corrosion products in radiation fields and the problems which could follow from transfer of such activated species to otherwise 'clean' parts of the circuit.

22. Additionally it is desirable to be able to control fission products which would be released in the event of fuel element failure.

23. Conventionally, in fossil fired installations, it is customary to minimize corrosion by raising pH by means of alkali or ammonia addition and by reducing oxygen concentrations to very low levels (<0.005 ppm) by efficient deaeration followed by hydrazine addition. Usually the boiler section of the system is fabricated from carbon steels, the condenser from brass or cupro-nickel and the feedheater train from copper based alloys or carbon steel.

The direct cycle nuclear system

24. In a direct cycle reactor, oxygen (with stoichiometric hydrogen) is produced by radiolysis in the fuel channels and its resultant concentration is approximately 0.1 ppm and 20 ppm in the water and steam phases respectively. Raising the pH of the system by addition of alkali is not attractive because of possible consequences of high caustic concentrations arising on heat transfer surfaces. Similarly, raising pH by adding conventional concentrations of ammonia is unacceptable because under irradiation it is destroyed and gives rise to oxides of nitrogen which would tend to produce acid conditions in the circuit. Thus conditions in the boiler circuit of a direct cycle nuclear installation are basically different from those which pertain in fossil fuelled conventional stations, the 'natural' reactor conditions being neutral pH with oxygenated (and hydrogenated) water and steam. This led to water reactor primary circuits (e.g., Dresden) being constructed in austenitic stainless steel; at the time the Winfrith SGHWR design had to be frozen, there was inadequate evidence to justify the use of materials other than stainless steel, although preliminary evidence was just becoming available to show that the corrosion resistance of carbon steels might be very much better than anticipated from consideration only of the oxygen levels of the environment (ref. 5).

25. Alternative systems based on the use of reducing conditions, which repress water radiolysis, were examined and developed. A process in which ammonia could be added in 'massive' quantities (5-10 ppm) to produce a hydrogen/nitrogen instead of an oxygen/hydrogen environment was investigated at Chalk River in association with our Canadian colleagues (ref. 6). Provision was made to operate the Winfrith SGHWR under such conditions, but it was subsequently shown to be unnecessary. Also, the addition of free hydrogen to repress radiolysis has been examined by our

Table 1
Specifications for polished condensate and primary circuit water

		Polished condensate	Primary circuit water
Conductivity μmho cm^{-1} (25°C)		< 0.1	< 1
pH		7 $\mp$0.2	7 $\mp$0.2
Total solids ppm		< 0.005	< 0.5
Cl$^-$	ppm	< 0.002	< 0.05
SiO$_2$	ppm	< 0.002	< 0.05

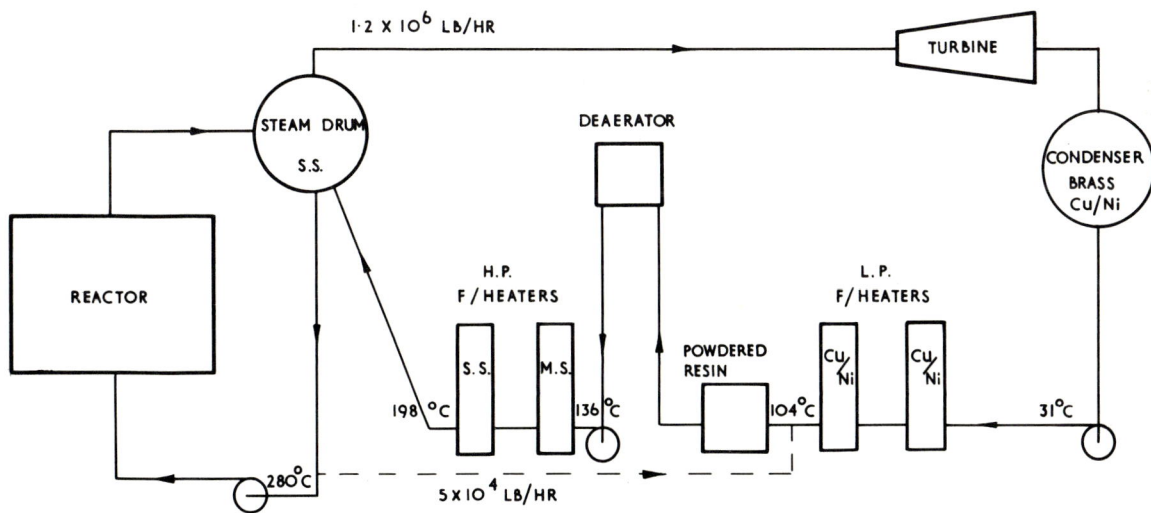

Fig. 3: Schematic diagram of primary and condensate system in the Winfrith SGHWR

own staff from the Culcheth laboratories.

26. Thus the primary circuit of the Winfrith SGHWR was constructed in stainless steel to be operated at 280°C under neutral conditions in the presence of oxygen and hydrogen. In parallel with the main primary circuit, however, a loop rated at several MW and fabricated in carbon steel was incorporated in the original design for large scale test and demonstration purposes.

Requirements

27. Analysis of published data obtained from conventional recirculating installations, closed water loop experiments, etc., indicated that little net release of corrosion products would occur in the primary circuit itself and that the major contribution to impurities in the primary water would be derived from the feedtrain. The objectives, then, were to clean-up the condensate return at a point as high up the feedtrain as possible and to clean-up those impurities which reached and concentrated in the primary circuit. Calculations indicated that a satisfactory primary water quality could be obtained if condensate clean-up was effected just prior to the de-aerator, and a primary circuit clean-up rate of 50,000 lb/h (total condensate flow 1.2×10^6 lb/h) was employed.

28. The polished condensate and primary circuit water specifications adopted are set out in Table 1.

Clean-up procedures

29. Conventionally in water reactor installations, primary circuits and condensate streams were treated by means of ion exchange units, with or without filters. The resins were in bead form, and could be regenerated; their operating temperature was limited to about 50°C. At the time the decision had to be taken for the Winfrith SGHWR, preliminary information on the use of 'throwaway' powdered resin systems at temperatures of about 100°C in conventional power stations was becoming available (ref. 7). These systems could be operated without resin regeneration in the vicinity of the deaerator instead of at the condenser outlet, and combined the functions of ion exchange and filtration in a single unit. Such factors, when considered in the SGHWR context, afforded an opportunity to reduce the amount of equipment required and offered advantages in reducing and simplifying the effluent treatment and waste storage facilities, since activity which was removed on the resin would be in a 'fixed' condition.

30. It then became attractive to 'blow-down' the primary circuit clean-up stream into the condensate upstream of the powdered resin unit which provided full flow condensate polishing. The load on the powdered resin unit was increased only marginally, a separate clean-up for the

primary circuit was eliminated together with its waste arisings, and the heat content of the blow-down was recovered in full, albeit at somewhat lower quality.

31. This unit consisted of two 75% capacity Graver-Davis filters fitted with stainless steel leaves. Each unit had an available area of 400 ft^2 and will normally be coated with a 2:1 cation/anion powder resin mixture applied at 0.15 lb/ft^2 of filter area. Since the decision to instal the unit was made, the ability of powdered resins to remove silica efficiently at high temperatures has become suspect, but in most other respects they appear to give good performance (refs 8, 9).

32. An outline of the water/steam circuits of the Winfrith SGHWR is shown in Fig. 3 and an engineering description is to be found elsewhere (ref. 10).

Developments

33. Since the time when decisions had to be taken concerning the materials to be used in the Winfrith SGHWR, intensive investigations on the behaviour of carbon steel under primary circuit conditions have been carried out within the Authority and its suitability is no longer in doubt (ref. 3). Use of carbon steel will not only be very attractive economically, but will eliminate the potential hazards of failure by cracking associated with the use of stainless steel. At the same time it will make decontamination of primary circuit equipment very much simpler (should this ever become necessary) on account of the structure of the protective surface layers.

34. The current tendency to replace tubular feedheaters by direct contact feedheaters in the LP stages is reducing enormously the amount of surface available to release corrosion products to the condensate stream, and so reduces the need to operate the polishing unit at high temperature. It will, therefore, become possible to increase the life of the powdered resin and possibly its efficiency also.

35. At the present time processes are being developed to remove impurities from high temperature water so that a simple unit at the top of the feedtrain and/or in the primary circuit itself would maintain impurity levels in the primary circuit at appreciably lower levels than even those being obtained at present.

ACKNOWLEDGEMENTS

36. This paper is published by kind permission of the Managing Director, The Reactor Group, UKAEA, Risley. The authors wish to record the assistance given by their colleagues M.C. Tanner and I.J. Smith, and associates in other establishments who have contributed to the development of procedures for controlling environment qualities.

REFERENCES

1.   SGHWR Symposium, I. Mech. E., London,
May 1967.

2.   GREENHALGH F.G. et al. Calandria and
neutron shields. SGHWR Symposium,
I. Mech. E., May 1967.

3.   TYZACK C. et al. Some
compatability aspects of SGHWRs.
Paper 9A to this conference.

4.   UK Patent 1,080,974.

5.   VREELAND D.C., GAUL G.G. and
PEARL W.L. Corrosion. Vol. 17(6),1961 and
Vol. 18(3),1962.

6.   LE SURF L.E., BRYANT P.E.C. and
TANNER M.C. Corrosion. Vol. 23(3), 1967.

7.   DUFF J.H. and LEVENDUSKY J.A.
Powdex - A new approach in condensate
purification. Am. Pow. Conf., 1962 and
1963.

8.   BALTHAZAR J. VGB Speisewassertagung,
1966.

9.   LEVENDUSKY J.A. and OLEJAR L.
Condensate purification applications of the
powdex process in high pressure utility
plant cycles. Am. Pow. Conf., 1967.

10.   KNOTT H. SGHWR Symposium, I. Mech. E.,
London, May 1967.

Safety of the SGHWR prototype

D. R. POULTER, MA, AMIMechE, UKAEA, Risley
F. G. JOHNSON, M Eng, AMICE, UKAEA, Risley
C. B. COWKING, BScTech, AMIMechE UKAEA, Risley
G. V. WINDLE, BScTech, UKAEA, Risley

SYNOPSIS   The paper opens by reviewing the approach to safety considered in the UK. The vented containment system of the prototype SGHWR is described along with development of the concept for future reactors using enriched fuel. An outline is given of the development work carried out on the release, fate and clean-up of fission products, the propagation of failures, fuel can performance at high temperature and containment design. Reference is made to emergency cooling and the provisions for inspection and testing. The method of safety assessment and supporting analytical work are discussed and the paper ends with a statement on the results of fission product release assessments for the Prototype reactor.

INTRODUCTION

1.   In the safety design of a reactor system, it is the practice in the United Kingdom to endeavour to predict reactor behaviour under all fault conditions and to assess the effects over a range of accidents, rather than to limit analysis only to the ultimate accident. Added support to this approach is provided by the recent method of siting assessment proposed by Farmer in which the consequences of an event are set against its probability of occurrence (ref. 1). To this end, research and development are directed towards those features which are essential to the safety of the system and these are studied in detail. This paper discusses some of these features and the work carried out to support the design of the prototype SGHWR at Winfrith, particularly where the work has application to further commercial designs.

2.   The control and shutdown provisions of the reactor (see Paper 6 to this conference) are such that, in combination with the negative void coefficient selected, it is extremely difficult to envisage large scale failure of fuel in an intact coolant circuit. Isolated fuel failures would release fission products through the turbine and off-gas system. After passing through the off-gas system, which incorporates a clean-up plant for volatile and particulate fission products, particularly iodine, the effluent is directed to the stack where discharge would take place safely. Accidents of the greatest importance are therefore those due to breaches of the primary coolant circuit and it is towards these that most attention has been directed and on which this paper concentrates.

CONTAINMENT

Design objectives for the Prototype

3.   The SGHWR can be housed in any type of containment. When consideration was being given to building the Prototype, it was decided to explore the possibility of designing a containment system which did not involve storing fission products at pressure. Double containment also appeared attractive since all fission products could be processed in a clean-up plant before discharge to atmosphere in a controlled manner from a stack. The design objectives for the containment of the Prototype were therefore set as:

(a) use of double containment with clean-up of the interspace;

(b) avoidance of high pressures and high leak-tightness standards;

(c) containment plant requirements to be met by the use of static devices or plant normally in operation, situated outside the primary containment and thus readily accessible for maintenance;

(d) use of conventional building materials for the containment structures.

It was found possible to meet these objectives with the vented containment.

Prototype vented containment

4.   The containment system for the Prototype is shown diagrammatically in Fig. 1. It comprises a primary containment situated within a secondary containment and

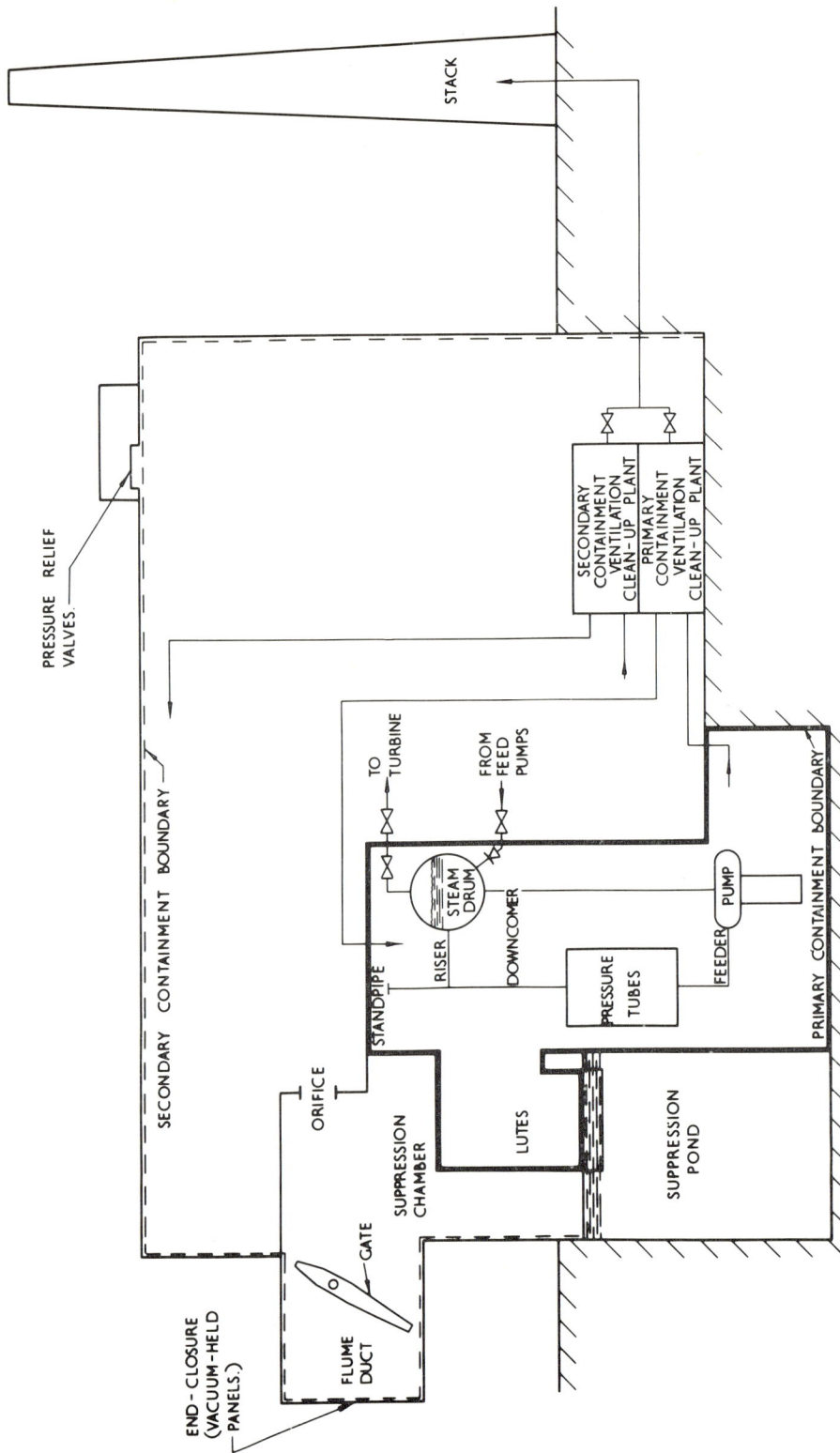

Fig. 1: Schematic arrangement of prototype SGHWR containment system

connected to it but sealed from it by a water lute. The primary containment is formed essentially by the concrete biological shield surrounding the core and reactor coolant circuit, but the boundary also envelops that part of the refuelling machine above the rotating shield. Pressure build-up in the primary containment following a breach in the reactor coolant circuit is relieved through the lute, which comprises two sets of pipes each dipping into a suppression pond. The purpose of the water lute is three-fold:-

    1. to reduce the volume of effluent to be handled by condensing a large portion of the steam arising in the discharge;

    2. to reseal the primary containment automatically following a discharge;

    3. to provide some decontamination of the effluent.

5.   Above each suppression pond is a re-inforced concrete chamber provided with fairings to reduce the resistance to flow of uncondensed effluent (mainly air). An orifice at the top of each suppression chamber allows discharge of the effluent to the secondary containment. However, a route to atmosphere is also provided from each suppression chamber via a flume duct, but this is normally sealed by a set of vacuum-held panels. In the event of a large rupture of the coolant circuit, these panels are blown off and a hinged flume gate rides on the air flow until this falls to a level which can be passed through to the secondary containment without causing overpressurization. At this time, the flume gates close completely under the influence of gravity to reseal the building.

6.   The secondary containment is formed by the power hall building which surrounds not only the core and primary containment but also the fuel storage pond and the turbo-alternator. To prevent overpressurization of this building, it is provided with eight dead-weight relief valves in the roof which discharge clean air at the end remote from the reactor. The building is a conventional steel-framed building with external steel cladding and a sealed internal skin of steel sheet cladding. Since the required leak-tightness standards are not high, access to the building is through a number of vestibules with double doors which act as air-locks, thus providing easy and rapid access for personnel to and from the secondary containment if required.

7.   The arrangements made for clean-up are an integral part of the containment system. Following a depressurization accident, valves in the ventilation system operate automatically to isolate the secondary containment from atmosphere and initiate air circulation through the clean-up plant. This building is maintained at a slightly subatmospheric pressure by discharging up the stack a volume equal to the total in-leakage to the building. Thus, the only

air passing to atmosphere from the secondary containment passes first through a clean-up plant having a high decontamination factor for fission products other than the rare gases. Two clean-up plants are provided so that one can always be available while the other is being re-conditioned. The clean-up plant is in operation continuously, treating ventilation air from the pond storage area, and its efficiency can be checked while it is running.

8.   The specification for the primary containment called for a leakage rate of about 5% per day at a pressure differential of 1 lb/in^{2}g following pressurization to the maximum design pressure of 8 lb/in^{2}g. The secondary containment was designed for a positive pressure of 3 inches water gauge and a negative pressure of 2 inches water gauge together with forces due to wind and snow. The leak-tightness was specified to be about 200% per day at a pressure differential of 2 inches water gauge. Tests on the Prototype have shown that the leakage specifications for both containments have essentially been met. It is interesting to note, however, that the safety of the reactor is not dependent on the strict maintenance of these leak-tightness standards; furthermore, any gross deterioration of the standard will become obvious from the consequent disturbance to the balance of the ventilation system. Facilities are provided for the periodic testing of the relief vent lifting pressures.

Development of the vented system of containment

9.   Development and refinement of the prototype vented containment design has taken place in formulating more advanced designs of reactors using enriched fuel. Improved understanding of the performance of the system has permitted the discharges from all accidents to be vented through the secondary containment. This development requires the secondary containment to be designed for higher pressures but eliminates the flume gates. The pressure relief valves have also been sited at ground level thereby improving the efficacy of the secondary containment as a holding and trapping facility.

10.   The advantages which can be claimed for the vented system of containment are:-

    (a) no high pressures have to be accommodated;

    (b) high standards of integrity are not required and the leak-tightness is continuously monitored;

    (c) the most important equipment of the containment system, namely the clean-up plant, is unaffected by an accident and is accessible and running during normal operation. Pressure suppression duties during post-accident conditions are largely met by the primary containment air-coolers which also run continuously during all reactor states. As can be seen, therefore, no commissioning of containment plant is required following an accident;

(d) it is possible to use conventional building materials leading to low costs and short construction times. Furthermore, building work can be completely separated from mechanical and other work.

DEVELOPMENT WORK IN SUPPORT OF VENTED CONTAINMENT

11. In support of the design work and the safety analyses required for the Winfrith Prototype form of vented containment, an extensive programme of experimental development work has been carried out by the UKAEA both in their own establishments and elsewhere. This is illustrated below, where certain aspects that are of particular significance and which have some relevance to succeeding designs of a similar type are discussed.

Fission product release, fate and clean-up

12. A major programme of work on fission product release and clean-up has been carried out. This has concentrated mainly on fission product iodine, in particular iodine-131, as constituting the principal hazard to public health. Besides elementary iodine, the main forms in which it is possible for iodine-131 to survive are methyl iodide, and an iodine aerosol.

13. Methyl iodide is not so easily trapped as the other forms and it was, therefore, important to determine the extent to which it would be released from fuel under accident conditions. Work at Windscale laboratories of the Authority in which the cladding of irradiated fuel elements was punctured in a steam atmosphere indicated that the fractional escape of iodine from the can is about one-tenth of the fractional release of xenon-133 (ref. 2). Of the iodine escaping, one tenth or less was found to be in the form of methyl iodide (ref. 2). These tests also confirmed that up to about 50% of the iodine inventory would be released on fuel melting.

14. Experimental work on passing iodine-containing vapours through a water lute has shown that decontamination factors for molecular and particulate iodine vary between 14 (with pure air) and several hundred for steam/air mixtures over a wide range of steam-to-air ratios and discharge rates. Much of this work was carried out with large scale lutes of similar geometry to those of the Winfrith Prototype. It was found that methyl iodide is essentially unaffected by passage through a water lute.

15. When non-penetrating forms of iodine are mixed with water and steam, the iodine is likely to be preferentially held in the water phase, resulting in a reduction in the amount reaching the lute. Some plating out on exposed surfaces in the primary and secondary containments may also occur but this is likely to be a longer term effect. Because of uncertainties in both these mechanisms in general no credit has been claimed for them in assessing fission product releases.

16. Experimental work at Windscale indicated the best combination of filters and demisters and the appropriate impregnation for the charcoal for the clean-up plant in order to handle air of high relative humidity which would arise following a depressurization accident (refs 2, 3). With this impregnated charcoal, decontamination factors for methyl iodide better than 10^5 can be achieved with laboratory scale plant. The work has also indicated the useful life to be expected from the charcoal when the clean-up plant is in continuous use as it is in the prototype reactor. Tests on the actual clean-up plants have shown decontamination factors for methyl iodide of about 10^3, which is nearing the practical limit of sensitivity for full scale tests.

Propagation of failures

17. In the Winfrith prototype reactor it was important, because of the containment design, to avoid the propagation of a reactor coolant circuit failure which could lead to a larger failure than the containment could handle satisfactorily. Also, and this may apply more critically to other forms of containment, it was particularly important to ensure that a failure in one half of the reactor coolant circuit did not lead to a breach in the otherwise intact other half of the circuit.

18. The region of particular interest is the core itself where there is no physical separation of the pressure tubes of the two halves of the core apart from the calandria tubes and moderator. Any additional protective barrier in this area would incur a reactivity penalty or result in undue complication of the calandria. It was shown theoretically that failure of an adjacent pressure tube could only occur as a result of impact by missiles. Work carried out abroad suggested that failure propagation would not occur, but these experiments were of an ad hoc nature and not directly applicable to the design of the Prototype. A more relevant programme was formulated and is at present being carried out at the Foulness Establishment of the UKAEA.

19. The method of testing is to fire a projectile at a pressurized tube and to measure the energy of any resulting fragments. By comparing the energies of the projectile and missiles, it is possible to ascertain whether failure propagation is possible. Using bare cast iron tubes to simulate embrittled pressure tubes, early rig commissioning tests showed that propagation was possible. However, subsequent

Fig. 3: Steam condensation rig

Fig. 4: Model to assess secondary containment performance

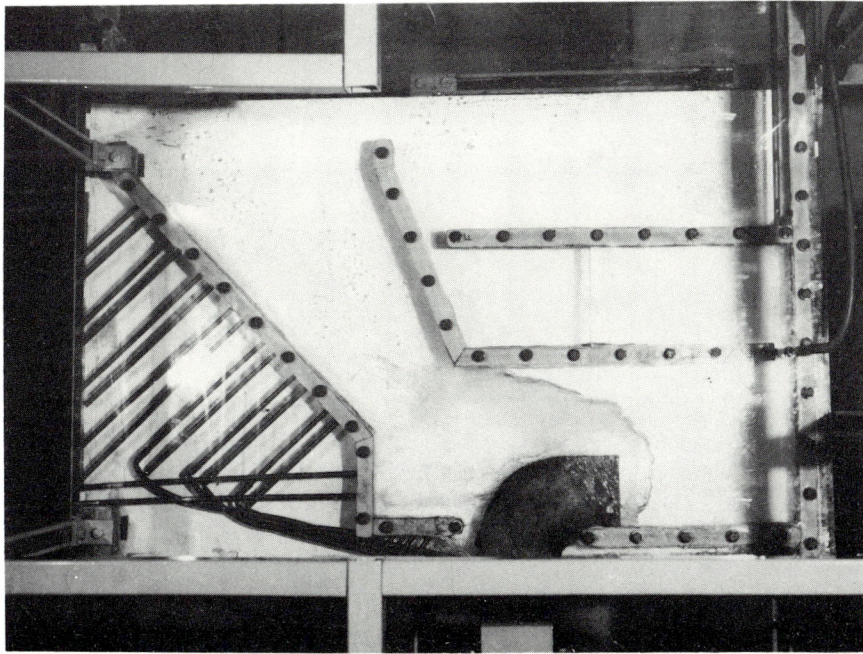

Fig. 2: 1/28-scale air and water model of lute system

11 147

experiments to determine the performance of a cast iron tube surrounded by an aluminium calandria tube have given confidence that the calandria tubes will, in practice, prevent failure propagation. Tests are continuing over a range of conditions. Experiments on zircaloy hydrided and irradiated to the extent expected in the reactor have shown that failure is by ductile fracture at temperatures above about 300°F (150°C). Favourable results from the Foulness tests on cast iron tubes should obviate the need for any further experimental work since it can be argued that zirconium alloy under reactor conditions, being less brittle than cast iron, will not fail in a manner which will lead to failure propagation in the reactor.

20. This work is supported by a monitoring programme in the Prototype to ensure that the actual pressure tubes do not unexpectedly reach an embrittled condition.

Fuel cladding performance at high temperature

21. As an aid to understanding the behaviour of the reactor fuel pins in a loss-of-coolant accident, out-of-pile tests on unirradiated cladding specimens have been made at temperatures up to 1200°C. A loss-of-coolant accident may lead to an early breakdown in heat removal from the reactor core and, since stored heat and decay heat are present even following reactor shutdown, there could be a significant temperature increase in the cladding with associated weakening. Depending on the amount of weakening and also on the stresses imposed by the fault, cladding may fail and release some of the fission products which are free inside. The major imposed force on the cladding is the net pressure difference between the internal gases and the external coolant, and this will change during an accident. For any one pin, the pressure load may initially tend to cause the cladding to collapse onto the fuel but subsequently reverse to become a dilating force as the coolant pressure falls below the internal pressure.

22. The tests on cladding reflected these two different conditions. Under net internal pressure tubular cladding dilates, bulges and fails at a point of strain concentration. Tests of this type were carried out in a furnace using short empty tubular specimens which were suddenly stressed by connection to a high pressure reservoir. A wide range of combinations of temperature and stress was examined and the results have been used to build up a comprehensive picture of the cladding failure behaviour in this mode. Under net external pressure, the cladding is largely supported by the solid pellets of uranium dioxide fuel and will generally have a good resistance to failure, but it may be envisaged that there would be a few interpellet gaps or fuel surface defects permitting cladding collapse. To test the cladding behaviour over such discontinui-

ties, specimens were filled with uranium dioxide pellet stacks incorporating accurately sized circumferential gaps and placed in a furnace within a stronger outer vessel. Pressure was applied to the outside of the cladding at the appropriate temperature and the collapse behaviour noted; combinations of pressure differential, temperature and gap width were tested.

23. In combination with calculations of internal pressure, these results have been used to form best estimates of the extent and timing of cladding failure in the early stages of the most severe loss-of-cooling accidents.

Work in support of the containment design

24. The development work required to support the vented form of containment started with a 1/28-scale air and water model of the primary containment and suppression lute system (Fig. 2), built at the Reactor Engineering Laboratories of the UKAEA to study the effects of different lute designs and layouts and to find the relationships between injection flow rate, lute immersion and peak containment pressure. This was followed by a $\frac{1}{4}$-scale model, constructed by Babcock and Wilcox Ltd, in which a drum containing steam and water at reactor conditions was discharged into a volume which vented through a lute system. The results from these experiments confirmed those from the smaller model and showed additionally that sufficient water would remain to reseal the lutes by an adequate submergence after the discharge. In addition, valuable information was obtained on the variation with time of the discharge rates from orifices and pipes.

25. In parallel with this work, a programme of tests was carried out by the Authority to study the steam condensation performance of the lutes. One series of experiments was done on a lute at 1/3-scale (Fig. 3) with a range of total flow rates and of air/steam mixture ratios, which showed condensation efficiencies varying from 74 to 100%. This work supported further tests on the performance of the secondary containment using a 1/16-scale model built by the British Hydromechanics Research Association (Fig. 4) in which gases of different densities were used to simulate the injection of mixtures of hot steam and air into the containment which would occur following a major coolant pipework failure. These experiments, with a wide range of simulated accident flow rates, were augmented by a much smaller programme of supplementary tests on the actual prototype containment designed to establish the behaviour at low flow rate (Reynolds Number) at full scale. Application of the combined results to the prototype system, over the range of possible accident sizes, shows that activity would not escape from the relief vents for any type of failure.

OTHER SAFETY FEATURES

Channel emergency cooling system

26. On the prototype SGHWR, a channel emergency cooling system has been installed which will prevent any large scale release of fission products from the fuel in the event of a rupture of the primary circuit. Cold water is injected at several levels into the fuel element cluster through rings of small holes located in the centre tie tube, or sparge pipe, of the cluster. The water is supplied initially from a high pressure tank containing water pressurized by nitrogen to about 200 lb/in^2 above primary circuit pressure. This tank holds sufficient water to provide adequate cooling of the fuel under the most adverse conditions until the primary circuit has been depressurized; thereafter cooling water is supplied by gravity from an elevated tank. Emergency cooling is initiated automatically by detection of rate of change of pressure or pressure rise in the primary containment and, apart from tripping of valves, is completely independent of moving parts or prime movers. Water is fed to the fuel at full circuit pressure almost instantaneously upon the occurrence of a rupture and no operator action to maintain the supply is required over about the first hour.

27. The system was developed after extensive experimental work at Winfrith, culminating in a series of tests on heated 36-rod clusters to determine the efficiency of cooling for various water flow rates, sparge pipe designs and channel pressures down to atmospheric. (It had been found previously that spraying water from above the fuel elements could be ineffective; even with quite low steam velocities the cooling water could be blown away before it was able to enter the cluster.)

28. The installation of such an emergency cooling system can significantly reduce the probability of a partial or full core melt-out. Important additional advantages of an efficient emergency cooling system in the event of an accident are the mitigation of the damage which could occur to the fuel and core structure and therefore the ensuing rehabilitation work required, and the protection of the commercial investment in the fuel.

Inspection and testing

29. The assurance that plant will run satisfactorily and not fail depends not only on design but also on the inspection and tests instituted during manufacture and commissioning and on regular and periodic inspection and tests during subsequent operation. During manufacture and erection of the prototype plant, stringent stage inspection and tests were instituted. Wherever possible reactor components have been shop fabricated and, in fact, no major fabrication work has taken place on site. In addition to this, the design has been orientated so that, as far as possible, full inspection and testing facilities during operation are made available to enhance the safety of the plant.

30. In the case of the reactor coolant circuit of the Prototype, the cold hydraulic pressure test at 1600 lb/in^{2}g properly tested only the stainless steel components of the circuit. The zirconium alloy pressure tubes were subjected to a stress that did not approach the stress to which they are subjected in normal operation when temperature effects are taken into account. A hot test at 1300 lb/in^{2}g and 577°F (303°C) was, therefore, carried out after completion of the construction in order to simulate actual design conditions much more closely. Subsequent to reactor operation it is proposed that, at agreed periods, the reactor will be shut down and the circuit subjected to a cold hydraulic test followed by a further hot hydraulic test. By these proof tests, it is intended to continue to demonstrate confidence in the life of the primary circuit and, particularly, the pressure tubes.

31. The channels can be inspected in situ by television cameras and the pipework layout is arranged so that, if considered necessary, complete channels can be removed for full examination. A comprehensive in-core monitoring programme will supplement data from out-of-pile and materials reactor tests. The larger components of the primary circuit can be fully inspected. In particular, it is possible to isolate each steam drum from its circuit to permit full visual and direct inspection of both internal and external surfaces without removing fuel from the core.

32. Arrangements have been provided to allow the operation of the channel emergency cooling system to be tested whilst the reactor is running. Similarly, the liquid shutdown trip valves are designed for testing individually whilst the reactor is in operation.

33. With the comparatively high leak rates acceptable for the primary and secondary containments, it is possible to monitor the leakage continuously by measuring the purge flows from the containments. The clean-up plant and coolers are in continuous operation, supplied by guaranteed electrical and water supplies; the decontamination factor of the clean-up plant can be checked whilst it is in operation.

34. It is considered that the above features will result in a high integrity and reliability for the reactor plant and, if an accident should occur, will give maximum assurance that the containment system will function satisfactorily.

HAZARD ANALYSIS

Method of assessment

35. The safety of SGHWRs, in common with other reactor types, is being assessed within the Authority on the basis of probability as outlined by F.R. Farmer in Vienna in April 1967 (ref. 1). This method recognises that plant as installed is not perfect and that failures are possible, however unlikely. Farmer suggested that release of iodine-131 was an appropriate criterion, although other criteria might also be suitable.

36. It is possible, on the basis of the data discussed above on fuel behaviour, fission product release from fuel, containment leak rates, and fission product clean-up, to assess the iodine-131 release to atmosphere for a range of possible accidents. The basic fission product release assessments are made assuming that all protective systems work as intended. The calculations are then repeated assuming that plant does not function properly and, in general, show a higher fission product release to atmosphere. However, the probability of occurrence is lower.

37. At present, there is insufficient statistical evidence available to assign a complete set of absolute values to the probability of failure of various components in the system such as pipes and pressure vessels. A method of comparison based on judgement has therefore to be relied upon. The failure probability will depend on such factors as:

    (a)   the extent of knowledge of the design and constructional techniques used;

    (b)   the accuracy to which the loads applied to the components are known; and

    (c)   the effect of environmental factors, including the influence of irradiation, on material properties.

Analytical support and interpretation of experimental work

38. Many analytical techniques have been developed in the course of the studies in support of the prototype reactor, both to assist in the interpretation of experiments performed in the development programme and also to predict the behaviour of the reactor system itself. An indication of the range of these methods is given below, illustrated by the nature of the different applications. Many of the techniques require so much calculation that the only practical form is that of a computer code.

39. In some safety studies, the fault temperature history of the fuel is basic to the prediction of cladding failure, cladding reaction and fission product release, and a method of calculating the transient temperatures within a fuel cluster has accordingly been developed. Coolant flow rate along the fuel largely dictates the level of heat transfer from the fuel under fault conditions and a calculation method has been devised which evaluates the short-term space and time-dependent coolant movements following coolant circuit failure. A less elaborate alternative method is available to calculate the long-term system blowdown behaviour as influenced by emergency cooling and feed-water flows and by stored heat being released from the fuel and circuit steelwork.

40. The rate of coolant discharge immediately following a water pipework failure is not amenable to simple calculation. In this respect, the role of analysis has been in the interpretation of experiments on the discharge of a pressurized vessel containing saturated water and steam, and formulae have been derived which describe the fall-off in discharge rate from an initial level approaching hydraulic flow to a lower value in which steam flashing occurs during expulsion. The same experiments provided information on the response of a $\frac{1}{4}$-scale model of a primary containment of the vented type and a computer simulation method has been developed which combines theoretical considerations with practical factors for the coolant injection rates, as above, and also the air resistance of the condensation lutes. This method provides a good simulation of the pressure response of the model containment over the range of injection flow rates tested and can confidently be used to predict full-scale behaviour.

41. The efficiency of a vented secondary containment in retaining fission products is predicted from analytical work which applies the results of experiments on both the 1/16-scale model and the actual prototype building.

Results for the Prototype SGHWR

42. The containment system, although not specifically designed to handle a steam drum failure, can accommodate the complete severance of any pipe in the primary circuit discharging full bore from both ends. All such failures have been examined and an assessment made of the resulting fission product releases. When assessed on a probability basis it was found that there were two accidents of greater significance than most:-

    (a)   failures in the feeder header system which can produce very low flow in a large number of channels (the so-called 'stagnation' accident), occurring at a frequency of, say, 10^{-4} per reactor year;

    (b)   single channel accidents of higher probability (frequency of 10^{-2} to 10^{-3} per reactor year) in which fission products could be released almost instantaneously due to mechanical damage.

43. The prototype containment is unique in that, because of the flume gates, it is sensitive to the actual time at which fission products are released from the fuel. Those accidents which involve the flume gates have been assumed to be associated with a premature release of fission products (i.e., release earlier than would normally have been predicted) to take account of uncertainties in fuel can behaviour due to irradiation effects or possible gaps between fuel pellets.

44. From the assessments carried out to date there is no evidence that any accident will result in an iodine-131 release falling outside the boundary line proposed by Farmer for ground level releases at an urban site (ref. 1). Indeed, even though the assessments of releases and probabilities are considered to have been biased on the high side, there is, in general, a margin of more than an order of magnitude between estimated and permissible release. It is therefore unnecessary to discuss in detail whether the suggested accident probabilities are precisely accurate.

CONCLUSION

45. The basic principle adopted in the safety design and analysis of the prototype SGHWR has been to understand and to be able to predict the behaviour of the reactor under all conditions. The vented containment system depends upon the detailed analysis of the course of each accident and the fate of fission products released from the fuel for a demonstration of its satisfactory performance.

46. Much of the development and analytical work carried out in this connection is equally applicable to any other type of containment that might be used in future SGHWR designs, and forms a firm base for the assessment of fission product releases to atmosphere. This, coupled with the probability method of assessment, gives confidence that SGHWRs are suitable for any size of station on any site.

ACKNOWLEDGEMENT

47. This paper is published by kind permission of the Managing Director, The Reactor Group, UKAEA, Risley. Thanks are due to many colleagues throughout the Authority who were responsible for the work reported.

REFERENCES

1. FARMER F.R. Siting criteria - a new approach. Atom, No. 128, June 1967, pp.152-170. (Also to be published in the Proceedings of IAEA Symposium on the Containment and Siting of Nuclear Power Plants held in Vienna in April 1967.)

2. COLLINS R.D., and others. Air cleaning for reactors with vented containment. TRG Report 1318(W), 1967.

3. COLLINS D.A., and others. The development of impregnated charcoals for trapping methyl iodide at high humidity. TRG Report 1300(W), 1967.

Commissioning and operating experience with the Winfrith SGHWR

D. SMITH, BSc, AInstP, UKAEA, Winfrith

D. ENGLISH, BSc, UKAEA, Winfrith

J. McCRICKARD, BSc, AInstP, UKAEA, Winfrith

SYNOPSIS   This paper describes the commissioning and initial operating experience with the Winfrith SGHWR. The paper is divided into two main parts. Part A covers the operational aspects of commissioning and early operation and Part B gives the technical performance results which have been obtained during this period.

INTRODUCTION

1.   Earlier papers to this conference have provided an outline of the work that led to the completion of the construction of the Winfrith SGHWR. Whilst a substantial amount of performance testing and proving had been undertaken before commissioning, the objectives over the first four months of operation have been to demonstrate that the overall plant:

(a)   was capable of being operated as a power producing unit;

(b)   functioned in a manner which closely confirms the performance predictions made for it.

2.   Since the Winfrith SGHWR first achieved sustained full load capability on 25th January, 1968, it has already generated 135 million units and achieved an average plant availability of 79% which has risen to 96% since 1st March, 1968. Thus, while the time that has elapsed is too short to constitute a full demonstration, there are substantial and encouraging grounds for believing that the design objectives are being achieved. This paper provides the bases for this opinion and is divided into two main parts.

3.   Part A summarizes the commissioning programme and describes the more significant events from the commencement of fuel and heavy water loading including operating experience until mid-April, 1968.

4.   Part B describes the results of the main core performance measurements made during commissioning and initial power operation and their agreement with prediction.

PART A

Organization and training

5.   In building up the Operations Division for the Winfrith SGHWR, a balance was struck between personnel with experience of commissioning and operating nuclear power stations and those with experience of experimental or prototype reactors. The team was supplemented for the commissioning and early stages of operation by staff with particular expertise.

6.   A training programme was introduced which included specialized courses and attachments to nuclear and non-nuclear plants. A training simulator of the control system was built which could be coupled to the Winfrith PACE analogue model of the SGHWR on which all operators and technologists received several hours of training. The operational shift team were responsible for the operation of plant during the functional tests which preceded the commissioning programme.

Planning

7.   The planning of various stages of the commissioning programme began with the preparation of outline proposals for each individual procedure or test. These identified equipment requirements, safety and operational aspects and provided an estimate of the time that would be taken. Special test or experimental procedures were written for repetitive measurements, e.g., period measurements The final programme was formulated by arranging the essential work in a manner which would occupy the minimum time.

Operational aspects of commissioning

8.   The commissioning period was divided into three main sections as follows:

Stage 1   Fuel and heavy water loading, zero power physics measurements and hydraulic tests (24th August-16th October, 1967).

Stage 2   Completion of construction and safety circuit testing (16th October-20th December, 1967).

Stage 3   Raising to full power
          (20th December, 1967-
          24th January, 1968).

The principal events during these three
periods will now be described.

Stage 1

9.   Following the practice developed with
heavy water materials testing reactors of
the DIDO class, the moderator system had
been completely tested using light water.
During this, the volumes of the calandria
and dump tanks were calibrated and it was
then necessary for the moderator circuit to
be thoroughly dried to prevent degradation
of the heavy water. The complete drying
operation occupied six days. Subsequent
measurements indicated that this was completely successful since the isotopic concentration of the heavy water suffered a
reduction of only 0.02% upon loading to
give a final value of 99.75 mole per cent.

10.   Fuel loading commenced on 24th August,
1967, as indicated on Fig. 1 which shows
the principal programme events from that
date. The fuel had been assembled under
dry conditions in the pond area and was
loaded directly into the reactor by a temporary building crane. Throughout this
period, the primary circuit was full of
light water but the first 69 fuel assemblies
were loaded with the calandria empty. At
this stage, 39 tonnes of heavy water were
loaded into the dump tanks. The remaining
35 fuel assemblies were then loaded with
the heavy water at dump level. Criticality
was achieved on 14th September, 1967, by
raising the moderator height to 172 cm from
a datum at the base of the calandria. The
cold, zero energy physics experiments were
then carried out over a period of ten days:
the results are discussed in Part B of this
paper.

11.   A plant proving run was begun on the
4th October, 1967. The pressure and temperature of the primary circuit were raised
to full operational values of 925 lb/in^2
and 280^oC using heat generated by running
the four primary circulators supplemented
by electrical heaters mounted temporarily
on the downcomers from the steam drums to
these pumps. The total heat input was
2500 kW which allowed the pressure to be
raised to 1020 psig for the purpose of re-
checking safety valve pressures. A number
of physics and thermal/hydraulic measurements were made at this point together
with a number of plant proving tests and
checks, which included the following:

    (a) primary circulator tests to
         determine cavitation limits and
         run-down rates and to establish
         the settings required for the
         rate of change of pressure trip
         units;

    (b) tests of the emergency cooling
         water (ECW) system to adjust flow
         to the required level;

    (c) operation of the blowdown to the
         centre pond to determine the rate
         of depressurization;

    (d) operation of the blowdown to the
         condenser to demonstrate the
         correct functioning of the system;

    (e) operation of the ventilation
         plant to set up the appropriate
         flow rates;

    (f) tests on the ancillary cooling
         water systems to establish and
         balance the flow of coolant and
         determine the heat loading;

    (g) measurement of thermal movement
         of the plant and associated pipe-
         work to check that these were
         satisfactory;

    (h) measurement of vibration levels
         to confirm that no section of the
         plant was subject to high
         stresses;

    (i) tests on the safety valves to re-
         check lifting pressures.

12.   The run at operating temperature was
terminated on the 16th October, 1967, by
full depressurization of the circuit. It
was followed by a detailed final inspection
of the complete plant, including the steam
drums, to check whether anything unexpected
had occurred during the early plant operation. This included removal of selected
channels of thin-walled fuel for visual
examination to verify that no wrinkling had
taken place during the hot run. Nothing
was observed which might have given cause
for concern.

Stage 2

13.   The main commissioning programme was
interrupted at this point to allow completion and final testing of the safety
circuits. Immediately prior to the planned
commencement of the power raising phase,
two unrelated delays occurred in the
programme. The first was a leak in a
superheat channel liner. These liners are
thin, helically-wound tubes of zirconium
alloy and the damage to the liner concerned
had been caused by the application of an
excess pressure differential across it
during a special pressure test which was
made on a section of the primary circuit
pipework. It was decided to remove the
complete superheat channel tube assembly
and, although it had been lightly
irradiated (10 h at a power of 2 MWt), this
gave rise to no problems. The whole operation including blanking-off the connections
to the channel, took only four days because
equipment was available for channel tube
removal and a procedure had been formulated
during the design and construction stages.

14.   The second incident concerned the
booster pump unit. This provides an augmented coolant flow to four channels for
testing advanced fuel assemblies. The pump
was found to have seized during an attempt

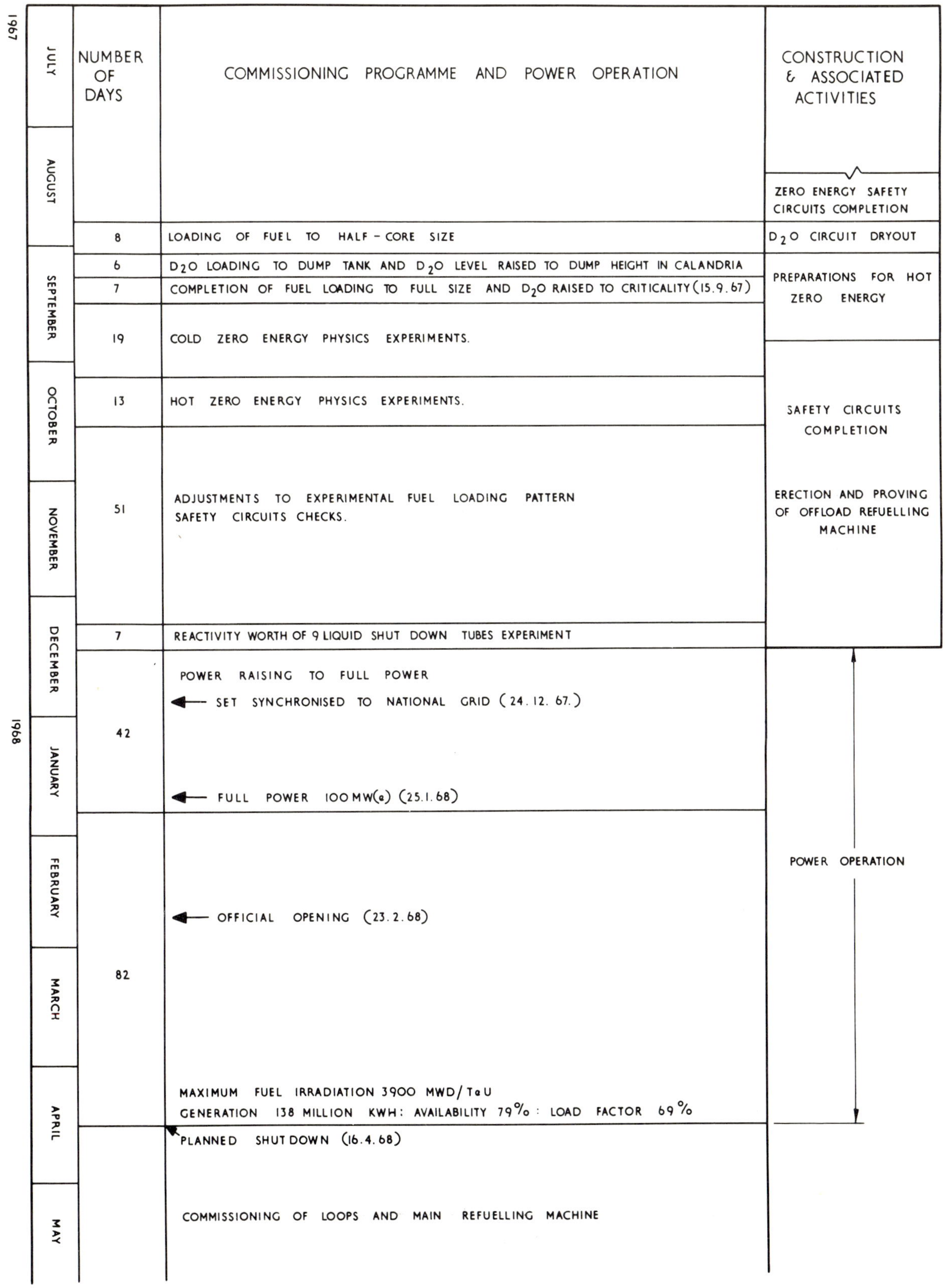

1967		NUMBER OF DAYS	COMMISSIONING PROGRAMME AND POWER OPERATION	CONSTRUCTION & ASSOCIATED ACTIVITIES
	JULY			
	AUGUST			ZERO ENERGY SAFETY CIRCUITS COMPLETION
		8	LOADING OF FUEL TO HALF – CORE SIZE	D_2O CIRCUIT DRYOUT
	SEPTEMBER	6	D_2O LOADING TO DUMP TANK AND D_2O LEVEL RAISED TO DUMP HEIGHT IN CALANDRIA	PREPARATIONS FOR HOT ZERO ENERGY
		7	COMPLETION OF FUEL LOADING TO FULL SIZE AND D_2O RAISED TO CRITICALITY (15.9.67)	
		19	COLD ZERO ENERGY PHYSICS EXPERIMENTS.	
	OCTOBER	13	HOT ZERO ENERGY PHYSICS EXPERIMENTS.	SAFETY CIRCUITS COMPLETION
	NOVEMBER	51	ADJUSTMENTS TO EXPERIMENTAL FUEL LOADING PATTERN SAFETY CIRCUITS CHECKS.	ERECTION AND PROVING OF OFFLOAD REFUELLING MACHINE
	DECEMBER	7	REACTIVITY WORTH OF 9 LIQUID SHUT DOWN TUBES EXPERIMENT	
1968		42	POWER RAISING TO FULL POWER ◄— SET SYNCHRONISED TO NATIONAL GRID (24.12.67.) ◄— FULL POWER 100 MW(e) (25.1.68)	POWER OPERATION
	JANUARY			
	FEBRUARY	82	◄— OFFICIAL OPENING (23.2.68)	
	MARCH			
	APRIL		MAXIMUM FUEL IRRADIATION 3900 MWD/TaU GENERATION 138 MILLION KWH: AVAILABILITY 79% : LOAD FACTOR 69% PLANNED SHUTDOWN (16.4.68)	
	MAY		COMMISSIONING OF LOOPS AND MAIN REFUELLING MACHINE	

Fig.1. Principal programme events from commencement of fuel loading: Winfrith SGHWR

to start the unit and the fault was traced to the windings of the driving motor, necessitating the removal of the unit to the manufacturer's works. The motor was completely rewound and the pump replaced in circuit after works bench tests, the complete operation again taking only four days. The cause of the overheating of the windings was ascribed to excessive friction in the main bearings which may have resulted from the deposition of solids from the water, since the condition arose after the pump had been shut down. Improvements have been made to the display of pump motor current loadings so that repetition of this incident should be avoided.

Stage 3

15. Power raising commenced on the 20th December, 1967 and, by the 25th January, 1968, an output of 104.6 MWe had been achieved and the plant was considered to be available for sustained full-power operation. Fig. 2 shows the stages by which power was raised; it will be noted that the turbo-alternator was first synchronized to the national grid on the 24th December, 1967, and full-power attained for a limited time on the 7th January, 1968. It will be evident from Fig. 2 that a substantial load factor was achieved during March and the first half of April.

16. During the power raising process a number of measurements and plant checks were performed as follows:

(a) Radiation surveys. These were conducted throughout power raising around the plant and showed no unexpectedly high levels. The values in the turbine hall are close to those predicted and have caused no problems either during operation or when access was required for maintenance. The principal source of radiation is nitrogen-16 (half-life 7 s), which is carried over to the turbine from the steam drums and eventually passes up the discharge stack via the condenser and off-gas system. A typical radiation survey of the turbine hall is shown in Fig. 3 while the variation of the radiation level at a point in this area with reactor power is shown in Fig. 4. From this, it will be seen that the levels vary approximately with power in accordance with a [reactor power]^2 relation.

(b) Turbo-alternator checks. Only a very limited number of tests were needed on the turbo-alternator itself as the majority of the initial proving of the machine had been carried out using a temporary commissioning boiler before the nominal plant completion. The additional tests

performed during Stage 3 were:

(i) load throw-off at 25 MWe and 53 MWe (tests at 100 MWe were done subsequently);

(ii) bus-bar heat run to measure maximum temperature attained;

(iii) on-load overspeed tests at 15-20 MWe (NB, overspeed tests are carried out at zero output every time the turbo-alternator is synchronized);

(iv) automatic voltage regulator (AVR) setting up and checking;

(v) overspeed-limiting gear operation.

Operation with the package boiler had not permitted all the auxiliary and ancillary plant to be loaded to capacity so that only during this phase could the commissioning of such items as the rotary air pumps, condensate extraction and feed water pumps, feed heaters and the associated bled steam system, and deaerator controls be undertaken.

(c) System vibration measurements. The vibration measurements that had been made during the engineering tests and low-power phases of the programme were repeated. They showed that the system was free of vibration except when certain steam lines were being warmed-through and when a blow-down line associated with the primary circuit clean-up was operated. Simple modifications to operating procedures, provision of a limited number of additional physical restraints and the insertion of a nozzle in the blow-down pipework rectified these defects.

(d) Performance checks. Various physics and thermal performance measurements were made to check the reactor performance and to confirm that operating limits were met. These are described in Part B. In addition, the overall performance of the turbine and feed train and auxiliary equipment has been checked and appears to be satisfactory although the final acceptance tests have not yet been made on the turbine and cooling towers.

(e) Commissioning of the automatic control system. Only minor adjustments have been required to the parameters of the automatic

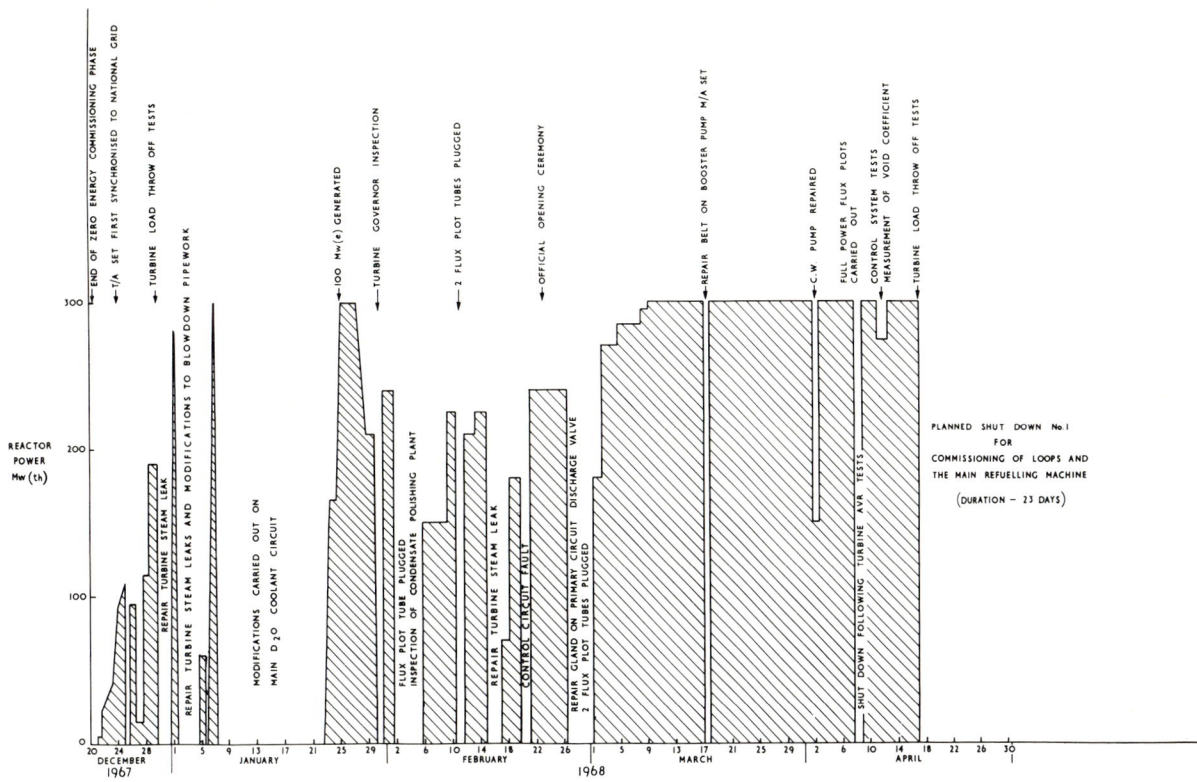

Fig.2. SGHWR: power history

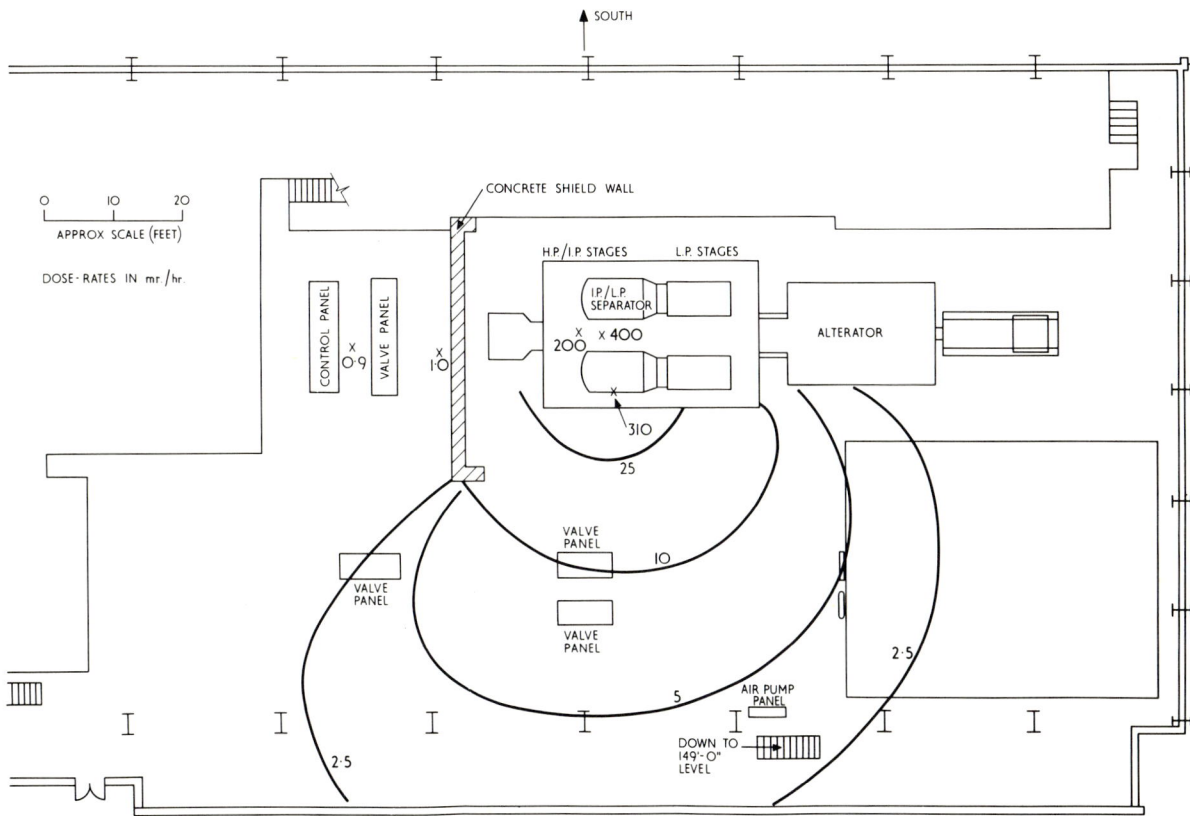

Fig.3. Plan view on turbine floor showing dose rate contours at 100 MW(e)

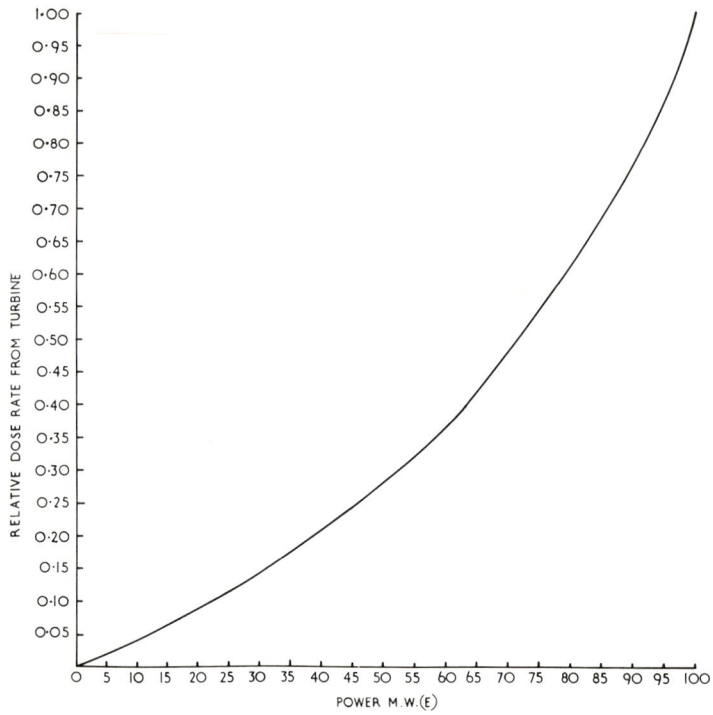

Fig.4. Dose rate from turbine as a function
of electrical power

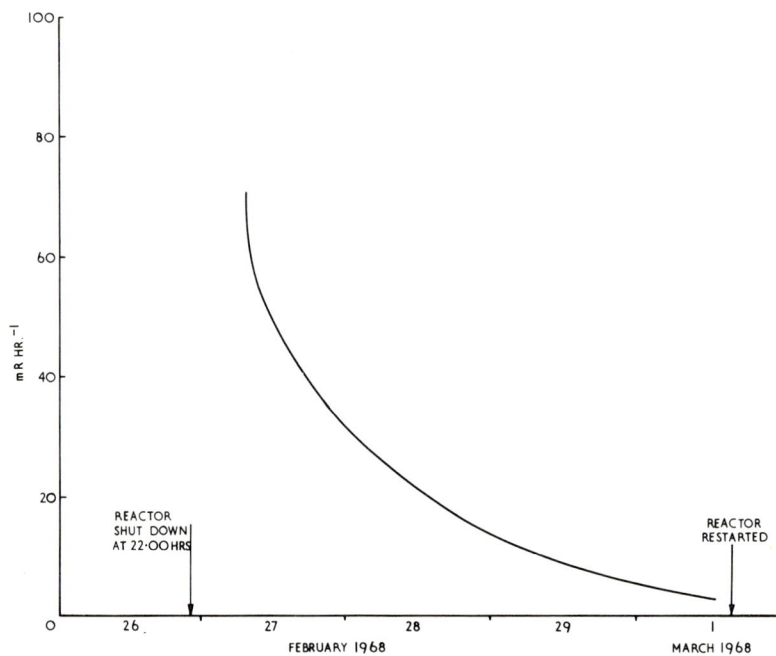

Fig.5. Primary containment radiation levels
in main plant area following a period
at 80% full power

control system which had been chosen on the basis of simulator studies. The only significant modifications have been associated with the characteristics of the turbine governor.

17. Outage during this period of power raising resulted principally from a spillage of heavy water. This occurred when the plant was at a power near to 100 MWe and a controlled shutdown was initiated. The unit was fully shut down within 30 min. After access had been gained to the primary containment, it was found that the leakage was from one of the two plate-type heavy water coolers which had been wrongly assembled.

Early operational experience with the Winfrith SGHWR

18. Since achieving full power, the operation of the reactor has been very satisfactory. Generally the plant has been operated at or near full-power with only very limited periods of part-load for tests or the correction of the occasional minor plant problem. The main plant performance parameters have agreed closely with predictions. Table 1 gives the basic operational figures up to the 16th April, 1968, when the reactor had a planned shutdown to allow commissioning of the experimental cluster loop and the main refuelling machine.

Table 1

	Since 25.1.68 (first full power)	Since 1.3.68
Availability	79%	96%
Load factor	69%	90%
Generation	134.841 $\times 10^6$ units	101.052 $\times 10^6$ units

Total generation since 24.12.67 - 138,372,000 kWh

19. The performance already achieved indicates the considerable progress made in the very few months since commissioning with the elimination of equipment defects that are commonly experienced when bringing any major plant into operation. It also reflects the growing experience of the operating team which will enable subsequent operating programmes to be formulated with confidence.

20. Radiation and activity levels. Direct experience has been obtained of access to and work in the primary containment and also of maintenance on the turbine and feed train. Radiation levels in the primary containment after the reactor has been in operation have not prevented essential work or access on any occasion. The general radiation level in the main primary con-

tainment plant area is shown in Fig. 5 as a function of time after shutdown. Contamination has been localized to areas near the occasional minor steam or water leak. Provided the basic health physics precautions are taken, no difficulties arise. Most of the activity from any such steam and water leakage is associated with activation products which have been retained by the pipework lagging. This, incidentally, has given a useful method of leak detection when the reactor is shut down and depressurized. The feed heater cell is classified as a restricted radiation area principally because it contains bled steam pipes and the primary circuit polishing plant. However, access has been possible at all times for visual inspection, and some maintenance work has been performed with the reactor at full power.

21. Chemistry. Experience with water reactors has shown the importance of water chemistry conditions. For this reason, the design of the Winfrith SGHWR included a polishing plant capable of taking the full feed flow, together with a fractional by-pass of the primary circuit water. The quantities of prime interest have been 'crud' (iron and copper), silica and chloride. The polishing plant has been effective in maintaining acceptable levels of crud and chloride. However, while the silica has been kept to a suitable level, the polishing plant has not been very effective in achieving its removal principally because of the temperature conditions that exist local to this plant.

22. The chemistry of the moderator circuit is discussed in detail in another symposium paper (ref. 1). Operationally, the two main aspects have been the control of boron level and the concentration of deuterium in the helium blanket above the moderator. The addition and removal of boron is easily performed although it is not yet fully automated or automatically monitored. The deuterium levels have been higher than predicted but the concentration has been kept below the maximum permissible level of 7%. An increase of the recombination capacity by about 50% is proposed.

23. Reactor control. Simulator studies had predicted that manual control of the reactor would be satisfactory. This has been confirmed on the plant. However, because of the operational advantages and the need to demonstrate the load following capability of the unit to support commercial designs, it was decided to commission the automatic control system at an early stage of the programme. This maintains key parameters such as system pressure, drum level and steam flow to the turbine at pre-set values. The system pressure is controlled directly by the position of the turbine governor valve, this control action being performed through a conventional governor gear. Some difficulties have been experienced with this and, although it is now giving an acceptable performance, further modifications and optimization of the system are proposed.

24. Drum level control assumes a major role in a direct cycle system since it constitutes the interface between the reactor and the turbine - feed train. Control has been satisfactory at full-power but less so at very low powers. However, no significant attempt has been made to optimize the system for these conditions and studies suggest that no inherent difficulty exists with control at low power. Problems have been experienced with noise in the transducer signals. The difficulty was associated with only one of the two halves of the main reactor coolant circuit and was found to be related to the geometry of the pipe runs to the instruments. The effect has now been greatly reduced by re-routing some of this piping. The steam flow to the turbine is controlled by variation in the reactor power which results from adjustments to moderator height. This system has performed very satisfactorily. Use is made of a switch installed to vary the gain of the system thereby providing improved response over the full power range. Steam flow control is normally engaged above 30 MWe. Below this level, reactor power is controlled by use of a neutron flux signal from an out-of-pile ion chamber. The pattern of operation employed in bringing the plant to full power involved a number of single power cycles. These were accomplished very smoothly. On one occasion, the reactor was shut down and the booster pump stopped to allow the replacement of a damaged fan belt on the motor alternator which supplies this pump. The whole operation, including the repair work, was completed within 10 h.

25. Fuel performance. The reactor fuel charge contains approximately one third experimental channels and has performed very well with the exception of a leaking fuel element which was detected at the end of March. The defect fuel cluster is of an experimental type which is used to monitor the effect of primary circuit water conditions on zirconium alloys. After the initial rise in radiation levels, there was no alteration in the activity from this defect during approximately three weeks of full power operation until the April shutdown. This period of operation included four power cycles, one of which was a reactor trip. The defect gave valuable experience in checking operational procedures and monitoring levels throughout the plant. In fact, it had been intended to load a deliberate defect into the reactor in order to obtain the experience which has been gained from this defect. This experiment will not now be performed. The activity discharged from the reactor was well within acceptable levels.

26. Outages. Operational time has been lost for a variety of reasons. Since the 25th January, 1968, the following have been the major causes of system outage:

   (i)   turbine feed train problems;

   (ii) spurious trips (mainly in first few weeks of operation);

   (iii) failure of experimental flux scanning thimbles;

   (iv) mechanical problems associated with faulty construction of the primary circuit polishing plant.

The lost time has been almost equally divided among the above plant problems all of which have now been overcome. They are thought to be of a non-recurrent type and again represent typical initial or commissioning problems which occur during the first few weeks of plant operation.

PART B

CORE PERFORMANCE MEASUREMENTS IN THE WINFRITH SGHWR

Objectives of the measurement programme

27. The programme of performance measurements was planned with two aims:

   (i) to provide data necessary for the safe and efficient operation of the Winfrith SGHWR;

   (ii) to provide accurate tests of theoretical models under operational conditions and so achieve a firm basis for design developments in later reactors.

28. Up to the present, emphasis has been placed on the first of these objectives. Sufficient information has been assembled to demonstrate that safety and operating criteria have been met; attention is now being turned to the more refined measurements needed to attain the second objective.

Operational aims

29. In order to achieve the design output of 100 MWe, satisfy the safety criteria and meet the needs of the irradiation programme, it was necessary that the initial core loading should satisfy the following main conditions:

   (1) possess sufficient reactivity to be taken critical and raised to full power with Xe and Sm poisons;

   (2) at initial full power to possess sufficient excess reactivity to run subsequently for 300 ± 30 equivalent full power days;

   (3) possess reactivity coefficients and control and shutdown variable responses compatible with the design tolerance of the control system and within limiting values allowed for in the hazards analysis;

   (4) give rise to a coolant flow distribution within the tolerances needed to achieve an adequate margin to dryout;

(5) give rise to a power distribution
such that

(i) no standard fuel channel
exceeds 4 MW thermal out-
put,

(ii) the 'enriched design'
boosted channel experi-
ments operate at thermal
powers close to but not
exceeding 5 MW,

(iii) the 'natural design'
boosted channel experi-
ments operate at 3.5 MW.

Initial core loading

30. The initial core loading chosen to
satisfy the requirements is shown in
Fig. 6. The reasons for this choice of
loading have been discussed in companion
papers (refs 2, 3 and 4). A basic 3-batch
arrangement of 2.28%, 1.56% and 1.24% fuels
has been perturbed to include a number of
irradiation experiments (ref. 4). The most
important perturbations are:

(a) the so-called boosted channels
(A9, C9 ('natural' design) and
A11, C11 ('enriched' design))
which are provided with an additional pump and are fuelled with
relatively highly-enriched
experiments;

(b) four 3.0% enriched fuel elements
(E19, S21, U17, W15) intended for
extra long irradiations;

(c) two small (pencil) loops in
positions H16 and R16 which are
at present unfuelled;

(d) the superheat channels, at
present unfuelled, but causing
local flux disturbances.

Prediction basis

31. It was evident that the accurate
prediction of reactivity levels and power
distribution for such a complicated loading
would provide a severe test of the
PATRIARCH computer codes (refs 2, 3). In
many cases, it has been necessary to use
the SOLOMON synthesis code to obtain an
adequate representation. This combines
the AIMAZ XY-reactor physics model with
the CUSH multi-channel primary circuit
representation and the TIRAZ coupled
nuclear-thermal-hydraulic single channel
model.

Scope of the measurements

32. Valuable reactor time was saved by
carrying out some of the preliminary
reactor physics measurements with the power
reactor fuel loaded into a core mock-up in
the tank of the DIMPLE zero energy
assembly. However, due to the limited size

of the DIMPLE tank, a maximum of 68 fuel
elements were all that could be accommodated
and some extrapolations from these results
were still necessary.

33. Performance measurements were made on
the power reactor itself during the following phases of the commissioning programme:

(a) hydraulic tests before fuel
loading;

(b) cold zero energy experiments;

(c) hot zero energy tests;

(d) power raising;

(e) full power operation.

The more important results will now be
reviewed.

REACTIVITY LEVELS

Cold zero energy

34. The reactor was taken critical with
moderator boron concentrations ranging from
4.1-12.7 ppm and immersed fuel heights from
109-360 cm. A convenient indicator of the
accuracy of reactivity calculations is
provided by the closeness of the predicted
K_{eff} to unity for states known to be just
critical. Over the range of states

$$\text{predicted } K_{eff} = 1.0068 \pm 0.0015.$$

Hot zero energy

35. Similar tests with the H_2O coolant and
D_2O moderator raised to full operating temperatures (280°C and 65°C respectively) by
electrical heat gave

$$\text{predicted } K_{eff} = 0.9995 \pm 0.0004.$$

These results, showing the disappearance of
small overprediction bias in reactivity
levels at operating temperature, were consistent with expectations from previous
zero energy measurements.

Full power operation

36. At full power the reproduction factor
is reduced by the build-up of Xe and Sm
poisons, the action of the fuel temperature
coefficient (mainly due to Doppler broaden-
ing of U-238 resonances) and the presence
of steam voids. The boron concentration in
the moderator must therefore be reduced to
compensate. Since the zero energy tests
show that the influence of boron on reactivity has been accurately predicted then a
comparison between the calculated and
measured boron concentrations with the
reactor operating steadily at full power is
a direct indication of the accuracy of
calculations of reactivity level. Since
the fuel was necessarily slightly burnt up
during the preliminary operations at less

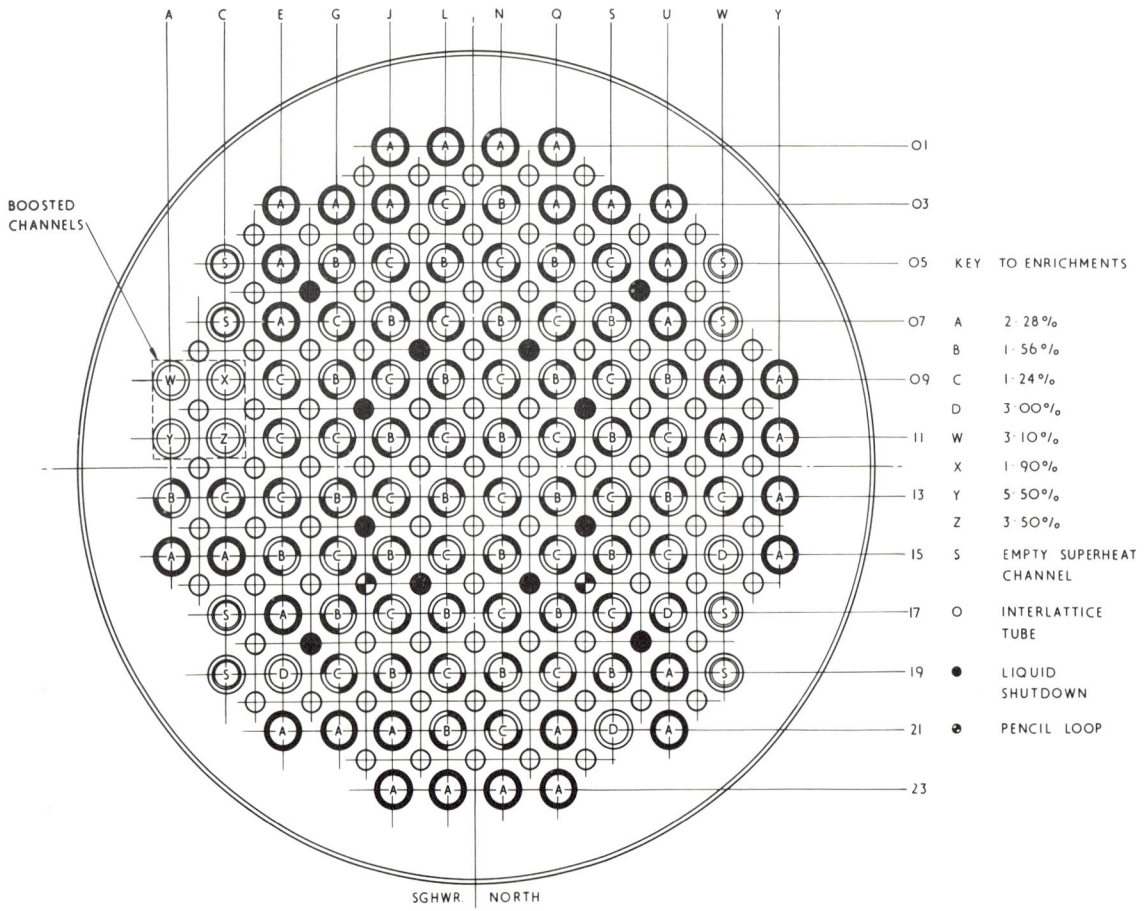

Fig.6. SGHWR prototype core plan

KEY TO ENRICHMENTS

A	2·28%
B	1·56%
C	1·24%
D	3·00%
W	3·10%
X	1·90%
Y	5·50%
Z	3·50%
S	EMPTY SUPERHEAT CHANNEL
O	INTERLATTICE TUBE
●	LIQUID SHUTDOWN
⊗	PENCIL LOOP

BOOSTED CHANNELS

SGHWR. NORTH

Fig.7. Prompt power deficit experiment

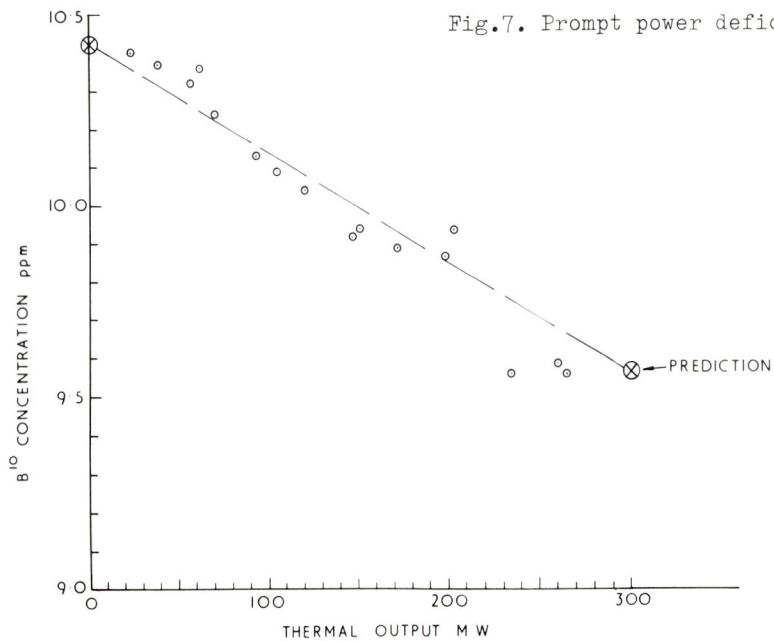

than full power it is necessary to apply some small corrections to the measurements. These have been reduced to a standard state in which the core is operated with equilibrium Xe and Sm poisons at zero irradiation. The following comparison emerges:

measured B^{10} concentration = 6.66 ± 0.20 ppm

SOLOMON prediction = 6.36 ppm.

Since 1 ppm $B^{10} \simeq 1\% \Delta K_{eff}$ these results suggest that the core is approximately $\frac{1}{4}\%$ more reactive than expected in the hot full power condition.

REACTIVITY CHANGES

Burn-up

37. It is still too early in the first cycle of fuel burn-up to make firm predictions of the cycle length. Nevertheless during the month of March when the reactor was operating essentially at steady full power:

observed B^{10} burn-up rate = $1.9 \pm 0.2 \times 10^{-2}$ ppm/EFPD (Effective Full Power Days)

SOLOMON prediction = 1.7×10^{-2} ppm/EFPD (Effective Full Power Days).

When taken in conjunction with the agreement on initial B^{10} level previously noted, this suggests that a cycle length within the design tolerance of 300 ± 30 EFPD will be attained.

Steam void reactivity effects

38. Zero energy measurements made in the core mock-up using H_2O/D_2O mixtures to simulate coolant of various effective densities showed that

measured void coefficient K_V = -0.016 ± 0.001

calculated $K_V = -0.016$

where K_V = (fractional reactivity change)/ (fractional void change).

Since the mock-up contained only 68 fuel elements against the 104 of the power reactor, there was more neutron leakage and the void coefficient correspondingly more negative. The same method of calculation gave for the complete power reactor at full power

$K_V = -0.009$

for perturbations involving small increases in reactor power.

39. A first check on the magnitude of void reactivity effects in the power reactor was made by perturbing coolant flow by partially opening and closing two of the four pump discharge valves with the reactor running at a thermal power of 75 MW. No discernable change in the slow drift of critical height with xenon build-up was detected. This was consistent with the very small effective void coefficient of $K_V = -0.0002$ computed for this type of flow perturbation.

40. A further experiment was made with the plant running at about 90 MWe. Two high pressure feed heaters were disconnected in succession while the reactor was operated at constant neutron flux. The sub-cooling at channel entry was therefore increased and less steam voids created. This produced a perturbation in critical height which was interpreted as equivalent to

$K_V = -0.007 \pm 0.002$

compared with (for this type of perturbation)

predicted $K_V = -0.006$.

Power deficit

41. It is difficult to separate the true power-void coefficient from the fuel temperature coefficient since both operate approximately simultaneously. For many practical purposes, e.g., assessment of the adequacy of the shutdown system, it is not necessary to make this separation. Estimates of the combined effects of coolant voids and the fuel temperature coefficients were made during power raising since this often lasted for several hours. It was necessary to apply corrections for changes in coolant and moderator temperature and in xenon reactivity. The latter correction was facilitated by using a xenon computer with the equilibrium value normalized to a SOLOMON estimate. Not surprisingly, there is a considerable scatter in the data and a typical run-up is shown in Fig. 7.

42. To summarize the available evidence on void and power coefficients:

(1) the power coefficient (combined effect of voids and fuel temperature coefficient) is certainly negative, probably rather more so than predicted;

(2) the void coefficient is small and negative and well within the control system tolerance;

(3) it is likely that the fuel temperature coefficient is more negative than expected.

Moderator and coolant temperature coefficients

43. These coefficients were measured during the hot zero energy phase of the programme. As expected they are about 5 mN/°C (1 mN = 10^{-5} $\Delta K_{eff}/K_{eff}$) less

Table 2
Moderator and fuel temperature coefficients

Boron concentration (ppm)	Moderator coefficient mN/°C		Coolant and fuel coefficient mN/°C	
	Experiment	Calculation	Experiment	Calculation
9.35	14.5 ± 0.5	20.47	-8.4 ± 0.2	-12.30
11.48	19.8 ± 1.6	23.69	-7.8 ± 1.3	-12.64

Table 3
Circuit flows

	Measured gall/min	Predicted gall/min
N circuit	16,800 ± 200	17,160
S circuit	17,300 ± 200	17,180
Total:	34,100 ± 300	34,340

negative than predicted. Similar discrepancies have been observed in other liquid moderated systems. The effect is, however, small and of little practical significance in SGHWR. Results of the measurements are presented in Table 2.

Control variable effectiveness

44. As has already been discussed the zero energy experiments have confirmed closely the predicted influence of moderator boron and hence its predicted effectiveness as a control variable.

45. Measurements of moderator height coefficients have been made by measuring reactor periods with excess moderator height. The coefficients are 25% smaller than predicted but are within control system tolerance. Smaller discrepancies of about 8% had previously been observed in zero energy measurements in DIMPLE.

Liquid shutdown tube worth

46. Pulsed source and rod drop techniques were used to estimate the worth of the 12-liquid shutdown tubes. The agreement with prediction through the zero energy phases was in all cases within $\pm 0.15 \Delta K_{eff}$ and the combined worth was $3.4\% \Delta K_{eff}$ at hot zero energy with a full tank.

47. It was demonstrated, by measurements of critical boron concentration, that even if three liquid shutdown tubes near to the booster channels failed to fire then the remaining nine tubes would hold down $2.1\% \Delta K_{eff}$. This is considerably larger than the combined power deficit and is therefore sufficient to ensure shutdown.

PRIMARY CIRCUIT HYDRAULICS

Total flow

48. Estimates of coolant flow in the circuits were based on data derived from full-scale tests on most of the major components including the fuel elements. In view of the complexity of the pipework, it was difficult to prejudge the likely accuracy of the overall prediction. Total flows were measured by Dall tubes situated in the main downcomers to the pumps over a range of thermal powers ranging up to 300 MW. The predictions were within the scatter of the measured points. At full power the comparison was as shown in Table 3.

49. These results indicate that the flow in the South circuit is about 3% higher than in the North. This is due principally to the fact that one of the pumps in this circuit, although of the same design as the others has a higher head versus flow characteristic.

Flow distribution

50. An important feature of the Winfrith reactor is that each channel is fitted with hydraulic instrumentation in the form of inlet and outlet Venturi meters. The inlet Venturis measure the total flow and have shown that the distribution of flow at full power is well predicted. Individual channel flows are predicted to $\pm 5\%$. Only at zero power was there a significant difference between the measurements and prediction, and this was a local effect observed in the channels fed from the four sub-headers nearest to the main circulating pumps. With no steam voidage in the core these channels were receiving 10% to 20% less flow than the average value for the core as a whole. It is believed that this starving of the end sub-headers at zero power was due to momentum effects in the bottom header (not included in the model) and the sharp radius of curvature of the pipe joining the pump to the bottom header. At power the effect was less significant due to the increase in the total circuit pressure drop associated with core voidage.

POWER DISTRIBUTION

Zero energy measurements

51. Provision has been made in the Winfrith reactor for the insertion of flux measuring wires along the axes of the fuel elements. Wires may be loaded or withdrawn with the reactor on power. Copper wires were used during the zero energy experiments to check the radial and axial neutron flux distribution.

52. At cold zero energy with a high concentration of boron in the moderator some large discrepancies amounting to a 40% underprediction of copper reaction rates were observed in the vicinity of the boosted channels. As the core was raised to operating temperature and the critical boron concentration was reduced from 13 ppm-10 ppm, the discrepancy was greatly reduced and fell to the few per cent overprediction level which had been expected on the basis of DIMPLE experience with high enrichment perturbations. As a precautionary measure to avoid possible delays at the beginning of power operation reactivity was reduced in the booster channel area by changing channels E11, C13 and A13 to the enrichments shown in Fig. 6. Previously these channels had been fuelled with 1.24%, 1.24% and 2.28% fuel elements respectively.

53. Subsequent theoretical studies have suggested that the form of coarse mesh diffusion theory used in the standard applications of the AIMAZ code does not represent the high local current flows from relatively highly enriched fuel to a highly borated reflector with sufficient accuracy. The problem is, however, much less significant at the lower boron levels arising at power operation.

SOUTH

A C E G J L N Q S U W Y

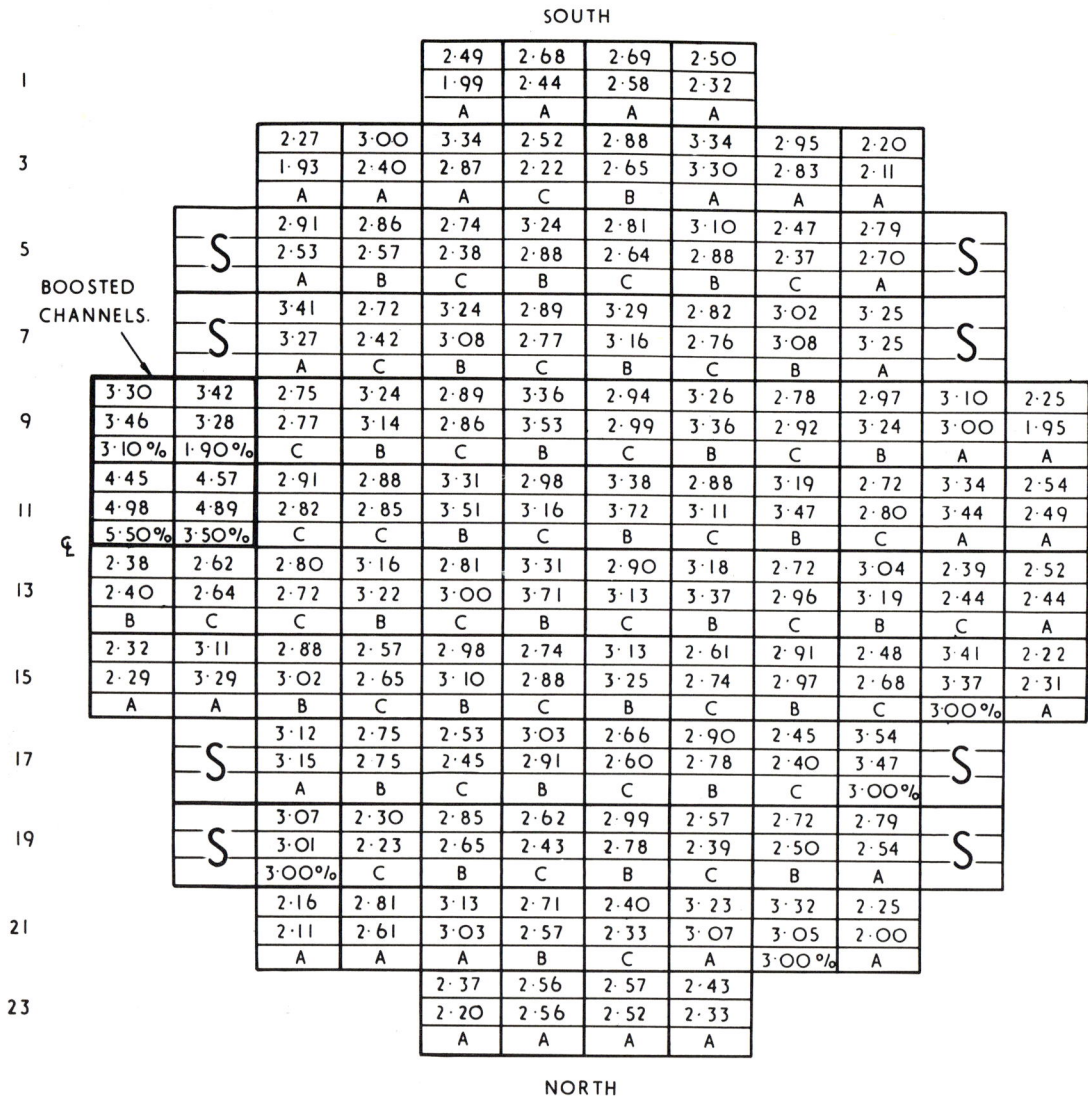

Row	A	C	E	G	J	L	N	Q	S	U	W	Y
1					2.49 / 1.99 / A	2.68 / 2.44 / A	2.69 / 2.58 / A	2.50 / 2.32 / A				
3		2.27 / 1.93 / A	3.00 / 2.40 / A	3.34 / 2.87 / A	2.52 / 2.22 / C	2.88 / 2.65 / B	3.34 / 3.30 / A	2.95 / 2.83 / A	2.20 / 2.11 / A			
5		S	2.91 / 2.53 / A	2.86 / 2.57 / B	2.74 / 2.38 / C	3.24 / 2.88 / B	2.81 / 2.64 / C	3.10 / 2.88 / B	2.47 / 2.37 / C	2.79 / 2.70 / A	S	
7		S	3.41 / 3.27 / A	2.72 / 2.42 / C	3.24 / 3.08 / B	2.89 / 2.77 / C	3.29 / 3.16 / B	2.82 / 2.76 / C	3.02 / 3.08 / B	3.25 / 3.25 / A	S	
9	3.30 / 3.46 / 3.10%	3.42 / 3.28 / 1.90%	2.75 / 2.77 / C	3.24 / 3.14 / B	2.89 / 2.86 / C	3.36 / 3.53 / B	2.94 / 2.99 / C	3.26 / 3.36 / B	2.78 / 2.92 / C	2.97 / 3.24 / B	3.10 / 3.00 / A	2.25 / 1.95 / A
11	4.45 / 4.98 / 5.50%	4.57 / 4.89 / 3.50%	2.91 / 2.82 / C	2.88 / 2.85 / C	3.31 / 3.51 / B	2.98 / 3.16 / C	3.38 / 3.72 / B	2.88 / 3.11 / C	3.19 / 3.47 / B	2.72 / 2.80 / C	3.34 / 3.44 / A	2.54 / 2.49 / A
13	2.38 / 2.40 / B	2.62 / 2.64 / C	2.80 / 2.72 / C	3.16 / 3.22 / B	2.81 / 3.00 / C	3.31 / 3.71 / B	2.90 / 3.13 / C	3.18 / 3.37 / B	2.72 / 2.96 / C	3.04 / 3.19 / B	2.39 / 2.44 / C	2.52 / 2.44 / A
15	2.32 / 2.29 / A	3.11 / 3.29 / A	2.88 / 3.02 / B	2.57 / 2.65 / C	2.98 / 3.10 / B	2.74 / 2.88 / C	3.13 / 3.25 / B	2.61 / 2.74 / C	2.91 / 2.97 / B	2.48 / 2.68 / C	3.41 / 3.37 / 3.00%	2.22 / 2.31 / A
17		S	3.12 / 3.15 / A	2.75 / 2.75 / B	2.53 / 2.45 / C	3.03 / 2.91 / B	2.66 / 2.60 / C	2.90 / 2.78 / B	2.45 / 2.40 / C	3.54 / 3.47 / 3.00%	S	
19		S	3.07 / 3.01 / 3.00%	2.30 / 2.23 / C	2.85 / 2.65 / B	2.62 / 2.43 / C	2.99 / 2.78 / B	2.57 / 2.39 / C	2.72 / 2.50 / B	2.79 / 2.54 / A	S	
21			2.16 / 2.11 / A	2.81 / 2.61 / A	3.13 / 3.03 / A	2.71 / 2.57 / B	2.40 / 2.33 / C	3.23 / 3.07 / A	3.32 / 3.05 / 3.00%	2.25 / 2.00 / A		
23					2.37 / 2.20 / A	2.56 / 2.56 / A	2.57 / 2.52 / A	2.43 / 2.33 / A				

BOOSTED CHANNELS.

NORTH

KEY

MW	SOLOMON PREDICTION.
MW	BEST FIT TO QUALITY METER MEASUREMENT.
%	ENRICHMENT:—

A = 2.28%
B = 1.56%
C = 1.24%

Fig.8. Comparison of predicted and measured
power distribution in SGHWR
normalized to 300 MW(th)

166

Power operation

54. The outlet Venturi meter fitted to individual channels in the Winfrith SGHWR provides a means of measuring exit steam quality and hence channel power. The equation relating quality meter differential pressure Δp, channel flow w, and steam quality x, were obtained from out-of-pile tests using an electrically heated facsimile of the fuel cluster in a full scale model of the channel and riser pipework under reactor conditions. A general relationship for the normal operating range of quality was demonstrated of the form

$$x = \frac{a\ (\Delta p - 17.0\ w^2) + b}{w^2}$$

where a and b are constants for a particular channel pipework configuration.

55. During commissioning, channel measurements were made at various reactor powers using the inlet flow meters and quality meters. At zero power, i.e., with no steam quality, checks were made of the channel flows as measured by the inlet and outlet Venturi meters respectively, and where they did not agree within 5%, those channels were excluded from the subsequent analysis of core power distribution. In addition certain of the channel instruments had developed faults and could not be repaired at this stage because access is only available during shutdown. Nevertheless the instrumentation in 77 out of the 104 channels proved to be satisfactory and provided a detailed survey of core power distribution.

56. In order to facilitate comparisons with theory by smoothing random errors in meter calibration ($\pm6\%$) and to fill in gaps where the instrumentation is not operative, the results have been processed through the SAMSON code, which produces a best fit consistent with neutron diffusion theory. Fig. 8 shows the results and presents a comparison with the SOLOMON predictions. It is clear that the peak standard channel is operating at below 4 MW and the booster channels at just under 5 MW as required. It also appears that SOLOMON follows the channel to channel variations associated with the enrichment loading pattern quite closely. However there is a systematic tendency for the observed powers to be about 10% higher in the booster channels and other high flux regions and proportionately lower elsewhere.

57. The quality meter power distribution measurements at steady full power operation are now being supplemented by wire activation scans made with 1.5% Cu/titanium alloy. At the time of writing the first results have not been fully analysed. There are indications that the axial power form factor will be 1.56 $\pm$ 0.02 which is 8% higher than the original figure used in the design analysis. The difference appears to be related to the effect of the bottom reflector but is not of great practical significance since sufficient thermal design tolerances exist, especially as the

peak channels are operating at below the 4 MW design limit.

CONCLUSIONS

58. The time taken to bring the Winfrith SGHWR to full-load capability from the nominal completion of construction and initial fuel and heavy water loading bears favourable comparison with that taken to commission a conventional power plant containing equipment which replicates that already proved in existing generating stations. This has resulted, in part, from careful planning and training but also from the design which permits extensive component testing and proving before assembly on site and follows closely many aspects which are well established in conventional power plant. In the first $2\frac{1}{2}$ months after reaching full-load capability, the plant availability has been high while the system has demonstrated that it is flexible, readily controlled and affords simple access for maintenance and adjustment.

59. As regards the performance of the Winfrith SGHWR, measurements have shown that this is close to prediction. In particular, the core has been brought to full-power without exceeding the channel output limits and it provides sufficient reactivity margin to give the designed burn-up.

ACKNOWLEDGEMENTS

60. This paper is published by kind permission of the Managing Director, The Reactor Group, UKAEA, Risley. Thanks are due to the many colleagues, particularly at Winfrith, responsible for the work reported.

REFERENCES

1. DICKSON G.K., BURTON W.R. and RILEY J.A. Chemical control in SGHWR circuits. Paper 9B, BNES Conference, May 1968.

2. HICKS D, JOHNSTONE I and O'DELL F.P. Nuclear design of SGHWRs. Paper 4, BNES Conference, May 1968.

3. HOLMES J.A.G., OBERTELLI J.D. and ROBERTS H.A. Thermal and hydraulic design of SGHWRs. Paper 5, BNES Conference, May 1968.

4. PICKMAN D.O. SGHWR fuel design and materials. Paper 3, BNES Conference, May 1968.

Session C: Discussion

PAPER 8

Mr P.G. Boiron, GAAA, France

1. One interesting conclusion of the studies presented in the Paper is that the length of defect which will produce failure of a pressure tube is several orders of magnitude greater than that which could be detected by inspection techniques which can be applied throughout in service. It seems that inspection in service is intermittent. Have any tests been made to evaluate the time-lag needed for an initially non-detectable defect to reach critical size? What is the frequency of inspection in service, and what is the process used? How are such defects differentiated from normal leakages from the rolled joints?

2. Could the Authors indicate what the consequences of a leak in the pressure tube would be for the calandria tube with such a high pressure primary coolant?

Mr L.M. Wyatt, Central Electricity Generating Board

3. Mr Nicholls has presented some very cogent arguments to show that the increase in diameter due to creep is well within acceptable limits, and also that the possibility of stress rupture does not appear to be serious. He has not, however, mentioned the possibility of distortion leading to bowing, due to creep or other effects during irradiation. There must be a considerable flux gradient across many of the pressure tubes of the reactor, and this will also lead to internal heating. From this might follow differential straining effects under power cycling conditions. Could the Authors say if they are confident that these effects will not lead to outage and replacement costs which could seriously affect reactor economics?

Authors' reply: Paper 8

4. In reply to Mr Boiron's questions, information on low cycle fatigue and creep shows that extension of defects from detectable size to several inches which would be needed to produce failure will not occur under the design conditions for SGHWR pressure tubes in their required economic life.

5. On the basis of these results such aspects do not control the frequency of tube inspection, provided that the inspection and pressure testing of the tubes before they are put into service is adequate. Testing and inspection of a particular station will depend on such matters as the statutory requirements applying to a particular site, and the extensive surveillance programme adopted for the prototype should not be regarded as a precedent for civil stations but rather as a source of additional data. One requirement for inspection would be if other observations, such as evidence of light water leakage or of unusual behaviour of a fuel element, indicated the possibility of trouble in a particular channel. The inspection equipment provided for the prototype includes provision for optical viewing of a pressure tube, ultrasonic testing, measurement of scores and scratches, and dimensional measurement. The use of such equipment would, of course, distinguish between defects and leakage from rolled joints.

6. On his final question, it is impossible to say exactly what would happen to the calandria tube, as this would depend on the nature of the leak. If the calandria tube is not penetrated, pressure in the carbon dioxide vault round the calandria will rise a little and be relieved to the primary containment through bursting discs. If the calandria tube is penetrated, for example by jet action, pressure build-up in the calandria will be similarly relieved through bursting discs.

7. The possibility of bowing of pressure tubes as a result of flux and temperature differentials to which Mr Wyatt refers must be considered for each individual design. This has been done in detail for the SGHWR and we are satisfied on all of these aspects. A considerable surveillance programme of measurements and sample exposure in the prototype has been set in hand which will provide added confidence.

PAPERS 9(a) and (b)

Mr D.E. Anderson, Ontario Hydro, Canada

8. Under certain conditions, particularly on a start-up, the radiolytic decomposition

at the Douglas Point and the SGHW reactors has been considerably higher than was anticipated, with the result that re-combination units were undersized for maintaining the deuterium at a safe level in the helium. Interaction with moderator conductivity has been identified as one factor, but the specific mechanism has not. Oxygen addition has been necessary at Douglas Point, but not with the SGHWR. Would the Authors care to comment on any UK investigations into this problem?

Mr P.G. Boiron, GAAA, France

9. Could the Authors please indicate the minimum boron concentration which will be used? Is this value approached in the actual operating period?

10. Are there any difficulties due to displacement of boron fixed by the other anions? The suppression of the preliminary weak anion bed is an economy if problems of control are not involved. Accidental anionic pollution is always possible.

11. The in situ regeneration system des-cribed is attractive but the investment, including the necessary heavy water, is considerable. Taking operating experience into account, do the Authors think that the complication introduced by on-line regeneration is economically justified. In particular, is on-line cation regenera-tion worthwhile? There is no mention of it in the description of the Brandy system.

Mr V. Machacek, Czechoslovak Atomic Energy Commission

12. I would like to ask how the corrosion products are extracted from the moderator circuit after fixation on the ion exchange resins? These can be eliminated either by using a deuterized agent, in which case recovery of the heavy water from the eluant material will be necessary, or by ordinary agents, when the resins have to be redeuterized. Which procedure is used in the SGHWR operation?

Mr E.C. Perryman, Atomic Energy of Canada Ltd

13. I would like to know how the proposal to use neutral high oxygen coolant con-ditions, as described in Section (b) of the Paper, is reconciled with the now over-whelming evidence that this leads to very high oxidation rates for Zircaloy-2 in the reactor core.

14. In view of the relatively high Fe content now being seen in the SGHWR, are the Authors concerned about the much higher iron contents which might be obtained in a mild steel system with neutral high oxygen coolant?

Dr D.J. Ferrett, UKAEA, Winfrith

15. I would like to add a few remarks to Paper 9(b) on the main chemical effects observed in the moderator and primary circuits during operations at power between January and April, 1968.

16. The ion exchanger system for control of the purity of the D_2O and its boron content has met the specified working con-ditions. The boron capacity and reaction times of the columns have been similar to those predicted. Boron levels have been monitored continuously by Technicon auto-analysers using carminic acid colorimetric techniques. These have worked reliably and well and results have agreed to within ± 0.2 ppm with manual checks ($\pm 2\%$ at the 10 ppm level). The purity of the moderator has been maintained at a high level by operation of the columns. Conductivity averages 1.0 micromhos, and the level of metallic impurity (e.g., Al, Fe, etc.) remains between 10 and 50 ppb.

17. It has been found more difficult than was expected to maintain the pD around 5.5. During power operations continuous running of both anion and cation columns for clean-ing tends to produce 'conductivity' water with a pD approaching 7. Control at 5.5 is maintained by more intermittent operation of the column or by dosing with DNO_3. The rates of gas evolution into the He blanket as a result of radiolysis are five to six times higher than predicted on the basis of UK MTR experience. This may in part be due to physical causes, in that gases may be stripped off more efficiently in the SGHWR, so that radiolysis rates may, in fact, be fairly normal. However, there is some inter-relation with chemical phenomena, in that rates of off-gas are kept to a minimum when anion and cation columns are operated continuously.

18. Chemical control of the primary circuit is principally dependent on the operation of the powdered ion-exchange water treatment plant. There have been a number of operational problems associated with the coating of these beds, which have lead to losses of small quantities of resin into the main circuit on about half of the recoatings. The radiolytic decomposition of this resin and consequent pH changes caused short temporary high N-16 levels at the turbine and increased crud levels in the circuit. We are gradually learning the tricks of the trade, and the peaks of these excursions are decreasing at each coating.

19. The beds have maintained a low level of Fe and other metallic impurities in the primary circuit, but little capacity has been demonstrated for SiO_2, in line with CEGB experience, and Si levels have been controlled to date by blow-down.

20. There have been 19 recoatings of powdered resin to date (May, 1968). Ten of these produced no measurable increase in crud levels and nine produced crud 'bursts' lasting two to three hours, the average of these being about 5 ppm.

21.   In reply to Mr Anderson's remarks, the theoretical G value for D_2O decomposition is about 0.4, but the net value observed is much lower as a result of recombination. In our material test reactors, where low temperatures and very high water purity are maintained, the net value is below 0.002. We estimated that this value would apply in the prototype SGHWR, and, in fact it is about 0.008.   There must therefore be some slight interference with the recombination reaction as a result of chemical or physical effects.   We are reasonably satisfied that the contribution of chemical effects is very small indeed; the most likely explanation is that some gas stripping of the heavy water occurs as the cool heavy water returned to the top of the calandria flows as a film down the calandria tubes before entering the bulk moderator.   Alternatively, we suspect that a small measure of nucleate boiling may be occurring on interstitial tubes in the calandria.

22.   In the prototype, the somewhat enhanced radiolysis rate observed causes no embarrassment.   The installed recombination unit handles the load satisfactorily.   The deuterium level in the helium blanket is approximately 4%, which is well below the minimum concentration of 8-10% necessary to support combustion.   Our design concentration of 1% could be achieved by adopting a higher gas recirculation rate (about 50 cfm) and we shall do this as soon as an opportunity arises to install greater recirculation pump capacity.

23.   Since the prototype helium blanket operates at approximately atmospheric pressure, loss of deuterium gas will be very low; in fact we have not detected any significant loss.   The situation could, of course, be embarrassing on a high pressure system.   In the prototype we have observed that the ratio of deuterium to oxygen in the blanket gas is about 25% above stoichiometric.   This ratio has remained constant and there has been no need to use oxygen.   When the cation resin bed is taken off stream a small increase in radiolysis rate has been observed, but this disappears as soon as the bed is introduced.   No measurable increase in conductivity accompanies this change.

24.   Mr Boiron has asked a number of questions which we will deal with in turn.

25.   The minimum boron concentration which one would expect in the bulk moderator at the end of a fuel cycle is 1 ppm: this could be reduced to about 0.3 ppm if xenon over-ride is required.   At the start of the fuel cycle, boron concentration is about 12 ppm.

26.   The only ion other than borate which is likely to be present in the system is nitrate.   With the cation exchange resin in frequent use to remove corrosion products and lithium, the nitrate ion concentration is very low indeed, and only a very small quantity needs to be removed at any one time in order to maintain pD.   Thus the amount of boron which is displaced is correspondingly low and the effect of this on boron concentration in 40 tonnes of heavy water is almost negligible.   In any case, the rate of change in concentration is slow, and compensation can readily be obtained by passing a small flow through a boron removal bed.

27.   As a matter of interest the boron-saturated bed can be used as a reservoir of boron, and if it is desired to increase the boron concentration in the moderator this may be achieved by injecting nitric acid or nitrogen with the nitrate removal bed in circuit.

28.   The heavy water investment using the Brandy system is lower than that when the Winfrith SGHWR system is used.   This may not be apparent from the diagrams since a single block on a diagram represents several items of equipment.   It would be possible to include an electrodialysis cell in the moderator circuit and such a procedure is under consideration.   However, this is proceeding at low priority, because in order to obtain adequate poison removal rates, the electrodialysis cells would be very large.   At present, we prefer to concentrate the boron on anion exchange resins and subsequently regenerate, recovering the poison and regenerants in closed cycle operation.

29.   In reply to Mr Machacek's questions, our extensive experience on materials test reactors has shown that the capacity of a single cubic foot of cation resin will suffice to remove corrosion products from circuits maintained at a pD of 5.5-6.5 for several years.   This very low load of corrosion products is being confirmed during the early operation of the prototype SGHWR by the fact that impurity levels are too low to be indicated by conductivity changes when the cation resin bed is removed from the circuit (although the radiolysis rate increases significantly). Because of this low load and consequently predicted long life of the 4 ft^3 cation resin bed in the prototype, it is not our intention to regenerate this resin. When it becomes exhausted we shall recover the heavy water and then transfer it to active storage.

30.   Should the load of corrosion products arising in the prototype substantially exceed estimates, it is possible to transfer the exhausted resin to the regeneration column and regenerate with deuteronitric acid.   Recovery of heavy water from the eluants may then follow the same procedure as for alkaline regenerants.   In civil versions of the reactor incorporating the Brandy system comparable procedures may be used.

31.   Finally, I would stress that we do not expect that the rate of corrosion will justify the regeneration of the cation resin and that heavy water recovery only will be justified.

32. As Mr Perryman says, there is considerable evidence to suggest that increased rates of oxidation of Zircaloy-2 occur in neutral oxygenated water environments. This does not, however, imply that the associated hydrogen pick-up by fuel or pressure tube is technologically unacceptable. In fact, one can say, as a rough generalization, that the higher the oxidation rate the lower the percentage corrosion hydrogen pick-up, so that to a rough approximation the two effects tend to balance one another out. To take a specific example, the corrosion rates on Dresden Zircaloy-2 fuel appear to be high, but the percentage hydrogen pick-up is stated to be only about 8%. If we take the case of a 0.2 in. wall Zircaloy-2 pressure tube operating at 100% load factor for 30 years with a corrosion rate of 1 mdd (which is pessimistic) and the above percentage hydrogen pick-up, this gives a total of 300 ppm of hydrogen from the water side. To this one should add, say, 100 ppm picked up from the gas vault side, giving a total of 400 ppm hydrogen at the end of life, which should be acceptable.

33. In relation to the question on primary circuit crud levels, we must first put the record straight in relation to the steady state crud levels in the SGHWR; these are not high, but only on average between 40 and 60 ppb. This, however, is not the main point in relation to a comparison of the likely deposition rates on fuel in a system with stainless steel and mild steel primary circuits. The total crud inventory derived from the primary circuit by virtue of its own corrosion is very small in comparison with the amount of corrosion material derived from the feed train - perhaps of the order of only 1%. This is because the primary circuit operates for most of the time at $285^{o}C$ and protective films are built up so that the corrosion rate falls off very sharply with time (about $t^{\frac{1}{2}}$); on the other hand, the feed train operates at lower temperatures where linear corrosion rates are observed, and these, coupled with the very large flow volumes (approximately 10^{6} lb/h) produce very large inventories of corrosion products, which are continually fed into the primary circuit. The use of mild steel in the primary circuit instead of stainless steel is therefore believed to make very little difference to the total crud inventory of the system.

PAPER 10

Mr P.G. Boiron, GAAA, France

34. One consequence of the failure of a pressure tube is certainly a pressure and temperature rise in the reactor vessel or calandria. Tests have been made by Euratom at Ispra on a full-scale mock-up of the ESSOR reactor core, with a view to determining the consequences of such an accident on the other components of the core. These tests have been of great interest to my company in relation to the larger organic cooled reactors such as the

ORGEL prototype which we are at present studying. What would be the consequences of such an accident for the reactor vessel and the shutdown tubes in the case of the SGHWR?

Major L. Cave, Atomic Power Constructions Ltd

35. In his opening address, Mr Booth emphasized that to be favourably received in the UK, the SGHWR would have to be shown to be at least as suitable for urban siting as an AGR in a concrete pressure vessel. The only meaningful way in which safety can be assessed in a comparative fashion is by a quantitative approach based on a probability analysis of both systems.

36. The need for an effective comparative method of analysis is also emphasized in Paper 3 in the comments on the desirability of pushing fuel rating to its limit. In general, increased ratings lead to reduced safety margins, and if there are four or five systems competing one with another, the pressure on licensing authorities to accept smaller and smaller safety margins could become intolerable unless an effective method of quantitative assessment can be developed.

37. I am disappointed therefore that the safety assessment of SGHWRs on a probability basis would appear to be proceeding so slowly. Might I suggest that the engineers concerned might make more use of an abbreviated method developed by my company? Its application to heavy water pressure reactor systems was illustrated in a paper at the Vienna symposium in September, 1967.

Mr P. Verstraete, Bonnard and Gardel, Switzerland

38. Would there by any limitation on the use of vented containment for a SGHWR plant of several hundred megawatts if one were to be built in the UK, where the concept is well known and has been approved. Possible limitations would be power on site rating. If there is no such limitation, why has vented containment not been retained for commercial designs?

Authors' reply: Paper 10

39. The answer to Mr Boiron's question on the consequences of a break in the pressure tubes is contained in the reply to an earlier question. Because pressure in the calandria is relieved, there will be no effect on the shutdown tubes.

40. We are certainly in agreement with Major Cave about the need for a method of comparing the safety of different types of reactor. However, he is, perhaps under a misapprehension about the actual position, and the speed with which a probability analysis of the SGHWR is proceeding. The safety of the larger reactors being designed at present is being assessed on a probability basis. A great deal of data

are at present being collected and safety analyses are, in fact, having their impact on the detailed design.

41. There seems to be no technical limitation in provided vented containment for SGHWR nuclear power stations as suggested by Mr Verstraete. However, as mentioned later in Paper 17, vented containment requires that the reactor containment and turbine building be designed as a whole, the latter being an essential part of the containment system. It therefore does not lend itself to stations in which the nuclear steam supply or reactor island is provided separately from the rest of the station.

42. Since the design of vented containment is governed by the rate of energy release from the circuit under accident conditions, careful attention has to be given to the maximum size of components, and this could place some limitation on economic design for stations of over about 600 MWe.

PAPER 11

Dr F. Accinni, CISE, Italy

43. I would like to ask why the wire scanning technique for flux mapping at power was preferred to the use of self-powered detectors. Was there any particular reason?

Major L. Cave, Atomic Power Construction Ltd

44. In the chronicle of the commissioning phase some events seem rather curiously timed, particularly the completion and final testing of the safety circuits after fuel loading. Possibly this timing was dictated by programme considerations, rather than being regarded as an ideal arrangement, but it would be helpful if the Authors could comment.

Mr W. Kirtley, Central Electricity Generating Board

45. The Authors make only brief reference to the commissioning of plant control systems. Could they explain what commissioning techniques were used, and also their usefulness in the light of experience?

Mr A. Forbes Gower, Central Electricity Generating Board

46. In para. 50 flow starvation of up to 20% at low flow due to header effects is mentioned. Clearly the CEGB is going to be very concerned about operation on spinning reserve at low power. Has low power operation at higher coolant flow rates been considered? For example, losing vacuum on the condenser would raise reactor temperature and thereby reduce the temperature rise across the reactor. With moisture traps in nearly every row of the turbine (as at Brown's Ferry) it might be

possible to reduce steam temperatures.

47. If there is any significant flow mismatching at low power, how confident are you that on raising power at the remarkably high rates suggested there will not be burn-out of some of the low flow channels?

Dr G. Peterlongo, CISE, Italy

48. Could the Authors give more details of the primary circulation tests to determine cavitation limits, for example a description of the tests, the limits as measured and predicted, and the effect of cavitation (total or partial loss of flow in the reactor)?

49. Which of the two systems for the measurement of power distribution, quality meters or flux scanning, is, in their experience the more accurate and reliable?

Authors' reply: Paper 11

50. In reply to Dr Accinni's question, at the time that the flux scanning method was chosen it was decided that wires would be cheaper and more reliable than self-powered detectors. However, a study of the performance of self-powered detectors is being carried out and two have been installed in the core. These are small enough to be mounted within a thimble in the control support tube of the fuel clusters and their installation does not involve penetration of the primary circuit pressure containment.

51. Major Cave queries the timing of part of the commissioning phase. For fuel loading and zero power testing, only a restricted number of the safety circuit inputs, i.e., trip parameters, were required. In addition whilst the nuclear shutdown trip actions were required, certain of the trip actions associated with power operation on a turbine trip, for example, steam dumping to the turbine condenser, were not essential. Programme considerations determined the installation of a number of these trip input parameters and output actions should be completed after the zero power testing, and a final full safety circuit check-out was carried out immediately prior to power raising. This approach did not constitute a relaxation of safety standards at any stage; in fact, additional nucleonic trip equipment was installed for the zero power phase of operation.

52. Mr Kirtley has asked for further information on the plant control systems. The simple control loops containing single controllers were commissioned by the usual techniques, and these remarks are therefore confined to the more complicated controls on pressure, power and drum level. The values of gain and time constant required were defined in the design study stage and confirmed by operation on the training simulator. Tests on the equipment at the manufacturer's works included gain and transfer function checks.

53. Once the control systems were installed, a PACE desk-top analogue computer was patched to close the feed-back loop of an individual control by a simplified simulation of the part of the plant to be controlled. This was of great value in several respects. It ensured that the entire system was tested completely long before it would otherwise have been possible. This complete live test ensured that all the local loops were correctly set up, that polarities were correct, etc. Finally, although the simple simulation precluded too much emphasis being placed on the control behaviour during the test, it was very informative and revealed unexpected characteristics in the components of the control early enough for these to be studied and, if necessary, changed. The design study values modified by these preliminary control results were used on the plant during the initial run-up to power and proved to be mostly correct.

54. The plant behaviour can be classified into two broad categories, steady state including response to small perturbations and the response to large transients such as turbine throw-off. All of these have been studied on the simulator and are now being tested on the plant to compare with and improve the dynamic model. With this achieved, it will then be possible to continue investigation on the simulation and restrict the testing on the plant. Limited perturbations have been applied, mainly by altering the demanded setting when in autocontrol. The responses have been used to determine the optimum setting of the autocontrols and have also yielded useful information on the plant dynamic behaviour.

55. Mr Forbes Gower has expressed concern about flow starvation. The reduction in coolant flow in a few channels fed by the outermost sub-headers was only significant at zero power; as power was raised and voidage developed the proportion of the total flow in these channels increased. The particular channels in question are on the edge of the core and their powers are much lower than those of the peak rated channels in the centre of the core. For this reason their dryout margin is higher than the average for the core over the whole range of reactor power, and there are no problems associated with flow starvation at any power level. The rates of power raising mentioned do not effect this conclusion.

56. Regarding the use of the SGHWR as a spinning reserve, it has been demonstrated that the prototype can operate over a very wide range of power with substantially constant coolant flow, circuit temperature and pressure. The autocontrol system ensures that increased steam demand is met by increase in reactivity, while pressure is maintained constant. There is, therefore, no requirement for the procedures suggested by Mr Forbes Gower.

57. Tests of the primary circulation pump flow cavitation limits of which Dr Peterlongo wishes more details, were made during the zero energy phases of reactor commissioning at different coolant temperatures. They confirmed our predictions, based on NPSH data supplied by the pump makers, Hayward Tyler Ltd. The method used was to record the pressure rise across the pump as the flow was progressively increased until a point was reached at which a fall-off of pressure was observed. This point was established by comparison with a previously established non-cavitating pump characteristic. The fall-off of pressure with flow beyond the cavitation limit was fairly rapid and the tests were not continued far beyond this point.

58. When operating at power, the sub-cooling provided by the feed-water flow to the drum is sufficient to ensure that the pumps are operating well clear of their cavitation limit.

59. The accuracy of channel power measurement by means of inlet Venturi meters and outlet quality meters is estimated to be about 5 or 6% (one standard deviation) for a mean channel power of 3 MW. Power measurement with higher power is more accurate because of the higher steam quality at exit. So far only a limited number of wire scans have been made at full power and an analysis of these in relation to the quality meter values is being carried out. It is estimated that the accuracy for relative channel powers is at least as good as that of the quality meters. The quality meters which are monitored immediately by the data reduction equipment, have important operational advantages over flux wire scanning at power, which requires the use of a special facility for loading and removing wires, involving rotation of the charge machine and time-consuming counting procedures.

Economic heavy water power reactors

W. BENNETT LEWIS, CC, CBE, FRS.

Senior Vice President (Science), Atomic Energy of Canada Ltd.

SYNOPSIS   Groups in Canada and India have already set themselves to large programmes of heavy water power reactors of Canadian design and a similar reactor is under construction in Pakistan.   Standard low cost natural uranium fuel with established irradiation performance that operates in either vertical or horizontal channels is used.   It is now possible to design natural uranium reactors using boiling light water instead of pressurized heavy water as coolant and a 250 MWe prototype is scheduled to start up in 1971. Flexibility and low cost of fuelling promises that these lines of heavy water moderated, neutron economical reactors can remain competitive for supplying large blocks of power into the indefinite future.

STATUS

1.   The present status of Heavy Water Power Reactors of Canadian design is that they have been adopted by utilities as economically competitive with any other reactor type or other available source of electricity in large sizes.   The total generating capacity so far committed exceeds 3000 MWe and a further commitment of another 3000 MWe is now being considered.   It is recognized that the selection of any reactor type by a utility in one set of circumstances gives little assurance that a similar choice would be made elsewhere.   Hitherto there have been very few open competitive international assessments for any nuclear power reactors and none yet for large generating stations of 1000 MWe or more for which the heavy water reactor shows to best advantage.   In the only two international situations where heavy water reactors have been offered and considered, the Canadian reactors have held a position among the first three and have shown the lowest prospective lifetime cost of power. Excluding such situations where no decision has been made, the present status of the Heavy Water Power Reactors of Canadian design is summarized in Table 1.

FUELLING

2.   It is characteristic of these natural uranium heavy water reactors that the cost of the complete fuel charge is relatively low, typically 200 kg/MWe at $40 to $60/kg or $8 to $12/kWe (ref. 1).   Moreover with the high burn-up of 9 MWd/kgU or 65 eMWh/kgU the fuel supply cost at equilibrium is 40/65 $/MWh or mill/kWh, that is 0.62 mill/kWh or 0.062 d/unit with the devalued penny.

3.   This low fuelling cost has been achieved not by accident but by a unique programme of development for commercial production.   At the symposium on heavy water power reactors convened by the International Atomic Energy Agency last September in Vienna, it was lamented by some speakers from other countries that no standard fuel had been established for their reactor designs.   We see no reason why the Canadian standard fuel should not be adopted and indeed many reasons why it should be.   Even in international reactor bids Canada has offered to include a complete plant for fuel fabrication from UO_2 to finished fuel together with specifications for less than a million dollars and any desired training on reasonable terms.   This makes a great deal of sense if some inappropriate ideas about international marketing as distinct from trade are abandoned.   So far India has adopted such a programme and will fabricate fuel for the RAPP reactors.   By deliberate Canadian policy two competing commercial manufacturers of this fuel have been established in Canada (ref. 2).   As the demand grows the unit cost of fabrication will fall.   The price of natural uranium may rise but that can be met in other ways as will be discussed later.   International sales of uranium and fabricated fuel have to meet conditions imposed by the political need for assurances and safeguards against diversion to nuclear weapons.

4.   It might be imagined that because the heavy water natural uranium fuelling costs are so low, there would be little advantage in striving for the lowest cost. This view overlooks the expectation that heavy water reactors will not be displaced by breeder reactors or any others, even when the use of nuclear energy becomes far more extensive than any harnessed energy in the world to date.   This wider use will only be accepted if fuelling costs are pushed even lower.   This prospect has been foreseen in Canada for many years and the

Table 1
Canadian Natural Uranium Heavy Water Power Reactors in operation, under construction or committed

Utility	Type	Power MWe net	Name or location	Nuclear design engineers	Date of first power
Ontario Hydro	PHW*	22	NPD Rolphton	AECL and CGE	June 1962
Ontario Hydro	PHW	203	Douglas Point	AECL	Jan. 1967
Karachi Electric Supply Corp. W. Pakistan	PHW	125	KANUPP	CGE	1970
DAE India	PHW	200	RAPP I	AECL and DAE	1969
Ontario Hydro	PHW	508	Pickering I	AECL and HEPC	1970
Hydro Quebec	BLW	250	Gentilly	AECL	1971
Ontario Hydro	PHW	508	Pickering II	AECL and HEPC	1971
DAE India	PHW	200	RAPP II	AECL and DAE	1972
Ontario Hydro	PHW	508	Pickering III	AECL and HEPC	1972
Ontario Hydro	PHW	508	Pickering IV	AECL and HEPC	1973
	Total	3032 MWe			

*To be converted to BHW in 1968

AECL   =   Atomic Energy of Canada Limited
CGE   =   Canadian General Electric
HEPC   =   Hydro Electric Power Commission of Ontario (Ontario Hydro)
DAE   =   Department of Atomic Energy, India
NPD   =   Nuclear Power Demonstration
RAPP   =   Rajasthan Atomic Power Project
KANUPP   =   Karachi Nuclear Power Project

Types: PHW   =   Pressurized Heavy Water coolant
BHW   =   Boiling Heavy Water coolant
BLW   =   Boiling Light Water coolant

fuel development programme and studies have been directed to its realization. It is well known that the irradiation testing of fuel to establish good performance is very costly. By choosing to design the standard fuel in relatively short bundles that can be easily handled, the number of tests that could be undertaken was increased. All this development testing has been carried out at AECL expense and made available to both manufacturers, who were co-operating fully in their share of the manufacturing development. The results are now available to others who may adopt this standard fuel.

5. In a paper presented very recently by G.R. Fanjoy of Ontario Hydro he explains their approach is to manage their fuel by letting long term raw material contracts and short term fabrication contracts (ref. 3). All contracts for the first charge fuel for the four Pickering units have been signed and show a total fuel cost of $40.70/kgU (1967 US dollars) for 375 tonnes U. At equilibrium this results in a fuelling cost of 0.63 mill/kWh assigning zero value to spent fuel. The use of plutonium in the spent fuel is under study and 'an equilibrium fuel cycle cost of 0.38 mill/kWh is expected around 1980'. This would result either from sale or re-cycle of plutonium to extend the irradiation of the natural uranium fuel.

6. Still other fuel cycle prospects have been studied and it seems most probable that when fuel reprocessing costs fall due to larger scale operations and when the price of uranium rises, most of the power will be derived from thorium. From each kilogram of uranium mined it is possible on such cycles to derive 40 or 50 MWd as shown in AECL-1916 (1964) and AECL-2274 (1965) (refs 4, 5). Even at a net station efficiency of 30%, which would by then be low for new reactors, the contribution to fuelling cost from uranium would be only $15.6/(7.2 \times 40) = 0.054$ mill/kWh for every $6/lb U_3O_8 ($15.6/kgU) in the price of uranium.

7. The gradual introduction of such cycles involving thorium does not carry any heavy conversion charges. Plain thorium fuel and highly enriched fuel can be intro-duced simultaneously in the small fuel bundles without even shutting down the reactor (ref. 6). The enriched fuel is costly but the thorium fuel is profitable. The total fuel cycle cost is likely to be kept below 0.6 mill/kWh.

OPERATING AND MAINTENANCE

8. Very good experience has been obtained in many countries over many years in the use of heavy water as moderator in experi-mental but quite high power (5 MW to 200 MW thermal) reactors. Little if any more difficulty is anticipated with the heavy water moderator in power reactors. It is true that maintenance operations become more difficult the higher the level of the tritium that builds up in the moderator, but exposure of open surfaces of heavy water of the moderator system need not arise very frequently and this has been the general experience.

9. Much more limited experience exists so far on operations with heavy water systems at high temperatures and pressures. As the systems grow more extensive without corres-ponding increase in trained operators and maintenance technicians, there is clearly a need for improvements in techniques, design and construction. Much is being learnt but it is not possible to apply all the lessons to designs of several years ago that are now in advanced stages of construction. Although it is appreciated that heavy water leaks need not become losses, leaks do impose demands on operators and technicians for a high degree of skill and discipline. They must wear full protective clothing with air masks to avoid absorbing tritiated water or water vapour through the skin or in breathing. It is not easy to work under these conditions, but poor work is likely to lead to further leaks and the need for further repairs. Flanged joints and other mechanical pipe connections, valve stem packings, interfaces with oil or water lubricating and cooling systems have all proved troublesome. Two most important aids have been introduced in the NPD reactor

- the dry vault atmosphere (ref. 7)

- leak detecting tapes (ref. 8).

The first is probably a lastingly sound provision. Large capacity and speedy adsorber driers are kept in operation in any spaces into which heavy water or its vapour can leak. This prevents heavy water condensing and accumulating on cold surfaces or penetrating into imperfectly sealed concrete. It does not, however, cope with large spills or high pressure discharges and for these it seems necessary to confine the spaces where they can more readily occur, such as the reactor faces where the fuelling machines operate.

10. The leak detecting tapes which change colour when water seeps up on their under-side have helped to speed finding the location of leaks, but it would be better to have fewer mechanical joints where leaks can occur.

11. Designers must remember the need to keep the small number of technicians from approaching their limit for exposure to tritium. Special consideration must be given to getting them out of their protec-tive clothing without showering in dry atmosphere regions and without exposing themselves to heavy water contamination on the protective clothing.

12. It is clear from the status described that there is, on the one hand, confidence and a determination to overcome these dif-ficulties and, on the other, the hope and expectation of greatly reducing the diffi-culties by adopting the boiling light water coolant system.

13. This system throws the operating and design problems back to the reactor physicist and the heat transfer engineer. Only a few years ago it was not believed to be practicable to meet the economic competition with a natural uranium fuelled boiling light water cooled system. Two alternative systems were studied. In the United Kingdom, as we have heard, enriched fuel was accepted and an ingenious means of minimizing power-reactivity coefficients was devised by having sufficient light water to contribute to the neutron moderation. The other alternative was to adopt light water fog cooling in which there would be so little light water in the form of drops that the absorption of neutrons would be minimized and hence the power coefficient and the need for enrichment. Another line, however, appeared that is being followed in the CANDU-BLW design. It is not a pure line but has four contributing features

   - increased uranium inventory

   - high feedwater temperature

   - several separate coolant loops

   - thin high strength pressure tubes.

The first two have the result that the total reactivity held by the coolant is kept low so that even if the channels were to void the reactivity rise would be well within the capacity of the several shut-down mechanisms. The object of the separate coolant loops is similarly to reduce any likely rate of rise of reactivity.

14. The first and last also have a common objective to keep the attainable burn-up of natural uranium so high, despite the neutron absorption by the coolant, that the fuelling cost is competitive.

15. There are many other important design features in the BLW such as the orificing of the channel inputs to curb any hydraulic instabilities due to the boiling. There are also improvements in fabrication and assembly techniques. For all these features reference may be made to several published descriptions (ref. 9).

16. The reactor under construction at Gentilly for Hydro Quebec is described as a 250 MWe prototype. It should be large enough to reveal all the points of over-design and discriminate between the precautions that are essential and those that are not necessary. The degree of input orificing of the channels would be a case in point. The attainable exit steam quality is another. There are also complexities provided in the control system that may prove unnecessary. Although some design work is in progress for higher power reactors of this type, it is not expected that our programme would involve a commitment to construct such large reactors before 1972 when there would be at least some operating experience.

17. In view of the very large scale of future operations my personal assessment is that far too little development work is being done throughout the world, including Canada. The result is that design decisions made for the early plants become frozen into the system because the features concerned are the only ones supported by experience. I am not advocating that every possible line should be explored for that would exclude the economies to be achieved by repetitive construction, but there is a wide range of middle ground. I am sorry to see the organic liquid coolant receiving so little support. With the limited effort made available in Canada, we had to drop it to very low priority on our programme but were encouraged that the United States and Euratom were at that time promising vigorous development. Our experimental 20 to 40 MW thermal reactor WR-1 at Whiteshell, Manitoba, is cooled by organic liquid and operates very successfully with the coolant close to 400°C (750°F), a temperature high enough to raise steam at high pressure, and much above the 290°C (550°F) temperatures that are optimum for the water cooled reactors (ref. 10). This type of reactor would share many of the advantages of the BLW and promises to be quite competitive assuming satisfactory materials development. We are now even more confident that the materials will prove reliable. The tricks necessary to control the hydriding of zirconium alloys and the deposition of fouling films have proved very successful.

18. The eventual heavy water moderated organic cooled power reactor was envisaged as attaining a net station efficiency of 40% or higher by combination with nuclear reheat of the steam (ref. 11). Nuclear superheat, when developed, could be applied to other neutron economical heavy water reactors. Some long range prospects are being explored in the research programme at Whiteshell. What is being sought is a fuel cladding of sufficient but not excessively long life with a low neutron absorption to operate at temperatures of 650°C or higher. We would like to see some competitive co-operation in this for our funding is limited.

19. Since the 1964 Geneva conference there has been a tendency to suggest that since economic nuclear power has now arrived, further development can be left to industry. This takes far too narrow a view of what we may expect the benefits of really low cost power to be and also shows no realistic understanding of the ways of industry. Take, for example, the development of zirconium alloys; those we have are good, but not likely to be near the best attainable. Since 1964 it has become progressively more difficult to secure the interest of industry in such development. The order books are full, the extrusion presses are busy, the experts are busy, and any development represents an interruption and loss of

immediately profitable work. Some of our own development effort has been diverted to assisting new manufacturing capacity to be set up in Canada.

20. Even with these difficulties, the developments achieved have been most significant. One question about the heavy water reactors is the expected life of the pressure tubes. We have designed on the basis that it must be practicable to change pressure tubes at any time. The life of the reactor is arbitrarily set at 30 years and although a 30 year life for the pressure tubes could be hoped for, we decided to face the prospect of changing tubes after 15 years. At first it was thought that the limit of life might be set by hydriding due to hydrogen picked up in the steady corrosion. We now know a lot about the control and effects of hydriding and although it needs attention there seems no cause for concern. On the other hand, only a few years ago it was found that the rate of expansion of the tubes by creep was considerably enhanced by fast neutron bombardment from the fuel. Extremely elegant studies of this have been made by precision gauging of actual pressure tubes, and special experimental tubes of stepped wall thicknesses irradiated in the experimental reactors (ref. 12). As a result, we now know that the cold working of pressure tubes enhances the radiation induced creep. The experiments call for extreme care and even when the results are precisely known there is a problem of extrapolation to fifteen or thirty years in a power reactor. We now forecast that a new heat treatment Zr-2.5%Nb alloy will have a much better performance than the cold worked zircaloy-2 used in the NPD and Douglas Point reactors. We still have reason to hope for 15 years of life of the Douglas Point tubes but thirty years seems not so likely for all the tubes.

21. On the practical side, pressure tubes have been changed both in NPD and Douglas Point, for reasons other than any suspicion of their failure. The operations were successful and confidence has been established that even changing all the tubes would not be economically impracticable, but there is little likelihood that the outer tubes would need changing. It is hoped that when any change becomes necessary our knowledge will have improved so that still better tubes can be installed with a very long life expectancy.

22. The major objectives of development are reduction in capital and operating costs. Both lead attention towards simplicity. Although the double ended symmetrical horizontal fuel channel design was adopted in the first place by the mechanical designers for simplicity, most economic studies have shown that the large floor area that results is relatively costly. Adopting a vertical structure and fuelling only from one end has been a prime feature of cost reduction in the design of BLW and in the CGE 'Venture' design for PHW (ref. 13). It makes possible the prefabrication of fuel channel joints, so that

the complete assembly may be inserted or removed from one end and connection made at the other by a relatively simple mechanical joint that has no other special function.

23. This is not the place to detail the many other design changes. One more may be mentioned. Very many heavy water leaks have been experienced at NPD at mechanical joints in auxiliary piping for differential pressure gauge lines and for coolant radio-activity monitoring for ruptured fuel. Means of measuring coolant flow and of locating ruptured fuel that do not require such auxiliary piping are being studied. One quite new principle for activity monitoring is promising and is being tested in NPD (ref. 14). A trap that consists of an extended surface of nickel, monel or stainless steel is installed in the feeder line of each channel. Escaping fission products are found to be adsorbed on these traps and it is possible to identify and obtain a usable measure of the deposited activity from Mo-99 and Te-132 in particular by means of a lithium drifted germanium gamma-ray spectrometer.

24. Again taking a broad view of the development required, we may note that the scale of effort to be devoted to the construction of nuclear power stations will rise over the next twenty years to a level for which there is no close precedent anywhere in industry. The rate of rise of power demand still far exceeds the rate of growth of Gross National Product. The individual nuclear power stations are enormous engineering projects requiring organization and training and in which a failure of any component or worker can have very costly results. Typically, industry is plunging into this competitively, which may be good, basing their methods on past experience, which is inadequate. What is needed is more co-operation not less, and greater development and dissemination of the basic knowledge.

25. Heavy water reactors are not alone in this predicament of needing more development. Those concerned may look with some jealousy at the much larger development efforts devoted to fast reactors, that seem to face greater problems even to gain a foothold in the economic world. It is my belief that the heavy water reactors will carry the burden of providing the bulk of the power needed when the scale of operations grows large and the price of uranium rises.

FUTURE PROSPECT

26. The fuelling cost in prospect for heavy water power reactors designed in the first instance to use natural uranium will be kept low by the gradual introduction of thorium. The important characteristics of thorium are that it is not only a cheap and efficient means of converting neutrons to energy but its residue contains about 15 g - U-233 per kgTh, the value of which greatly exceeds the initial cost of the fabricated thorium fuel. The provision of

the necessary neutrons at the lowest cost is a challenge to the nuclear physicists and engineers. By keeping the neutron wastage in the reactor low, the use of natural uranium to produce plutonium is practicable and may well compete with the extraction of U-235. It is perhaps unkind of nature that thorium should be a cheaper fuel material than U-238 but U-238 is given the benefit of a fissile isotope present in limited amount while thorium has none until it is irradiated.

27. Capital costs of heavy water reactors should certainly fall, especially if more design teams were formed and given the opportunity to build more generating plants in parallel, while enjoying free access to the basic knowledge being built up by a greater number of development organizations.

REFERENCES

1. PON G.A., LEWIS W.B., HAYWOOD L.R., PRIMEAU D.B., PHILLIPS G.J. and MERLO E.E. Prospective D$_2$O-moderated power reactors. AECL-2010. Paper p/10, vol.5, p.333, Proceedings 3rd U.N. International Conference on the Peaceful Uses of Atomic Energy, Geneva 1964
and
HAYWOOD L.R. and AIKEN A.M. Costs and economics of heavy water moderated nuclear plants. AECL-2946, SM99/36, IAEA Symposium on Heavy Water Power Reactors, Vienna, September 1967.

2. Canadian General Electric Co., Peterborough, Ontario. Canadian Westinghouse Company, Port Hope, Ontario.

3. FANJOY G.R. Nuclear fuel management-Ontario Hydro. IAEA Symposium on Economics of Nuclear Fuels, Czechoslovakia, 1968.

4. LEWIS W.B. How much of the rocks and the oceans for power? Exploiting the uranium-thorium fission cycle. DM-72, AECL-1916, April 1964.

5. LEWIS W.B. Heavy water reactor review and prospect. DL-67, AECL-2274, July 1965.

6. See ref. 1. Also LEWIS W.B. Outlook for heavy water reactors. AECL-2947, SM99/37. IAEA Symposium on Heavy Water Power Reactors, Vienna, September 1967
and
LEWIS W.B. Prospect for heavy water reactors. DL-83. Address at 25th Anniversary of First Nuclear Chain Reaction. University of Chicago. 2nd December, 1967.

7. HORTON E.P. NPD operating experience. SM99/27. IAEA Symposium on Heavy Water Power Reactors, Vienna, September 1967.

8. DOMBRA A.H. Location of heavy water leaks in Canadian power reactors. AECL-2755, October 1967.

9. PON G.A. and BOUCHER G.R. Gentilly Nuclear Power Station, Paper 5, AECL-2486. The 11th AECL Symposium on Atomic Power, October 1966
and
PON G.A. CANDU-BLW-250. AECL-2942, SM99/32. IAEA Symposium on Heavy Water Power Reactors, Vienna, September 1967.

10. MOORADIAN A.J., ROBERTSON R.F.S., HATCHER S.R., HART R.G., TEGARD D.R. and SUMMACH A.J. Current status of Canadian organic cooled reactor technology. AECL-2943, SM99/33, IAEA Symposium on Heavy Water Power Reactors, Vienna, September 1967.

11. LEWIS W.B. Designing heavy water reactors for neutron economy and thermal efficiency. DL-42, AECL-1163, Proceedings p.10, Symposium on Nuclear Power, D.A.E. India, Bombay, January 1961.

12. ROSS-ROSS P.A. and HUNT C.E.L. The in-reactor creep of cold worked zircaloy-2 and Zr-2.5% Nb pressure tubes. J. Nucl. Matls., March 1968.

13. WILLIAMS N.L. Design details of the GCE vertical heavy-water pressure tube reactor and some factors influencing the design. DM99/31, IAEA Symposium on Heavy Water Power Reactors, Vienna, September 1967.

14. LIPSETT J.J. and PALMER J.F. Locating fuel failures by fission product deposition in CANDU-PHW reactors. AECL-2786, IAEA Panel on Failed Fuel Element Detection, Vienna, November 1967.

Prospects of water cooling in heavy water moderated reactors

P. J. FONTERAY, Ing.Ec.Nav., Department of Pile Studies, CEA, France

S. GOLDSTEIN, Department of Pile Studies, CEA

R. NAUDET, Ing.Ec.Poly., Department of Pile Studies, CEA

SYNOPSIS   Among the various possibilities existing for heavy water moderated reactors, water cooling has the great advantage of being applied to a quite well developed and proven fuel. Moreover, a better use of the fuel can be obtained by using heavy water as coolant instead of light water, and disadvantages such as those related to stability are avoided. This is the reason why these reactors have been developed first.

Actually two concepts are being developed, according to whether the pressure is withstood by tubes or by a vessel enclosing the whole reactor, and sometimes the whole primary system. An analysis of advantages and disadvantages of these two solutions is made, taking into account the status of the art of the technological works proper to each one.

Boiling light water cooling has a number of advantages, among which avoiding treatment of hot and pressurized heavy water. From the construction standpoint, it could be considered as a direct continuation of the pressure tube solution. Even if as a first step, heavy water cooling is preferred, boiling light water cooling must be considered when a choice is made between the two constructive solutions.

The use of light water requires a compromise between neutron balance, general performances of the system and difficulties related to heat transfer and control problems. Characteristics are proposed and discussed, from the standpoint of continuity with respect to heavy water cooling.

INTRODUCTION

1.   The versatility of heavy water reactors is well known, and it is often quoted that almost all conceivable coolants have been proposed. In France, the Commissariat à l'Energie Atomique concentrated its development programme on CO_2 cooling, somehow by continuity from graphite reactors, in 1959, and decided the construction of the prototype EL 4 (70 MWe) in 1962. The plant delivered power through the grid on the 9th July, 1967.

2.   No major difficulty was met during the construction, and operation of the reactor itself, so far, has been satisfactory (refs 1, 2, 3). At the beginning of the year, failures appeared in heat exchangers, resulting in a lowering of the power; but it is to be noted that the damaged exchangers are of an entirely new type, and that the observed failures are not related to the use of heavy water as a moderator.

3.   The present fuel is made of stainless steel clad uranium oxide, but low absorbing can materials have been developed. Six channels of the reactor are loaded with zirconium-copper clad bundles, and their number will be progressively increased during the next two years, since irradia-

tion tests made in Pegase, at Cadarache, evidence a satisfactory behaviour. Moreover, an economic study has shown that, for a large reactor, the fuelling cost should be quite acceptable.

4.   Gas cooling, therefore, is a viable concept. Engineering studies have been made for large size reactors, and EL 4 will be a very useful irradiation facility in order to develop and test fuels (ref. 4). Nevertheless, it is clear that from the fuel standpoint, this concept is not in a so propitious position as water cooling. Zircaloy clad uranium oxide has been extensively developed; it is now a thoroughly proven fuel, and it can be produced at low cost. The commercial success of the light water reactors will emphasize this advantage. For the sake of realism, we must face this situation.

5.   Now, water cooling involves either heavy or light water. The use of heavy water leads to a better neutron balance and a lower fuel cost, and avoids a number of difficulties such as those related to the existence of a large positive void coefficient. As a matter of fact, in the case of light water cooling, if a very low enrichment of the fuel is searched for, many problems have to be solved, and the experience of a prototype is needed. This is the reason why the heavy water cooled

reactors have been developed first. But undoubtedly, removing that expensive and tritiated fluid from the primary circuit, and turning to direct cycle is an attractive feature.

6.   Thus, even though heavy water cooling is preferred, as a first step, light water cooling represents a potential improvement. This idea must be kept in mind if we have to select a design. This is the point we would like to develop further.

HEAVY WATER COOLING

7.   Two designs are being developed, according to whether the pressure is withstood by tubes or by a vessel.

Pressure vessel

8.   In this concept, the lay-out is more simple than in the case of pressure tubes; the neutron economy is about the same; the energy released in the moderator can be entirely recovered.

9.   But the present possibilities for the manufacture of steel vessels seem to limit the reactor output to about 300 MWe, for a plant operating with an indirect cycle. Beyond this power, pre-stressed concrete would be necessary.

10.   In this case, the development of a leak-proof medium thermally insulated from the concrete, with many through-tubes (control rods, secondary cooling system) is a technically difficult problem. Several solutions can be considered:

- the heavy water can be insulated by a gas gap maintained in a metal structure to avoid convection; a system for pressure balance must be provided and designed to compensate the transient variations without an external control;

- the vessel liner can be covered with a metal structure maintaining a stagnant water gap;

- a special concrete can be installed behind the vessel liner, which is thus at the temperature of the inner medium (300°C). Great thermal stresses cannot then be avoided.

11.   Presently, as far as we know, none of these solutions has been satisfactorily demonstrated, even at small scale. Developmental work, of long duration and of a large extent, would be required.

12.   On the other hand, the vessel design favours the integration of the fuelling machine, in order to lessen the heavy water leaks, and anyway, in a concrete vessel, it is not possible to have as many holes as fuel channels. The problem is then to develop devices operating in steam at 300°C. At present, no reliable design can be warranted.

13.   Lastly, the access, for maintenance, to the inner structures of the vessel raises difficult problems.

14.   Thus, the extrapolation of the pressure vessel design towards large size reactors still needs important development works (ref. 5).

Pressure tubes

15.   On the contrary, this design does not seem any longer to raise serious problems. It has passed beyond the prototype stage, and is well fitted to the search for high unitary powers. Indeed, the channels, their end fittings and feeding pipes, are modular components which will be almost identical, whatever the reactor size; these components can be wholly studied on smaller reactors.

16.   The only source of concern is the creep behaviour of a pressure tube under irradiation and at high temperatures. It would always be possible, if there is any doubt, to decrease the tube temperature by insulating the inner side. This solution, used in EL 4, is suitable to water cooling, although it leads to a mechanical arrangement a little more complex.

17.   Incidently, as far as the French experience is concerned, the essentials of the required technology for pressure tube reactors have been developed for the construction of EL 4: Zircaloy pressure tubes, metallurgical joints, vessel with many holes, remote welding, and so on.

18.   Thus, although the steel pressure vessel may be a good solution for small size reactors, and although pre-stressed concrete vessels may have good prospects for future, we think that the pressure tubes concept is in a better position from the industrial standpoint.

19.   At this point of the discussion comes the comment we made above. Light water cooling requires pressure tubes; if we think that this concept is really promising, and if there is a possible engineering continuity, we have another reason to prefer this design.

LIGHT WATER COOLING

20.   In order to preserve the neutron balance, the coolant cross section area must be a minimum and the steam quality not too low; this raises mechanical and heat transfer problems. On the other hand, a positive void coefficient cannot be prevented, whence three difficulties:

- control devices with high dynamic and mechanical performances are required. The response must be fast, and the usual noise of the reactor might result in almost permanent rod oscillations;

- even though spatial instabilities due only to void can be prevented, xenon instabilities are increased;

- the rupture of a feed pipe, through draining of cooling channels, would induce a large amount of reactivity. The system should have to be divided in several loops, so that this reactivity could never reach prompt criticality.

21. The void coefficient can be lessened by undermoderation, but once again the neutron balance is affected. A compromise must therefore be made, between two ultimate positions:

- either a safe operation is emphasized, then fairly enriched uranium must be used: this is the British solution for SGHWR;

- or a good neutron balance is emphasized, retaining the use of natural uranium, then some performances are to be lowered, and possible risks must be accepted: this is the Canadian solution.

22. An intermediate position, with a very slight uranium enrichment, seems to be eventually attractive. It happens to be the solution where one is readily led to, when one attempts to transpose as directly as possible the characteristics of a heavy water cooled reactor.

Study of a reference case

23. Let us consider the Canadian reactors of the CANDU-PWR type presently being built at Pickering. The Canadian General Electric has proposed a vertical version for these reactors, with the same channel and the same fuel (ref. 6). Let us see what would happen if pressurized heavy water was replaced by boiling light water in the channel.

24. It is recalled that the fuel is made of 28-rod bundles (UO_2 pellet diameter: 14.2 mm), Zircaloy clad, in a tube of 103.5 mm ID.

25. No difficulty seems to be expected from heat transfer for the same power (maximum conductivity integral ~ 42 W/cm), provided that the exit quality is low enough ($< 15\%$).

26. For neutron calculations, core parameters have been modified on the following features only:

- cladding thickness brought up to 0.6 mm (more severe corrosion problems);

- pressure tube thickness brought down to 3.2 mm (operating pressure changed from 100 to 65 bars);

- channel height limited to 5 m;

- smaller lattice pitch: two values have been considered: 26 and 24 cm (hexagonal lattice).

27. The average burn-up in steady operation and the initial void coefficient have been studied as a function of lattice pitch and uranium enrichment.

28. Computations with the CRUEL code, after readjustment on the experimental results obtained in ZED-2 for the same 28-rod bundles, gave the following results:

(a) Average burn-up in steady operation (on-power refuelling with good shuffling).

	Pitch: 26 cm	Pitch: 24 cm
Natural U +2 g/kg of U-235	12,660 MWd/t	
Natural U +3 g/kg of U-235	15,850 MWd/t	15,000 MWd/t
Natural U +4 g/kg of U-235	19,000 MWd/t	18,000 MWd/t

Note that the initial reactivity difference from pitch 26 cm to pitch 24 cm for an enrichment of 3 g/kg is 16.6 mk; if that difference was due to poisoning, the decrease of average burn-up would be about 1700 MWd/t. Actually, it is only half of this value: this is because the reactivity loss is due mainly to the factor p, and there is therefore an improvement in plutonium conversion. In other words, a fairly high burn-up leads to a smaller penalty of undermoderation.

(b) Total void coefficient ($\times 10^{-3}$) for the fresh core:

$$\frac{k_{eff}(\rho) - k_{eff}(1)}{k_{eff}(1)} \text{ for } \rho = 0,$$

ρ being the relative coolant density with respect to water at the same temperature.

	Pitch: 28 cm	Pitch: 26 cm	Pitch: 24 cm
Natural U +2 g/kg of U-235	90	82.5	64
Natural U +3 g/kg of U-235	85	77	59
Natural U +4 g/kg of U-235	81	73	55

As an indication, the coefficient for pitch 26 cm and an enrichment of 3 g/kg can be split as follows:

$\delta\varepsilon/\varepsilon$	+ 4.8
$\delta\eta/\eta$	+ 2.4
$\delta p/p$	+ 9.2
$\delta f/f$	+68.6
Leakage	- 8.1
$\delta k_{eff}/k_{eff}$	76.9

29. For a $10^{\circ}C$ sub-cooling and an exit steam quality of 15%, if the gradation of densities in the channel is properly taken into account, the reactivity is the same as if the relative density was uniform and equal to 0.42. This figure is smaller than the mean density.

30. If we consider a power rise, assuming that the flow rate, the pressure and the inlet temperature are maintained, we find the following reactivity coefficient (enrichment 3 g/kg):

pitch 26 cm: 0.173 mk/% power

24 cm: 0.122 mk/% power.

Discussion

31. In the case of the Canadian BLW reactor being built at Gentilly, the total void coefficient for the fresh lattice, defined as before, is of the order of 60 mk. In our case, it is therefore sufficient to decrease the pitch below 24 cm to be under more favourable conditions.

32. Now, it can be seen that under-moderation rapidly improves the void co-efficient without affecting the fuel cycle too much. If, for instance, the pitch was brought down to 22 cm, a burn-up of 15,000 MWd/t could still be warranted for a uranium enrichment of about 1.05%, and the total void coefficient could be lowered till about 40 mk. Then, the power coefficient would be about 0.08 mk per percent. of power only, and the reactivity induced by simultaneous draining of all channels from nominal operating conditions less than 20 mk; (thus the reactor safety could be insured in any circumstances with a reasonable number of loops).

33. The fuelling cost under those conditions remains quite low. Let us assume for instance that the natural uranium bundles could be manufactured at $55/kg, and that in a PHW the average burn-up be 9300 MWd/t; the fuelling cost is then 0.83 mill/kWh. If the fuel is enriched to 0.9% in order to bring the burn-up to about 15,000 MWd/t and if the marginal gram of U-235 is evaluated at $12 (with a provision for transport and chemical dissolution), the cost is then lowered for the same reactor to 0.72 mill/kWh. If now we consider a BLW with 1.05% enriched fuel and a 15,000 MWd/t

burn-up, taking the improvement in thermo-dynamic efficiency (from 29.5 to 31.5%) into account, the fuelling cost under the same conditions is 0.83 mill/kWh, i.e., a little more than for the PHW with optimum enrichment, but the same as for this reactor fuelled with natural uranium. We may therefore say that the penalty is in-significant.

34. On the other hand, changing the 28.2 cm square pitch of Pickering into a 22 cm hexagonal pitch results in dividing by a factor 2.25 the amount of D_2O moderator in the cell. Taking the additional saving from the cooling system into account, the heavy water inventory is brought down from 0.7 to 0.25 ton per MWe, thence a saving of 18 $/kWe.

35. Lastly, besides the operating advantages resulting from the removal of tritiated heavy water from the primary system, simplifications and savings are to be expected through direct cycle.

36. For these reasons, if an appropriate control in the presence of a power coef-ficient of the order indicated above can be provided, boiling light water cooling is likely to be beneficial, and there will be surely a large incentive to go this way.

37. We believe that it is very important for a heavy water reactor to retain the advantages of a very good neutron balance, i.e., a low fuelling cost and a good utilization of natural resources. But, in the case of light water cooling, a very slight enrichment has the following advantages:

- the operating conditions can be safer, with a greater margin with respect to burn-out and a smaller void coefficient;

- the performances of the best heavy water cooled reactors can be retained, in particular the mean specific power;

- the general core characteristics of these reactors can be retained, and consequently a minimum of new development work is required.

38. We believe that this is the best line to go along with, when thinking of boiling light water cooling in heavy water reactors.

CONCLUSION

39. Water cooling has the decisive advan-tage of a thoroughly proven, reliable and cheap fuel. The concept using pressurized heavy water in pressure-tubes is at present in the best position from the industrial standpoint, but light water cooling appears undoubtedly as a possible improvement. This is an additional incentive to select the pressure tube design, even though heavy water cooling is preferred for the moment.

40. As far as boiling light water cooling is concerned, the best design requires a

very slight uranium enrichment, consistent
with a low fuelling cost. This option has
the additional advantage of providing the
maximum of continuity from heavy water
cooling.

REFERENCES

1.   CARLE R. et al. Essais de la centrale
EL 4. IAEA Symposium on Heavy Water Power
Reactors, Vienne 11-15 Septembre 1967,
SM 99/52.

2.   GIRRARD Y. et al. Aspects physiques
des essais et de la montée en puissance de
la centrale EL 4. ibid, SM 99/51.

3.   MARTINOT G. Le contrôle commande de
la pile EL 4. ibid, SM 99/50.

4.   FONTERAY J. et al. Etudes sur les
piles à eau lourde refroidies par gaz
carbonique. ibid, SM 99/55.

5.   FONTERAY J. et al. Etude de centrale
à eau lourde refroidie à l'eau lourde
bouillante. ibid, SM 99/54.

6.   WILLIAMS N.L. Design details of the
CGE vertical heavy water pressure tube
reactor and some factors influencing the
design. ibid, SM 99/31.

German contribution to the development of D₂O moderated reactors

Dr Ing. K. F. W. KELLER, Works Director, Siemens AG, Germany

R. A. STUEGER, DipIng, Project Leader, Siemens AG, Germany

SYNOPSIS   This paper traces the work done by the Siemens Company and its associates in the development of reactors fuelled by natural uranium and moderated by heavy water. Both pressure tube and pressure vessel designs have been produced, the tube reactor being cooled by CO_2. The paper describes these reactors and also the 320 MWe power plant of the pressure vessel type that has recently been ordered by the Argentine CNEA. The further development of the D_2O vessel system to larger units involving concrete vessels and integral steam generators is outlined and the possibility of employing a thorium fuel cycle is discussed.

1.   In the last decade the Siemens Company has made some significant contributions towards the development of heavy water natural uranium reactors. Those efforts were rewarded by turn-key orders for two prototype reactors, viz:

- the D_2O cooled pressure vessel reactor MZFR, of a net power of 51 MWe, which became operational at Karlsruhe in December, 1965, and

- the CO_2 cooled pressure tube reactor at Niederaichbach, of 100 MW net, which is scheduled to be commissioned early in 1970.

2.   Quite recently Siemens were awarded a contract for a 320 MWe power station with a heavy water natural uranium reactor of economic size by the Argentine CNEA. The plant will be built on the river Parna and is scheduled to go into operation late in 1972.

THE 50 MW PROTOTYPE (MZFR)

3.   The heavy water pressure vessel reactor MZFR, the prototype of the plant ordered for the Argentine, has been on power since March, 1966 (ref. 1). The reactor went critical in September, 1965 and commenced power production 6 months later. Its gross electrical output is 57 MW. As the heavy water is pressurized the components of the reactor and the circuits do not differ to any large extent from those of light water reactors, except for the geometry of the core, the additional appliances for refuelling under load, a general feature of natural uranium reactors, and the equipment required for reprocessing any D_2O leakage from the system.

4.   After a construction period of exactly 5 years and all the contractual stipula-

tions had been fulfilled the MZFR was handed over to the client in November, 1966. During the commissioning period we had certain difficulties with the pumps, the fuelling machine, the hydraulic system and the fuel channel plugs, but none of these were of such a serious character as to make their solution unreasonably difficult or expensive.

THE MZFR TYPE HEAVY WATER REACTOR OF ECONOMIC SIZE

5.   The experience gained with the MZFR and the most remarkable success of H_2O pressurized water reactors provided a strong inducement to develop the MZFR concept of a natural uranium fuelled D_2O-PWR up to an economic size. This had been achieved when we tendered for the 320 MW Atucha unit in the Argentine last year.

6.   The heart of this plant is the pressure vessel with a diameter of 5.360 m, designed to operate under a pressure of 117 kg/cm². Steel vessels for such extreme requirements have not been made so far, but with the break-through of light water reactors some manufacturers have already provided the facilities for the construction of very large units. In consequence, the steel vessels that can now be fabricated are much larger than ever considered before (Fig. 1). Today's limitations of size are imposed less by manufacturing problems, than by the difficulties connected with the transport of large indivisible loads. A vessel of the size required for a 300 MW reactor will have to be transported by water direct from the factory to the building site. The location of the Atucha power plant, the vessel of which will be manufactured in Europe, will allow this to be done.

7.   When the MZFR core was about to be designed, small fuel rod diameters were chosen, because, for a given moderator to fuel ratio, they will result in a high power density and a small core. Today, the limitations on vessel size are no longer so severe, but, it is the capital investment, particularly due to the heavy water inventory, as well as to some extent to the price of the reactor vessel and the fuel which favour a core of high specific power. The most effective means to achieve this are 37-rod bundle clusters and fuel rods of small diameter.

8.   The production costs of a MZFR type fuel element which also apply to the fuel of the Atucha reactor amount at the present to approximately 55% of the total costs, with the balance of 45% for uranium and Zircaloy. It is thought that a significant reduction in future production costs is possible by rationalized manufacturing methods and standardized test procedures which go hand in hand with increased production capacities. The uranium costs may be assumed to remain constant in the period under review. In the long run it is therefore advisable to choose that fuel element design which will benefit most by the expected production cost reduction.

9.   The core of the Atucha reactor comprises 253 coolant channels generating a thermal power of 1100 MW. Moderator and coolant - both, of course, heavy water - are separated from each other by a container inside the pressure vessel so that the moderator can be given a lower temperature than that of the coolant. By reducing the former to about 180°C the final burn-up attainable can be increased significantly. The possibility of varying this temperature is a valuable means of using the reactor reactivity as a control element during the transition phase of the first core towards equilibrium.

10.   The coolant channels are carried individually through the head of the reactor vessel and are equipped with high pressure closures to which the fuel elements are attached. For refuelling and radial shuffling of fuel elements, which is done under load as in all other natural uranium reactors, a fuel rod cluster consisting of an undivided assembly of fuel rods is exchanged together with its closure. Fig. 2 shows the fuelling machine in the loading position above the reactor core. The design of the fuelling machine is very similar to that of the MZFR, its length corresponding to the increased length of the fuel elements. Apart from a device controlling locally the tightness of the seal between the machine mouth and the coolant channel to receive an immediate signal of leaks and a modified venting appliance no improvements of the design of the MZFR machine have been found necessary.

11.   On their way from the reactor to the cooling pond and vice versa the fuel elements must be dried so as to prevent the mixing of D_2O and H_2O. As an improvement over the MZFR design a drying station of significantly shorter drying periods has been developed, reducing the time for replacement of a fuel element from 9 hours to 5 hours. For the transport of the fuel element to the cooling pond a pivoting H_2O flask is employed to take the fuel element, which rests on a sledge.

12.   Analyses of different loading schemes has revealed that the obtainable gains in reactivity as well as in burn-up are not sufficient to justify axial shuffling of fuel elements. Undivided fuel element clusters, such as those provided, are less expensive. The reduction of the number of shuffling manoeuvres is welcome from the operational point of view.

13.   Arranging the control rod drives above the reactor vessel offers important technical advantages. The design principle, which proved successful with the MZFR, has therefore been retained without alteration. Twenty-nine control and shutdown rods are inserted at an angle into the pressure vessel from its periphery. It has been verified by calculations that undamped local power oscillations cannot occur in the core of the size of a 300 MW reactor, so that the reactor can be kept under control by two rods when operating at full power. While admittedly the inclined arrangement of the control rods reduces somewhat their effectiveness in the lower third of the core, their total reactivity suffices to shut down the reactor safely from any operating condition, and to keep it cold undercritical by at least 2%. The heat generated in the coolant channels is dissipated by two closed primary loops placed symmetrically to the reactor vessel (Fig. 3), each comprising a steam generator of usual design with U-shaped tube bank and a main circulating pump with controlled leakage shaft sealing - the type of design used at the Obrigheim H_2O-PWR. The problem of shaft sealing of pumps has been solved so well that they are suitable also for heavy water coolants. The advantages over canned motor pumps include better efficiency and easier access for maintenance. Furthermore, shaft sealed pumps complete with drives are considerably cheaper. The pressurizing system for the loops does not deviate from that of light water reactors with the sole exception of the blow-down tank, which is arranged in series with the pressurizer and equipped with sub-cooled steel bodies for coolant dumping.

14.   Fig. 3 shows the simplified flow diagram of the primary circuit. The heat generated in the moderator and received by heat transport from the cooling channels is dissipated in a separate circuit and employed for pre-heating the feed water. The moderator circuit is also kept under the pressure of the coolant, but otherwise independent of the main loop, comprising its own cooler and pumps. The independent moderator circuit has the great advantage that moderator cooler and moderator pumps may be used also for the removal of the residual heat as well as for emergency cooling. In the event of an emergency the coolers are connected in such a way as to form two independent heat sinks. The two

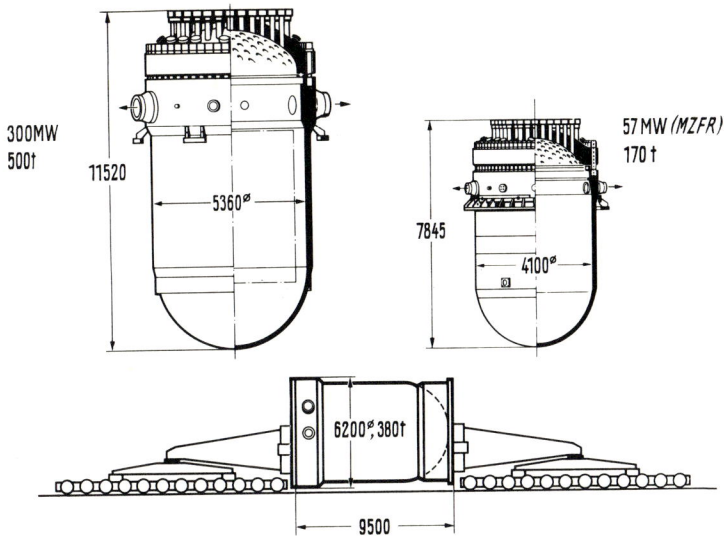

Fig. 1: Pressure vessels for heavy water reactors with natural uranium

300 MW
500 t

11520

5360 ⌀

57 MW (MZFR)
170 t

7845

4100 ⌀

6200 ⌀, 380 t

9500

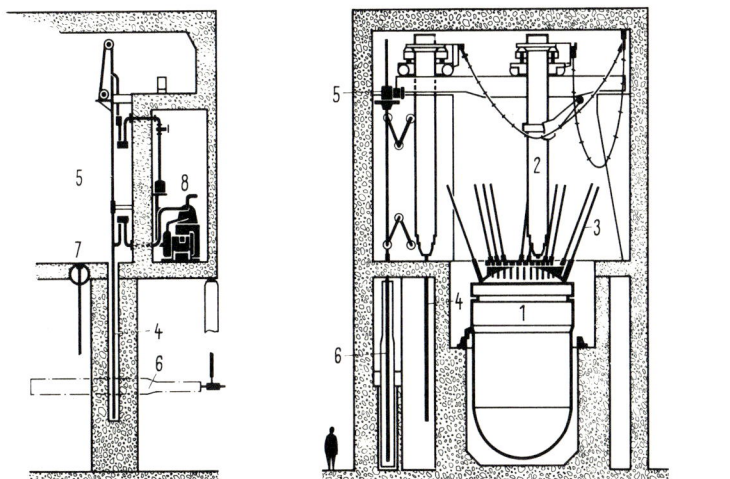

| 1 Reactor | 3 Control rods | 5 Drying chute | 7 Channel seal replachment |
| 2 Fuelling machine | 4 D_2O-storage positions | 6 Fuel transfer flask | 8 Drying system |

Fig. 2: Atucha nuclear power station - fuel transport system

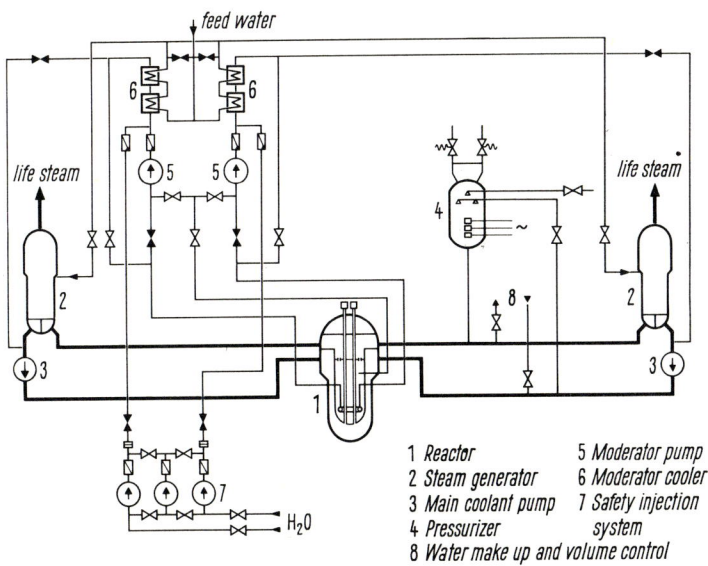

feed water

life steam

life steam

H_2O

1 Reactor
2 Steam generator
3 Main coolant pump
4 Pressurizer
8 Water make up and volume control

5 Moderator pump
6 Moderator cooler
7 Safety injection system

Fig. 3: Atucha nuclear power station - flow diagram primary circuit

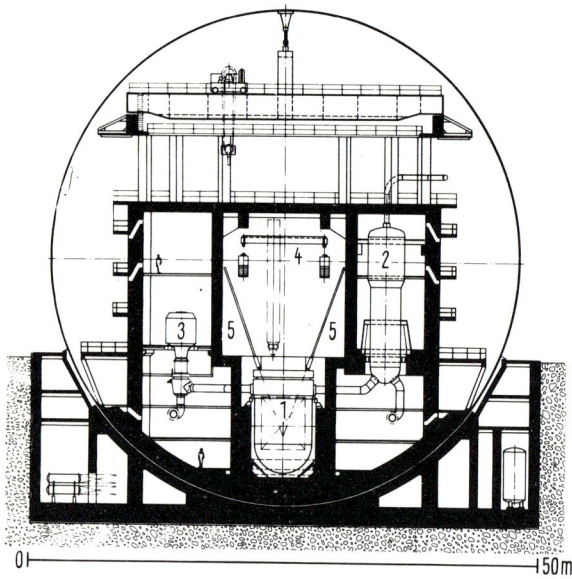

1 Reactor
2 Steam generator
3 Main coolant pump
4 Fuelling machine
5 Control rods

Fig. 4a: Atucha nuclear power station -
reactor building

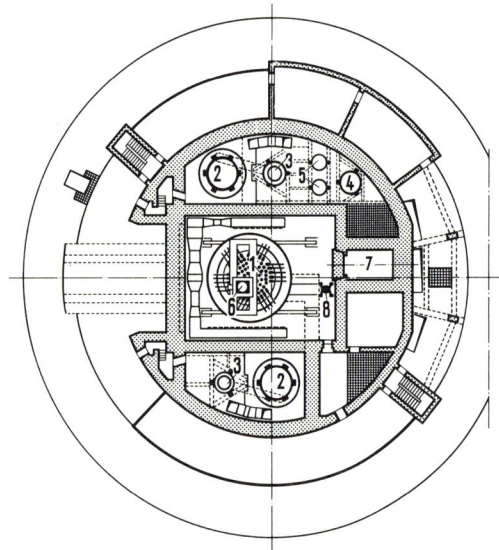

1 Reactor
2 Steam generator
3 Main coolant pumps
4 Pressurizer
5 Moderator cooler
6 Fuelling machine
7 Fuelling machine storage
8 Drying tube

Fig. 4b. Atucha nuclear power station -
reactor building ±0.000 m

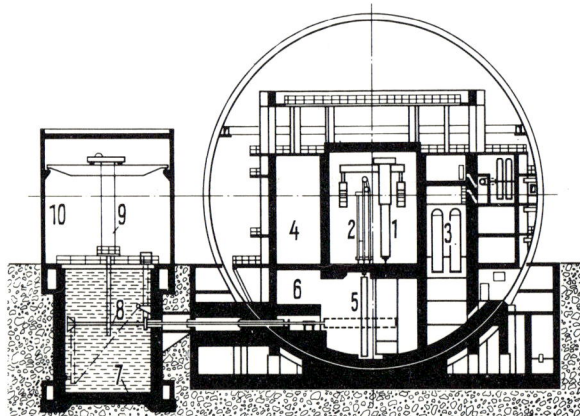

1 Fuelling machine	5 Fuel transfer flask	9 Fuel pit platform
2 Drying system	6 Fuel discharge chute	10 Fuel pit building
3 Moderator coolers	7 Fuel pit	
4 Fuelling machine storage	8 Pivoting chute	

Fig. 5: Atucha nuclear power station -
reactor building and fuel pit building

190

circuits that are normally operated in parallel will then operate independently of each other.

15. The nuclear plant is enclosed in a steel sphere of 49 m diameter and designed to withstand the full pressure. Figs 4 and 5 show the striking resemblance of this heavy water reactor to a light water PWR, the arrangement and design of the main components being in fact identical. It is worth mentioning in this connection that up to the present several years operational experience has been gained in 19 nuclear plants of this type with a total capacity of 3700 MW. The pressure vessel, the steam generators, the pressurizer and pumps of a PWR, no matter whether it is cooled by light or heavy water, are today of mature design, based on extensive experience in manufacture and operation. It will be obvious that with a D_2O system even minor modifications require an adequate degree of care, particularly with respect to absolute tightness. For these special problems the experiences gained with the MZFR prototype may be drawn upon. The same applies to the fuelling machine and the fuel element transport, representing the two technical features by which the heavy water reactor, requiring continuous refuelling under load, distinguishes itself from the light water reactor. The salient parameters of the Atucha nuclear power plant are given in Table 1.

THE EVOLUTION OF THE HEAVY WATER PRESSURE VESSEL REACTORS

16. The core dimensions characteristic of natural uranium reactors require pressure vessels of large diameter. Six years ago, when the design of the MZFR vessel was established, its parameters corresponded to the production capabilities at that time. Those limitations have meanwhile been transgressed and are no longer valid. The steel vessel for the Atucha power plant corresponds to an electrical output of 318 MW. Pressure vessels for reactors of still higher power are likely to necessitate site construction on account of the transport problems referred to above. From the manufacturer's point of view an escalation of the unit power of a steel vessel reactor up to 500 or 600 MW appears feasible.

17. A pre-stressed concrete pressure vessel has been under development for some 3 years by the Siemens Company, the design of which deviates in some respects from those used in Great Britain and France (ref. 2). The principle adopted by us is particularly suited for reactors operating under very high pressures - a necessary prerequisite for water cooled types, if a high efficiency is to be attained.

18. The thermal insulation of pre-stressed concrete vessels for water cooled systems is today still in the development stage. Among the various proposals put forward, a gas gap insulation rather than a wet insulation appears best suited for heavy water reactors, since it allows to utilize types of insulation already proved in gas cooled reactors. Our present state of knowledge of pre-stressed concrete insulation is, however, still considered insufficient by our company for establishing any binding conceptions.

19. With the well-known PWR design as a starting point Siemens visualize a series of steps towards the realization of D_2O reactors of very high power as shown in Fig. 6.

20. The next stage, and the first step in the application of pre-stressed concrete is relying upon the proved loop system PWRs', the only distinction being that the steel vessel is enclosed by a pre-stressed concrete container so as to relieve the former of any pressure loads. Instead of the usual pressurization by means of a pressurizer with saturated steam atmosphere, maintained by electric heating of the primary medium, the concrete container encloses a gas atmosphere in equilibrium with the coolant by way of an open D_2O surface which is not shown in the figure. Such systems of internal pressurization, which must comprise devices for preventing diffusion from one side to the other, have been studied carefully by our company in connection with the development of integrated CO_2 cooled heavy water reactors, and been found to represent a reliable system. The steel vessel is thermally insulated by layers of lagging attached to the outside of the vessel, while the pressurized gas is kept at low temperature by internal circulation. The pre-stressed concrete container must therefore be leak-proof, but need not be thermally insulated. A pre-stressed concrete container of this type entails no higher risks than the other well proven components of conventional design.

21. A further step in the development of the line of D_2O pressure vessel reactors can be the concept of an integrated pre-stressed concrete reactor, shown in Fig. 6. This design has been the subject of a previous paper, Fig. 7 (refs 3, 4). Similar to the gas graphite reactors all primary components are placed inside the pressure vessel, the high cost of the coolant calling for a particularly compact arrangement of the components. Nevertheless, the assembly and the possibility of removal of components in case of malfunction should be possible without excessive difficulty. The design of the wedge-fastened reactor lid offers free access in case of need to the inside of the pressure vessel over its entire width - a feature which might be considered ideal.

22. In line with integrated systems the fuelling machine is also arranged inside the pressure vessel. A D_2O vapour atmosphere is, for reasons of economy, provided above the reactor core for the space in which the fuelling machine moves, the vapour being supplied by net evaporation from the reactor core. Some delicate engineering problems caused by placing the fuelling machine inside the pressure vessel

300 MW *Loop system*   600 MW *Loop system*   600 MW *Integrated system*

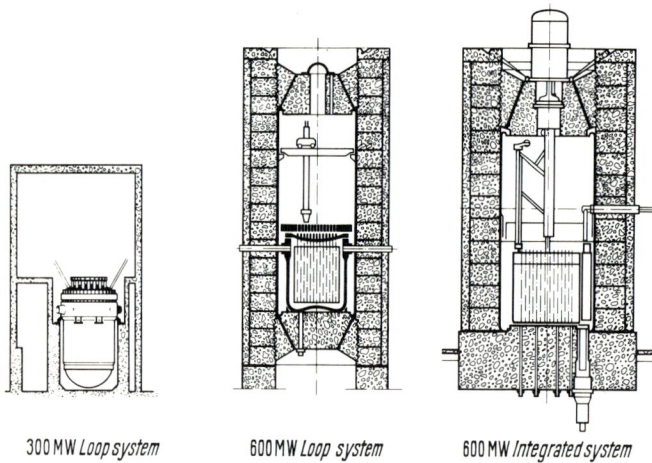

Fig. 6: Evolution of D_2O-pressure vessel reactor systems

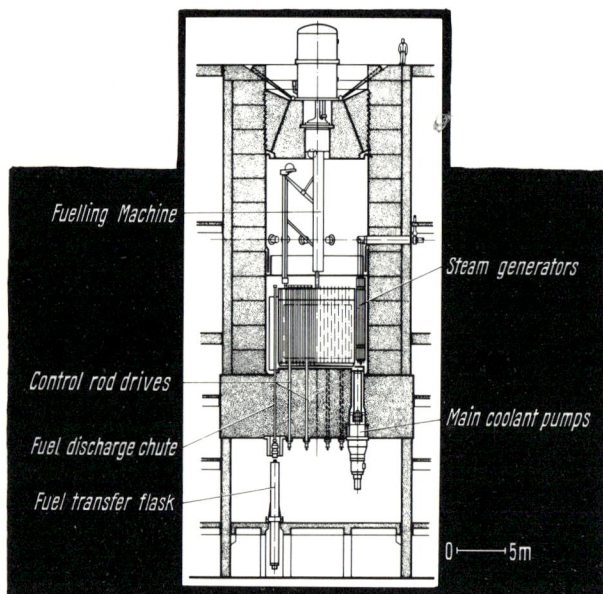

Fuelling Machine

Steam generators

Control rod drives

Main coolant pumps

Fuel discharge chute

Fuel transfer flask

0 ⊢——⊣ 5m

Fig. 7: Large size heavy water moderated reactor (SMR-600)

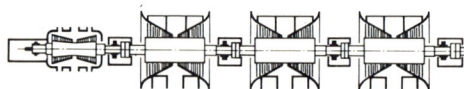

Steam Turbine
50 ata / 263 °C / 0,03 ata

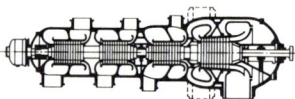

Feed water pumps

Helium Turbine
60 ata / 800 °C / 22 ata

CO_2 *Turbine*
300 ata / 520 °C / 84 ata

Auxiliary Compressor

0 ⊢————————⊣ 20m

Fig. 8: 300 MW 3000 rpm turbines for nuclear stations

Table 1
Selected data of Atucha Nuclear Power Station

General

Thermal reactor power	1,100	MW
Gross electric power	340	MW
Overall efficiency of the plant	29	%

Reactor

Moderator and coolant		D_2O
Number of coolant channels	253	
Lattice pitch, hexagonal	217.6	mm
Moderator to fuel ratio	16.8	
Coolant to fuel ratio	1.6	
Heat rating	26.6	MWth/tU
Specific D_2O inventory	0.75	t/MWe
Moderator temperature, nominal	180	°C
Pressure vessel diameter, internal	5,360	mm
Number of absorber rods	29	
Burn-up	8,000	MWd/t

Fuel elements

Fuel		UO_2 - natural uranium
Cladding		Zircaloy-2
Fuel element		36 rod clusters
Fuel rod diameter	11.9	mm
Maximum linear power	576	W/cm
Maximum heat flux	154	W/cm^2
Core length	5,350	mm
Core diameter	4,543	mm

Heat removal

Number of primary loops	2	
Operating pressure	115	kg/cm^2
Coolant flow	20,000	t/h
Reactor outlet temperature	305.4	°C
Temperature rise along the coolant channels	34	°C

Turbo generator

Live steam	256.3	°C/45 kg/cm^2 abs.
Feed water flow	1,727	t/h
Feed water temperature	120	°C
Coolant water temperature	17	°C
Coolant water flow	70,000	m^3/h
Electric power generator	425	MVA
Voltage	21	kV

---

are counterbalanced by a reduction in the number of ports through which coolant might possibly escape.

23. In the course of development some minor alterations in the design compared to the state of the feasibility study were decided upon (ref. 3). These were suggested partly by new technical considerations, partly by amplified practical experiences resulting from our co-operation with the Swedish ASEA and the French SOCIA companies as industrial partners. For example, the system of the fuelling machine was patterned on the principles of the Marviken machine, enabling us to profit by the practical operating experience obtained with this machine during its first years of service. A review of the operating data resulted in a reduction of the mean vapour content at the core exit to approximately 1%, which tends to lead to a self-sustained pressurized coolant system. The former highly positive void coefficient had required a reduction in steam generation in order to achieve a stably controlled reactor system.

24. A modification has also been made in connection with the control rods, which are now inserted into the reactor from below despite additional engineering problems, in particular with respect to heavy water as a coolant.

THE GAS COOLED HEAVY WATER REACTOR

25. The Niederaichbach nuclear plant is a prototype of a CO_2 cooled, D_2O moderated pressure tube reactor, with an output of 100 MWe (refs 5, 6). If construction proceeds according to schedule the plant will be commissioned in 1970. A noteworthy feature of this reactor is the high coolant temperature of 550°C at the reactor outlet, requiring, of course, steel as canning material for the fuel.

26. The further development of this reactor line is closely linked to the applicability of natural uranium. When the last hopes regarding the suitability of beryllium as cladding material vanished about two years ago, attention was focussed upon the development of suitable zirconium alloys. Hitherto, the evaluation of irradiated test fuel elements with zirconium-copper canning has been rather encouraging, but the experience gained so far is yet too small to form the basis of a commercial offer.

27. A substantial simplification of the CO_2 cooled reactor is required for reducing the investment costs, so as to make it more competitive with other existing reactor types. One way towards this end is seen by us in the adoption of the pre-stressed concrete technique for the gas-cooled heavy water type in the form of a pressure vessel reactor. Siemens participated in a design study of an integrated gas cooled reactor of this type, which was carried out last year in co-operation with the Sulzer company and the French CEA.

28. There is also a certain connection between the efforts to bring down the investment costs and the considerations and exertions for the development of CO_2-gas turbines aimed at the realization of a direct circuit, which could obviously be utilized as well for a CO_2 cooled heavy water reactor. Hot gas temperatures in the range of 500°C which, in connection with zirconium-copper as cladding may be regarded today as quite realistic, would result in a rather interesting overall efficiency of a plant. The most attractive point, however, in connection with a process based on an expansion to not less than about 80 kg/cm² - the kind of process we would prefer - is given by the remarkably small dimensions of the CO_2 turbines of such a plant.

29. The proportions in size of a steam, a helium, and a CO_2 turbine for 300 MWe (Fig. 8) show very drastically the great advantage of the CO_2 gas turbine, though this gain will admittedly be somewhat impaired by the larger heat transfer surface of the regenerative heat exchangers required.

THORIUM FOR FUEL

30. Under an association contract our company is co-operating with the Jülich Nuclear Research Centre in the development of D_2O cooled and moderated thorium converters. The aim of this study is a project for a 600 MW unit of the pressure vessel type and comprises a detailed R & D programme.

31. Our investigations have shown so far that the D_2O thorium converter with pressure vessel design offers an interesting advantage in fuel cycle costs, provided that highly enriched uranium is used as replacement fuel in a thorium converter optimized for minimum fuel cycle costs. While self-sustaining thorium and natural uranium cycles are possible in principle, the fuel cycle costs would go up. A comparison speaks in favour of the thorium converter. In addition a refuelling programme with large intervals similar to that of light water reactors - reshuffling would, of course, not be envisaged - and the reduced D_2O inventory give reason to hope that the investment costs offer this reactor a good chance to compete economically with the H_2O types.

CONCLUSION

32. The line of natural uranium heavy water reactors of the pressure vessel type pursued in Germany gained its first success abroad a few months ago. The contract for a 320 MWe nuclear power plant awarded by the Argentine CNEA was won by Siemens in open competition with all other reactor types. The further development of the heavy water pressure vessel reactor to very high unit ratings of 600 MW - in the more distant future to as high as 1000 MW - will provide the opportunity of being competitive with all other proven reactor types, even in countries of very high load density.

REFERENCES

1.   MZFR. Kraftwerk mit D_2O-Druckkessel-
reaktor atomwirtschaft. Heft 7/8,
Jahrgang 1965.

2.   GRUHL H. Spannbetonbehalter für
wassergekühlte reaktoren. Information-
stagung Brussel 7-8th November, 1967,
EUR/c/4281/67d.

3.   STÜGER R.A. Large heavy water power
reactor with pre-stressed concrete pressure
vessel. IAEA Conference, 11-15th September,
1967, Vienna, SM-99/8.

4.   STÜGER R.A. and FREI G. The primary
cooling system of an integrated heavy water
reactor with concrete pressure vessel.
EN-1/18 presented at Symposium on the
Technology of Integrated Primary Circuits
for Power Reactors, Paris, 20-22nd May,
1968.

5.   TEBBERT T., STRASSER W. and PLANK H.
Kernkraftwerkt Niederaichbach mit
gasgekühltem D_2O-Druckröhrenreaktor - Von
der projektierung bis zum baubeginn.
Atomwirtschaft, Heft 10/1966.

6.   ALTVATER W. and PREUß H.J.
Kernkraftwerk Niederaichbach mit
gasgekühltem D_2O-Druckröhrenreaktor -
Technik und aufbau der anlage.
Atomwirtschaft, Heft 10/1966.

The CIRENE reactor concept

S. VILLANI, DPhys, CIRENE Research and Development
Programme Manager, CISE, Italy

SYNOPSIS   The main characteristics of a typical 1600 MW(th) CIRENE reactor design are
discussed and some data reviewed in comparison with similar reactor concepts, namely the
SGHWR and the CANDU-BLW.

A basic difference between CIRENE and the SGHWR consists in reactor physics. The
former has to accept operation with a considerable coolant void coefficient: this fact
has to be duly taken into account in the design of the control and safety systems, which
are described in some detail.

A discussion is also summarized concerning the refuelling procedures.

The development of the CIRENE reactor is eventually justified on the economic ground,
in the frame of long-term forecasts for the growth of power demand in Italy.

GENERAL FEATURES

1.   CIRENE is a reactor concept belonging
to the family of the heavy water moderated
and boiling light water cooled systems.
The structure of the core, essentially made
of vertical pressure tubes insulated toward
the cold moderator, as well as the direct
cycle of the coolant give this reactor some
similarities with the SGHWR.

2.   It has to be noticed however that these
common aspects are mainly limited to some
general design features and to material
technology. The physical behaviour of the
CIRENE on the contrary is different from
that of the SGHWR in its enriched version.

3.   This is due to the fact that CIRENE
was basically conceived as a natural
uranium fuelled reactor. Particular care
has been therefore taken in order to
minimize the light water content in the
core: the coolant does not contribute substantially to moderation, as happens in the
SGHWR, but acts mainly as a neutron absorbing medium. A considerable coolant void
coefficient had to be therefore accepted.
The control of the plant, which might be
intrinsically unstable, is of course a
problem to be considered very seriously.

4.   The concern about keeping the water
content low leads to establish the core
height so as to balance the extra power one
can draw from longer power channels against
the penalties deriving from higher coolant
flow rates and pressure drops and from
lower steam exit qualities. The lower
neutron absorption in shorter power
channels is partly offset by the larger
leakage due to the pan shape, although this
can be tolerated to a certain extent.

5.   In Table 1 some representative data
are collected relevant to a typical 500 MWe
CIRENE design (ref. 1). They have been
compared with the corresponding data
reported for a 350 MWe SGHWR design and for
the 250 MWe CANDU-BLW reactor prototype
(refs 2, 3).

6.   Some significant differences of CIRENE
with respect to the otherwise similar
CANDU-BLW consist in the configuration of
the fuel element, the fast control system
and the start-up system.

7.   The CIRENE fuel consists of 19-rod
bundles of uranium dioxide. The bundles
are of a segmented type, with collapsible
Zircaloy-2 canning. The bundles are
axially free. Basically, they are designed
for a conductivity integral of 48 W/cm.
Average thermal rating is 12.8 MW/tU.
Refuelling is performed from the bottom of
the reactor. Representative values for the
average burn-up are 8500-8200 MWd/t, depending on the refuelling scheme.

8.   As for the control systems, they
deserve a particular attention and will be
considered in some detail below, also
because fast control is obtained through a
method which is novel in the reactor technique.

9.   The shutdown system is based on the
injection of poisoned liquid in vertical
tubes traversing the core. Unlike the
SGHWR, in which injection of poisoned
liquid is effected by means of a pressure
drive, the CIRENE poison injection system
relies on gravity only. A small CIRENE
prototype might have also the dumping of
the moderator to scram the reactor, but the

Table 1
Characteristics of three BLW-cooled heavy water moderated reactors

		CIRENE	SGHWR	CANDU-BLW
Power	MW(th)	1613	1082	800
Overall efficiency	%	31	32	31.3
Power channels	No.	600	310	308
Pressure tube ID	mm	106.1	130.6	103.4
Core diameter	cm	850	598	539
Core height	cm	500	396	500
Fuel		UO_2 - natural	UO_2 - enriched	UO_2 - natural
Bundle configuration		{ 19-rod segment	{ 36-rod full-length	{ 18-rod segment
Average rating	MW(th)/t	12.8	17.8	12
Average exposure	MWd/t	8500	18,000	7000
Refuelling		Off-load(?)	Off-load	On-load
Fast control system		Two-phase fluid	D_2O-level	Solid-rods
Scram system		Pois. liquid	Pois. liquid	D_2O-dumping
Start-up system		Steam blower	-	Enriched boosters
Coolant outlet pressure	atm	50	63.3	53
Exit quality	%	25	10.75	16.4

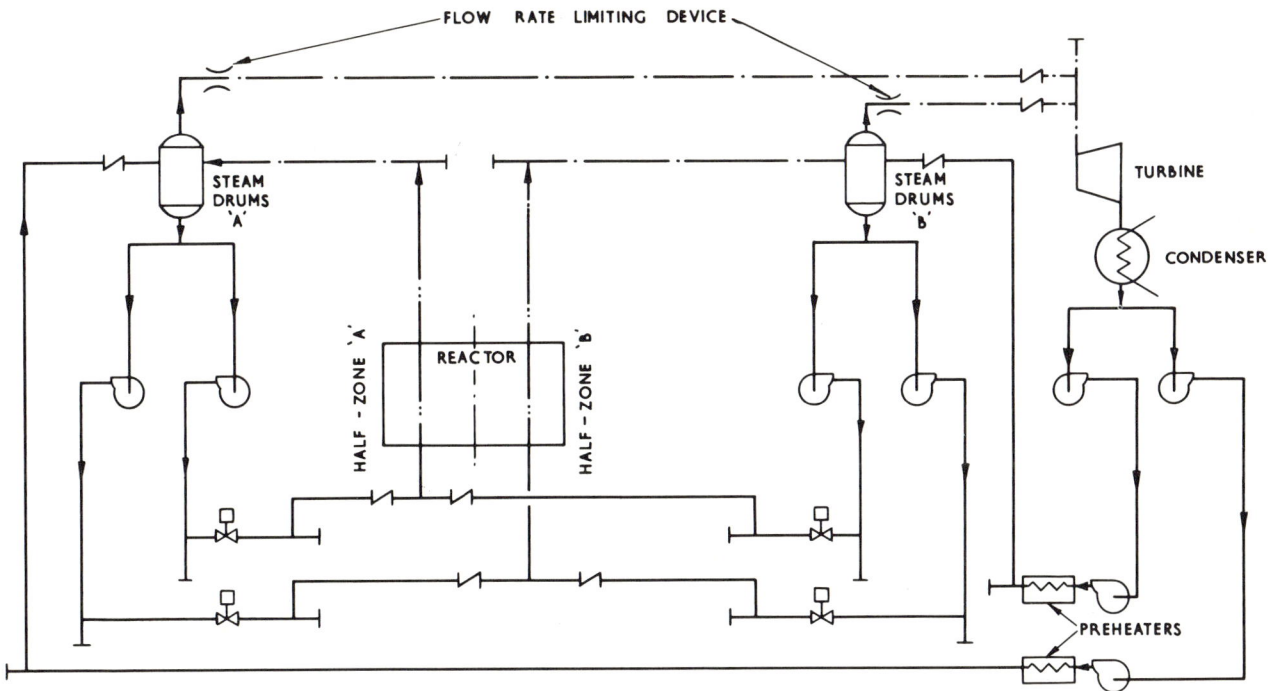

Fig. 1: Flow diagram of the cooling system for a typical CIRENE reactor

Fig. 2: An artist's view of the 35 MWe CIRENE prototype

adoption of such a system for the commercial units is still questionable.

10. Since the reactor is sub-critical when the power channels are flooded, the start-up requires either the insertion of enriched uranium boosters or the partial evacuation of water from the channel. As it will be seen later in more detail, the latter solution was adopted for the CIRENE reactor.

11. As it can be seen from the table, the CIRENE reactor is foreseen to operate with the highest steam exit quality: 25% by weight.

12. An upper limit for the steam quality or, correspondingly, a lower limit for the water content are substantially dictated by the heat transfer crisis. The CIRENE design is based on a critical flux correlation derived both from full-scale experiments performed in a purposely made 7 MWe heat transfer loop and from the analysis of literature data. A safety factor of 1.5 was adopted against the crisis (i.e., the ratio of channel power in nominal conditions to channel power at the crisis), including the intrinsic uncertainty margin of the correlation and the hot channel factor as well.

13. Since inlet enthalpy and pressure of the coolant are practically constant, the flow rate has to be diminished from the centre to the periphery of the core, in order to keep the safety factor at the same level everywhere. An excess of safety margin at the periphery would unduly increase the water content in the core.

14. The flow diagram of the cooling system for a typical 1600 MW thermal CIRENE reactor is shown in Fig. 1. Operating pressure was established at 50 atm, since the cost functions - both for the fuel and the plant - were found to decrease with decreasing pressure, levelling off at about 50 atm.

15. For safety reasons the core, consisting of about 600 power channels, is divided into four independent zones, so that coolant loss in one of them would not cause the sudden voiding of the rest. Each of these zones is divided into two partly independent circuits. In case of a sudden pressure loss in a steam drum (there are two of them for each zone), voiding would be fast in one half-zone only, while it would be delayed in the other half, so as to enable the safety and control systems to intervene.

16. There are two circulating pumps feeding each half-zone with the coolant coming from two different steam drums, so that a failure in one of them would not cause the coolant flow rate to go down to zero.

17. The steam ducts before the header are all provided with Venturi type devices, limiting the flow rate in case of a sudden rupture occurring in the header or in the turbine. The maximum flow rate is thus only 30% in excess of the nominal flow rate and voiding of the power channels is sufficiently slow.

18. The main assumptions on which the CIRENE 500 MWe reference design is based will be verified in a smaller prototype - about 35 MW electric - whose construction is going to be initiated at the same site of the Latina Magnox power station (ref. 4). Fig. 2 shows an artist's view of the small prototype plant.

CONTROL AND SAFETY

19. The main factors which have to be taken into account for fast transients in the design of the CIRENE control systems are the following:

- Void fraction in the power channel. At constant pressure a power rise increases the void fraction and thus reactivity, resulting therefore in a destabilizing effect.

- Fuel temperature. The fuel temperature coefficient is negative with fresh fuel, tending to zero after a certain operation period, when the fuel reaches equilibrium.

- Coolant pressure. A power rise increases the coolant pressure, tending therefore to decrease the void fraction. This is a stabilizing effect, but its feed-back is rather slow. Its time constant may be limited by reducing the plant volume filled with high pressure steam.

- Coolant enthalpy at the core inlet. This quantity depends on feed-water temperature. Its influence is important, although considerably slower than the pressure effect just mentioned.

20. Furthermore the control system has to compensate for slow transients connected with fuel depletion, variations of xenon and samarium concentrations and variations of fuel and coolant temperatures during reactor start-up or operation at reduced load. Spatial instabilities in the core arising from fluctuations both in coolant densities and in xenon concentration have to be also taken into account.

21. The time intervals involved as well as the values of reactivity to be controlled are quite different for each effect.

22. Velocities of the order of ten pcm/day with overall reactivity variations of some thousand pcm are needed to compensate fuel burn-up. A few pcm/s in the same range of reactivity variations are required by large load variations and xenon transients.

23. On the other hand, velocities of 20-40 pcm/s in a range of a few hundred pcm are required for fast control of the system.

24. The slow reactivity variations may be compensated by different means. The reactivity excess of fresh fuel up to equilibrium conditions may be balanced, for instance, by poisoning the moderator and by providing depleted uranium in the first batches. Other slow effects connected with power changes may be compensated by varying the moderator level and the coolant density.

25. The fast control system of the CIRENE reactor, which ensures also the spatial stability of the core, consists in a number of special control tubes placed vertically through the core.

26. The amount of reactivity absorbed in each of these tubes is varied by changing the void fraction in the flow of a two-phase mixture, made of helium and poisoned light water. Boron is used as a poison.

27. Fig. 3 shows the flow diagram of such a system. A pressure difference (2 atm) between the low pressure tank LP and the high pressure tank HP (at 5 atm abs.) is maintained by the helium blowers B. The two tanks are common to all the control tubes of the system; the pressure difference between the tanks is kept constant and thus independent from the flow rates in the various control tubes by the automatic valve VG placed on a gas line connecting the tanks.

28. The liquid is circulated by means of pump P and liquid level in HP is kept constant by an automatic control which actuates the valve VL placed on a liquid line connecting the two tanks.

29. Gas and liquid are fed to the various control tubes through independent ducts derived from the tank HP; a mixer M is placed at the inlet of each control tube.

30. The control of the void fraction inside the reactivity channel is achieved by means of an electro-pneumatic valve placed on the liquid feeding line; actuation of the valve results in variations of the liquid flow rate. The driving signal is independent for each reactivity channel.

31. It is possible to know the degree of insertion of the absorbing fluid by calibrating the position of the valve stem.

32. The gas flow rate varies with the liquid flow rate according to the pressure drop characteristics of the system. When gas only is fed to the control tube, the pressure drop in the circuit is almost wholly concentrated in the fixed resistance R (a valve or an orifice) on the gas feeding line. This resistance is also aimed at ensuring a convenient operating range to valve V.

33. The control tubes are U-shaped, passing through the upper plate of the reactor. Separation of the two phases coming out of the control tubes occurs in the low pressure tank LP. Two heat exchangers, on the gas line and on the liquid line respectively, are provided in order to eliminate the heat produced in the core by the neutron absorption reaction and outside the core by the circulators. A catalytic bed is also foreseen between the two tanks LP and HP in order to recombine radiolytic gases produced during the flow through the core.

34. A CIRENE reactor of 1600 MW thermal would require 19 control tubes like that here described, acting at a rate of about 30 pcm/s and covering an overall reactivity range of 600-800 pcm.

35. The application of two-phase control tubes - as compared to solid rods - simplifies the problem of penetrating the upper part of the reactor, where the coolant outlet ducts leave very little room available. Another advantage of the control tubes consists in the axial uniformity of neutron absorption.

36. The performance of this novel control system is being tested in a full-scale out-of-pile experimental circuit feeding two mock-ups of control tubes (ref. 5). The convenience is being presently considered to control for testing purposes a zero-power reactor by means of this novel system.

37. The scram system of the CIRENE reactor consists, as previously mentioned, in a number of tubes passing through the core and allowing injection of a poisoned liquid. Each of these tubes is a branch of a U-shaped duct, the other branch being placed outside the core. In operation the liquid column is maintained in the outside branch by an overpressure of the cover gas inside the in-core branch, which balances the hydrostatic head.

38. The scram signal actuates a by-pass between the two arms, so that the poisoned solution is pushed by gravity into the in-core branch.

39. About 9000 pcm have to be controlled by the scram system. According to the design specifications, 1.5-2 seconds are allowed from the scram signal to the full insertion of the poisoned liquid column. These times were satisfactorily met in full scale experiments.

40. The less stringent requirements as for the insertion time in comparison with the SGHWR, which permit the scram system to rely on gravity only without the need of a pressure drive, are due to a different approach to some safety problems. In fact, for the CIRENE reactor, one does not admit the sudden loss of flow due to pump failure since the pumps are provided with fly-wheels. Other emergency cooling means are also foreseen in case of pump failure.

41. Due to the strong influence of the coolant density on reactivity, the basic operating programme taken into consideration for the CIRENE reactor is such as to keep constant at different loads the coolant density, its value being the same as in nominal conditions, i.e., about 0.28 g/cm^3. Such a programme differs from

Table 2
Basic data on different refuelling schemes

Procedure	Load factor %	Flux peaking factor %	Average fuel burn-up MWd/t	Refuelling machines
On-load	80	1.2	8500	2+1
Off-load	80	0.3	8200	4

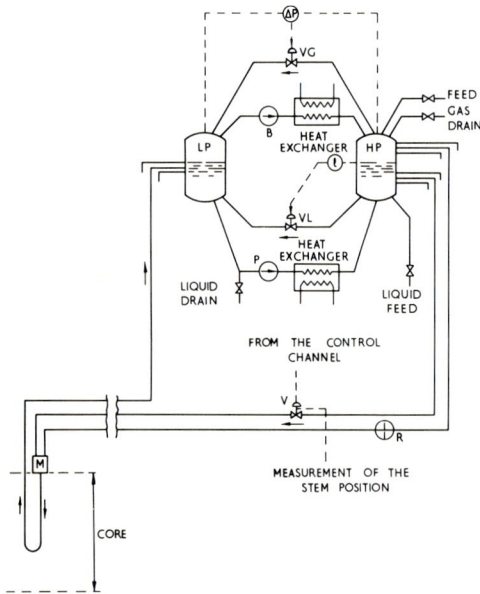

Fig. 3: Flow diagram of the two-phase fast control system

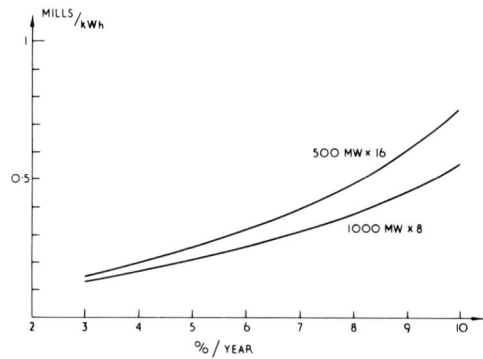

Fig. 4: Net saving on the energy unit cost (mill/kWh) as a function of the required capital remuneration (yearly interest rate, %)

Table 3
Forecasts for power production expansion in Italy

Year	Power production 10^9 kWh/year	Population (million)	Per capita production (kWh)
1965	80	52	1,540
1975	160	56	2,860
1985	320	60	5,330
1995	640	64	10,000

the usual operating programme of boiling water reactors, in which coolant density increases when the load lowers until the core is flooded at zero power.

42. It is obvious that in order to operate at constant coolant density one has to control the various thermal and hydraulic quantities on which the coolant density is dependent, namely the flow rate of re-circulated water. the inlet enthalpy of the coolant and the pressure.

43. Operation at reduced loads may be effected by diminishing the coolant flow rate. This is feasible down to about 25% of the nominal load value. At lower loads, the flow rates would attain a range in which flow instabilities and control diffi-culties could be expected.

44. For this reason, under 25% of the nominal load, the reactor is operated by reducing the coolant density. This is obtained by recirculating a portion of the steam to the core inlet through a steam blower. The steam flow rate is then established so as to ensure a stable coolant flow in the power channels.

45. The steam blower is therefore used for the reactor start-up. Start-up with re-duced coolant density also helps in overriding the xenon peak, at least to a certain extent.

46. This method, avoiding the use of enriched uranium boosters, has the advan-tage of inserting more uniformly the reactivity all over the core and also diminishing substantially the insertion of positive reactivity in case of a coolant loss when the reactor is operating at reduced load.

47. The possibility will be investigated of operating the steam blowers up to power values exceeding the 25% limit. This results in a reduction of the average coolant density.

48. One could also envisage operating the reactor in nominal full-power conditions keeping the steam blower running and thus having a positive inlet steam quality. This performance would have a number of beneficial effects. Fuel life would be longer. The reactor stability both overall and spatial, would improve, due to the absence of the sub-cooled portion of the power channel, which leads to a substantial reduction of the power-density feed-back. Obviously the smaller water content in the core would improve the safety aspects connected with the voiding reactivity coefficient.

49. The actual possibilities offered by the use of the steam blower will be tested during the performance of the CIRENE prototype.

FUEL MANAGEMENT

50. Different fuel management procedures, both with on-load and off-load refuelling,

have been taken into consideration for the CIRENE reactor. Three typical procedures are the following:

(a) On-load refuelling with a quasi-continuous charge and discharge of fuel slugs, at a rate of 5 slugs per day. It is estimated that the time required for the single refuelling operation is about $1\frac{1}{2}$ to 2 hours. During this period, the power channel is engaged for $\frac{3}{4}$ of an hour, the re-maining time being required for shuffling which is performed through a separate machine. In this case, two refuelling machines (one spare) and a shuffling machine are needed.

(b) Off-load refuelling with hot pressurized channels. This operation is foreseen to take place once every four weeks, during a weekend. A portion of the core would be replaced in 37 hours, by changing one slug per channel in a number of channels uniformly spread throughout the core, so as to perform a sort of radial and axial scatter loading. The number of slugs to be re-placed during each shutdown is about 125. Since the single replacement operation is assumed to last one hour, four refuelling machines are needed. Shuffling is performed by the same machines.

(c) Off-load refuelling with cold un-pressurized channels. The fre-quency of this operation is the same as in the previous case. The time required for replacing a single fuel slug is estimated to be only half an hour, but the outage period of 37 hours pre-viously considered is not en-tirely available for refuelling, because of the time needed to cool down the system and bring it up again to nominal temperature. Consequently four machines are still required in order to re-place 125 fuel slugs.

51. An outage of 37 hours during a weekend every four weeks could still maintain a load factor in excess of 80%. It could be accepted without economic penalties in a network including several CIRENE reactor units. In the case of a few units of such type, it is possible that during its outage the corresponding power should be supplied by another plant, having a higher marginal cost.

52. Representative data for the three refuelling schemes are given in Table 2.

53. The peaking factors are mostly due to radial flux distortions, since the axial buckling should be kept constant by means of the control system. Off-load refuelling is characterized by lower peaking factors due to the considerably larger number of channels in which fuel slugs are replaced.

54. For on-load refuelling, the burn-up loss with respect to the ideal continuous fuel cycle is negligible. In the off-load cycles, on the contrary, burn-up decrease is significant: about 300 MWd/t with respect to the ideal cycle.

55. The comparison of the three refuelling schemes is substantially affected by the cost estimates for the refuelling machines and by the differences in power marginal costs during outage of the nuclear plant.

56. If the latter factor has not to be taken into account, off-load unpressurized refuelling would be either equivalent to on-load refuelling or somewhat cheaper, depending on the cost evaluation for the refuelling machines. The advantage would result in about 3% of the total investment, capitalizing all the costs. On the other hand, if the differential fuel costs have to be taken into account during the outage of the nuclear unit, the off-load unpressurized scheme may result - in the worst case - about 1% more expensive than on-load refuelling.

57. All these comparisons are based on the assumptions that only 1% of the on-load refuelling operations produces some trouble leading to scram and that in 50% of such events it is possible to re-start very quickly, i.e., within half an hour. The picture could change quite substantially, if these assumptions are not verified.

58. In default of a practical experience (because no examples exist of what really happens when charging and discharging on power a full-scale boiling channel) and due to the relatively small economic differences among the various schemes, off-load refuelling - possibly in unpressurized conditions - is presently considered very seriously for adoption in the CIRENE reactor.

ADVANCED VERSIONS

59. Several improvements may lead in the future to more advanced versions of the CIRENE reactor design.

60. The possibility is being studied, for instance, of controlling the moderating power of heavy water by bubbling through it in a number of compartments a gas injected from the bottom plate. Variations of gas flow rate would correspond to variations of void fraction and therefore of moderating power. Two aims could be achieved by this means, depending on the moderator temperature.

61. In the case of maximum moderator temperatures considerably lower than the boiling point - for instance 80°C, like in the present design - a slow increase of the void fraction in the moderator could be employed to compensate slow reactivity variations, connected, for instance, with the fuel cycle or with operation at reduced loads.

62. Operation with gas bubbling, when the moderator is very close to the boiling point would allow, if feasible, an intrinsic fast control of the reactor power. In fact, a power raise would immediately cause the heavy water evaporation to substantially increase the initial void fraction corresponding to gas bubbling.

63. As for the fuel, which in the present design consists of 50 cm long slugs, an advanced version could foresee longer rods, for instance twice as long. This would simplify the refuelling procedure and also allow a significant reduction in fuel manufacturing cost.

64. The CIRENE reactor is being presently designed for natural uranium fuel, but it cannot be excluded that a very slight enrichment may improve its overall economy under particular circumstances. Very slight enrichment means here that the U-235 content in spent fuel is still so low as to exclude the economic convenience of its recovery.

65. In any case, the technology acquired in developing the natural uranium version can be utilized to a large extent also for a slightly enriched design.

66. Further in the future, if the expansion of demand and exploitation of low grade ore will raise the uranium price, plutonium recycle could be adopted for the CIRENE reactor, keeping constant the fuel cost in spite of substantial increases of uranium prices.

ECONOMIC CONSIDERATIONS

67. Preliminary economic evaluations concerning CIRENE 500 MWe plants found that energy unit cost data fall within the same range pertaining to other 'proven' reactors or to other reactor concepts being currently developed. Advantages or disadvantages are often measured in terms of a few tenths of a mill per kWh. Cost difference of this magnitude are also found between different design versions of the CIRENE reactor.

68. Since it is doubtful that more refined economic studies on paper may decide whether a new reactor concept is competitive or not, the question is rather to establish if such small differences in the energy costs are likely to compensate for the overall development cost (ref. 6).

69. A reasonable estimate for the development cost gives a total expenditure of about $80 millions, spread over a period of 20 years, say from 1959 to 1979. This sum covers the following stages of the development:

- research and design studies, leading to the construction of a small reactor prototype of 35 MWe;

- construction and operation of the small prototype;

- research and design studies for an intermediate power unit, of about 200 MWe;

- partial support to construction and operation of the intermediate power unit;

- research and development for scaling up the design to commercial sizes, i.e., 500 MWe.

70. A part of the above mentioned sum is aimed at covering the difference between the cost of power produced by a 200 MWe reactor plant, probably uneconomic, and the cost which could be obtained with a conventional plant of the same power.

71. One can assume that at the end of the 20 years period, i.e., by 1979, the first 500 MWe unit is operational and since then the cost of further development work is sufficiently low so as to be incorporated in the construction costs of the commercial units.

72. Both the development expenditures occurred before 1979 and the net savings obtained in power generating costs by operating a number of CIRENE reactors after 1979 may be referred to the year 1979.

73. Assuming a yearly interest rate of 5%, the present worth method gives an increase of 50% of total development expenditure as referred to 1979. The relatively low interest rate assumed in this evaluation may be justified by the indirect advantages of such an investment, considered on a national basis.

74. In order to evaluate the economic benefit deriving from power generation through CIRENE reactors, some assumptions have to be made about the total installed capacity with reactors of this type and about the rate of installation.

75. Let us assume an overall capacity of 8000 MWe to be covered by CIRENE type units of two different sizes, 500 and 1000 MWe respectively, installed at a rate of one unit per year. The remuneration one can expect from the operation of these plants can be evaluated as a function of the net saving on the production of the electric kWh. In the graph of Fig. 4 this remuneration, to be read on the abscissae, is expressed as a yearly interest rate on the capital invested in developing the reactor, taking the year 1979 as the reference date for the present worth of expenditures and revenues.

76. It can be seen that a net saving of about 0.2-0.25 mill/kWh would ensure a remuneration of 5% per year to the capital absorbed by development work up to 1979. Since there are serious reasons to believe that such values of the net saving will be met and perhaps exceeded, the whole enterprise appears to be basically reasonable.

77. The possibility of installing CIRENE type reactors for a total capacity of 8000 MWe needs some comments with respect to the growth of national power demand forecast for the next decades.

78. Table 3 gives, in round figures, the yearly power production - both total and per capita - in the next decades, assuming a demand doubling every ten years.

79. From this table, one can see that the per capita production data are not so high that a saturation could be predicted in the considered period. In fact today's per capita production in the United States is higher than the figure corresponding in the table to the year 1985 and the forecasts in that country are considering the doubling of per capita consumption within 15 years.

80. It is probable that also in Italy, like in other developed countries, the largest portion of the thermal power capacity installed from 1975 onward will be of nuclear origin. A proportion of 80% nuclear against overall thermal capacity seems to be a reasonable assumption.

81. In order to increase the power generation from 160 billion kWh per year in 1975 to 640 billion in 1995 it is necessary to install, roughly speaking, 100,000 MWe, out of which 80,000 MWe should be nuclear. During the periods 1979-87 or 1979-95 considered for the installation of CIRENE units of 1000 or 500 MWe respectively, the newly installed nuclear capacity should be correspondingly of 26,000 MWe and 69,000 MWe. The assumption to cover 8000 MW by CIRENE reactors, this capacity being roughly 30 or 12% of the total nuclear capacity installed in the considered period, does not seem therefore to be unduly optimistic.

82. Italy is relying more and more on fossil fuel importation, since domestic resources are very poor. The weight of this importation on the foreign payments balance is becoming heavier, as time elapses. Importation for power generation only would reach 80-100 million tonnes of equivalent coal in 1985, if power had to be produced entirely in fossil fuelled plants. The corresponding expenditure would be close to $1 billion.

83. Nuclear power plants would allow a substantial reduction of this expenditure nearly 60% for enriched fuel elements imported as a finished product or even 90% for natural uranium imported as uranium concentrate to be processed by domestic industry. The CIRENE reactor being fed by natural uranium, would give thus a substantial contribution in reducing expenditures for fuel importation.

84. It has to be mentioned at this point that feeding CIRENE reactors, like other heavy water converters, requires relatively low uranium amounts. Some comparative

figures are the following:

- Magnox reactors — 347 kg U/MWe - year

- Light water reactors — 200 kg U/MWe - year

- CIRENE reactors — 147 kg U/MWe - year

85. Furthermore generating costs with CIRENE reactors, as with other heavy water converters, are not very sensitive to price of natural uranium (ref. 7).

86. In the period foreseen for the installation of CIRENE type reactors, beginning only in 1979, fast reactor systems are likely to have reached industrial maturity. It is therefore interesting to examine the impact that CIRENE reactors could have on fast reactor penetration, in comparison with light water reactors.

87. We will assume that construction of commercial fast reactor units in Italy starts in 1985. In that year, the installed nuclear capacity should be around 20,000 MW and in the decade 1985-95 it should grow at a rate of 14% per year in order to meet a power demand of 640 billion kWh at the end of that period.

88. To have an idea of the advantages which may derive from a good converter like CIRENE with respect to a light water reactor, let us compare two mixed fast plus thermal reactor systems, in which the thermal share consists entirely of either CIRENE reactors or light water reactors respectively.

89. If we assume for fast reactors a load factor of 80%, an overall fuel inventory of 3.2 kg fissile/MWe and an integral conversion ratio of 1.30 their penetration would correspond respectively to 40% of the total nuclear capacity in the first case and to about 36% in the second case. These data refer to an overall nuclear load factor of 65% and a plutonium production of 0.33 kg/MWe - year for CIRENE reactors and 0.28 kg/MWe - year for light water reactors.

90. The larger penetration allowed to fast reactors by CIRENE type plants results in a reduced uranium requirement: about 35,000 t in the considered decade for fast plus CIRENE system against 55,000 t for the fast plus LWR system.

91. It can be seen from these figures that the installation of a substantial capacity of CIRENE plants could improve the conditions for launching a fast reactor generation.

REFERENCES

1. Prototipo CIRENE: Considerazioni generali, avan-progetto, analisi dei costi. CISE Report R-205, Milano, July 1966.

2. CARTWRIGHT H. The design of the Steam Generating Heavy Water Reactor. Atom No. 137, 1968 (February), 26-37.

3. PON G.A. CANDU-BLW-250. Paper No. SM-99/32, Symposium on Heavy Water Power Reactors, IAEA, Vienna, 11th-15th September, 1967.

4. CASAGRANDE I. The CIRENE prototype reactor. Nucl. Eng., 1967, 9 (September), 685-690.

5. PETERLONGO G., POSSA G. and VALLI G. Studio preliminare degli organi di regolazione rapida e di arresto rapido per il reattore CIRENE. CISE Report R-201, Milano, October 1964.

6. SILVESTRI M. Some remarks on H_2O fog cooled reactors moderated with cold heavy water and fuelled with natural uranium. Energia Nucleare, 1967, 9 (September), 509-18.

7. SEABORG G.T. Nuclear power - two years after Geneva. Annual lecture to the BNES, London, 24th October, 1966.

The Swedish programme on vessel HWRs

P. H. MARGEN, BSc(Eng), FIEE,   Manager, Reactor Engineering Dept., AB Atomenergi, Sweden

SYNOPSIS   Swedish HWRs use D_2O as moderator and coolant and pressure vessels.   The Ågesta PHWR has operated since 1963/64 with very low D_2O leakage and high availability. Commissioning of the Marviken 200 MWe BHWR is due for early 1969.   Features of these units and of designs for commercial BHWRs are discussed.

Current designs for large BHWRs use concrete pressure vessels and a project for building a model vessel in Sweden by Scandinavian funds has started.   Discussion of economic and technical parameters indicated that expected trends for the cost of uranium, plutonium, fuel fabrication and reprocessing and the size of units all favour the economics of natural uranium HWRs in general and the highly neutron economic BHWRs in particular.

Long term resource considerations and the important part which HWRs could play in this respect are discussed with reference to very recent international studies.

BACKGROUND (ref. 1)

1.   Sweden is a small country by most standards, certainly the smallest which has engaged in the task of developing reactor systems to the stage where they can be commercially exploited.   However, the electricity demand is high in relation to the population and should thus eventually provide a market of a reasonable size.   For instance, it is now estimated that at least 6000 MWe of nuclear plant should be installed by 1980 and around 15,000 MWe by 1985.   Swedish industry has also a good record of development and export including the conventional power plant field.   Hence, the desire to build up a strong position also in the nuclear field was understandable.   Lastly, it has very large though low grade uranium resources which create at least an alternative supply in possible emergency situations, eventually probably an economic home supply.

2.   With this general background, Sweden decided in the middle of the 1950s to prepare for an independent reactor development effort.

ÅGESTA (refs 2, 3)

3.   The annals of heavy water reactors (HWRs) in Sweden go far back in time.   As early as 1954, R1, a 600 kW research HWR (later uprated to 1 MW) designed by AB Atomenergi (AE) was commissioned in Stockholm.   It is still in satisfactory operation.

4.   By late 1958, a unanimous decision was reached by Swedish utilities (the State Power Board, SV, and Stockholm Electricity Board), Industry (ASEA) and AE to commit a prototype HWR of 65 MW thermal rating at Ågesta to gain general experience for power reactors of this type.

5.   The selection of D_2O as moderator was motivated mainly by

(a)   the ability to use natural uranium with implications of independence from a limited number of great powers with enrichment facilities, possibly to use own uranium resources, favourable trade balance

(b)   the very low fuel cycle costs and resulting favourable economy predicted for large units,

though of these (a) gradually assumed decreasing emphasis for the home market.

6.   A choice as important as that of the moderator was the selection of water (as opposed to gas or organic) as coolant. This made it possible to utilize directly the technology on materials and fuel elements and most of the technology on components built up by the vast US light water reactor (LWR) programme.   Pressurized water (D_2O) was preferred to boiling water at this early stage primarily because of the better known water chemistry and stability.

7.   The third significant choice was that of a vessel design preferred to pressure tubes mainly on the grounds of the simpler single moderator and coolant circuit; the reduced leakage problems (fewer joints);

Table 1

			Ågesta	Marviken	Concrete vessel BHWR	
1.	REACTOR TYPE					
	(a) General type		PHWR	BHWR	BHWR	
	(b) Cycle		Indirect	Direct+nuc.sup.	Direct	Indirect
	(c) Circulation		Forced	Natural	Natural	Natural
2.	POWER					
	(a) Electrical (net)	MW	10	196	600	600
	(b) Thermal (gross)	MW	65	591	1906	2002
	(c) Efficiency (net)	%	-*	34.4	31.5	30.0
3.	WORKING PRESSURES					
	(a) Primary	bar	34	49.5	69.0	80.7
	(b) Secondary	bar	14.3	-	69.0	45.5
4.	CORE					
	(a) Height	m	3.05	4.42	5.12	4.38
	(b) Diameter	m	3.60	4.30	6.84	8.08
	(c) Volume	m^3	1.75	64.1	188	224
	(d) Reflected vol.	m^3	31.0	94.6	312	372
5.	FUEL ASSEMBLIES			Boil. Sup.		
	(a) Number		140	147 32	346	459
	(b) Number of rods/ass.		76	36 45	37	37
	(c) Rod diam. (UO$_2$)	mm	17	12.5 13.0	14.1	14.1
	(d) Can material		Zr-2	Zr-2 Incoloy	Zr-2	Zr-2
	(e) Can thickness	mm	0.7	0.6 0.4	0.55	0.55
	(f) Mean enrichment	%	0.712	1.42	0.712	0.712
	(g) Burn-up	MWd/tU	~5000	~13000	9900	9760
6.	RATINGS					
	(a) Mean	kW/kg	3.25	16.9	19.2	17.9
	(b) Mean	W/cm	78.5	193 195	291	259
	(c) Max. transient	W/cm	314	560 540	665	627
	(d) Max. transient	kW/chan.	760	5500 5800	8650	6960
7.	INVENTORIES					
	(a) Uranium	tonne	18.5	33.6	99	107.5
	(b) D$_2$O (total in station)	tonne	69.2	180	452	470

*Heat used for district heating.

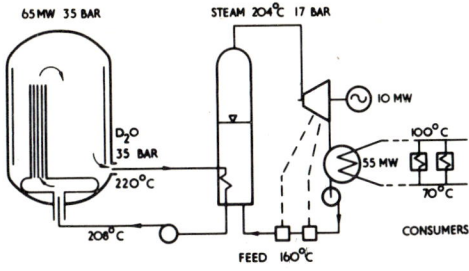

Fig. 1: Ågesta PHWR. Simplified flow diagram

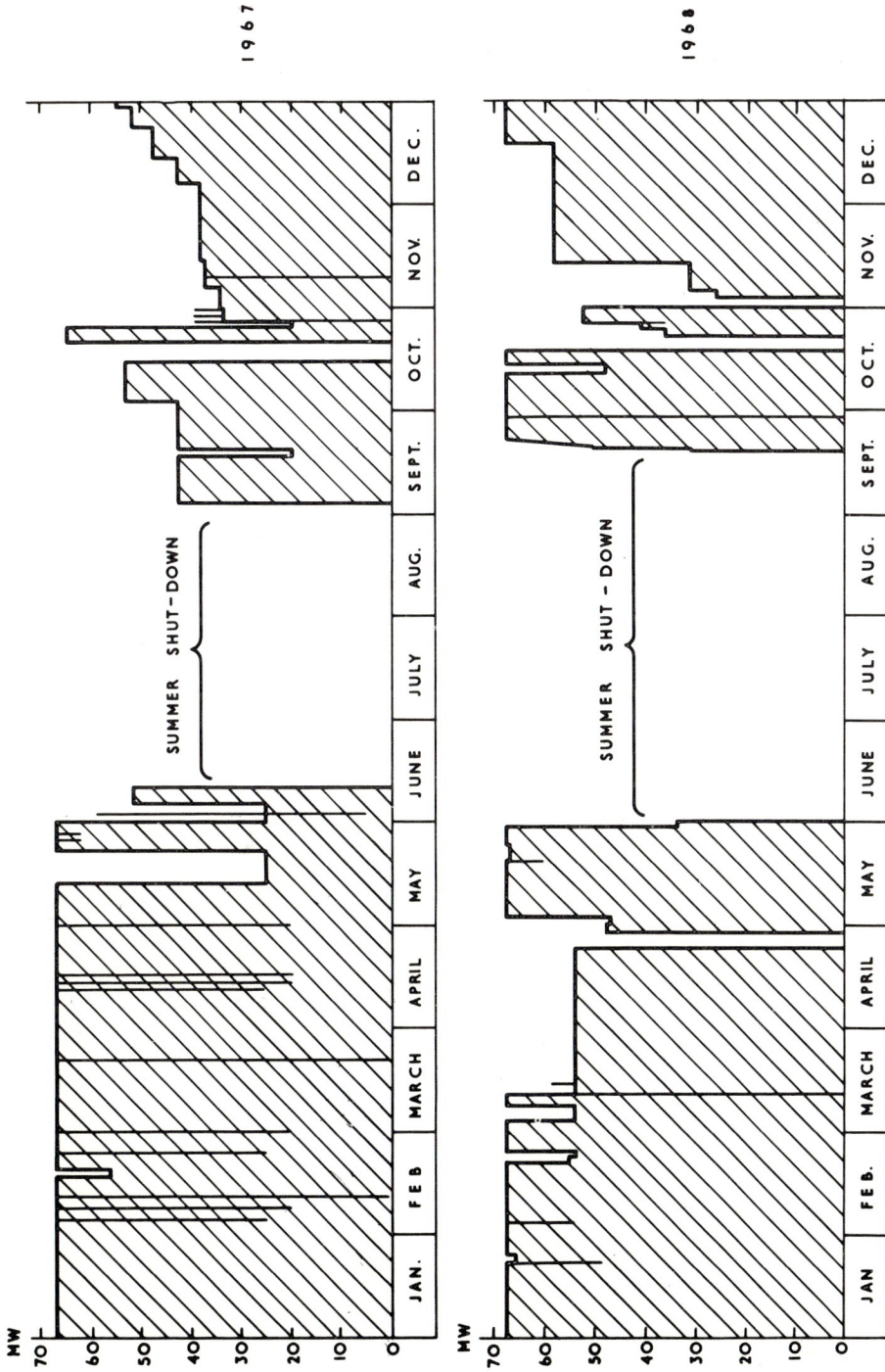

Fig. 2: Ågesta PHWR. Reactor availability, 1966 and 1967

and Swedish heavy engineering background applicable to pressure vessels aided by some US component experience.

8. Fig. 1 shows a schematic of the reactor and circuit, and Table 1, Column 1, some leading data. The reactor is used to supply 55 MW of heat for district heating of the Farsta suburb of Stockholm and 10 MW of electricity from a back-pressure turbine. The principle design was carried out by AE whilst the main contractor, ASEA, and sub-contractors carried out detailed design. The station was jointly financed by the previously mentioned utilities and AE.

9. Ågesta reached criticality in 1963 and full power in March 1964. Fig. 2 shows the operating record. One prolonged shut down occurred during the winter 1964/65 due to cracks on some sample tubes not forming part of the power reactor proper, but apart from this the availability was very satisfactory. The reactor is shut down each summer during a period when the heat demand practically ceases. Excluding this period, the average availability for the operating seasons 65/66 and 66/67 was 89% and the availability excluding routine outage for exchanging experimental fuel assemblies for later reactors exceeded 96%.

10. Leakage performance was particularly satisfactory. In the four years since criticality, the integrated net loss from all causes was only about 800 kg, corresponding to about 0.25% of the inventory per annum. Expressed per hour operation at full pressure, the total loss was 5 to 7 g and the 'chronic loss' around 2 g. These values have been determined by tritium activity measurements and checked by inventory. The loss curve for 1965/66 is shown by Fig. 3, illustrating the normal low loss gradient, the sudden increase when some leak occurs and the return to the 'chronic rate' as soon as this has been repaired. The leakage of H_2O has been practically non existent - some tens of kg over the four years of operation.

11. The excellent leakage record is partly attributed to the vessel design which reduces the number of joints to a minimum; partly to the careful detail design and workmanship with welding being used wherever possible; and partly to the absence of a D_2O recovery system from the reactor vault. The latter feature - together with the low basic leakage rates - assure a low activity level in the reactor vault, permitting initiating leaks to be promptly detected and remedied.

12. In summary, the Ågesta reactor has been the training object for Swedish design teams and nuclear industry but has also given valuable lessons in its own right - particularly regarding the manner of achieving a leak tight D_2O system.

MARVIKEN (refs 4, 5)

13. Even while Ågesta was being committed it was realized that it would have to be followed by a larger station to extrapolate the experience of manufacturers to larger components and to serve as a closer prototype to commercial units. Marviken became this larger prototype. After several years of comparisons between alternative designs it was decided to incorporate a number of advances compared to Agesta while retaining the three basic features of D_2O as moderator; water as coolant; and a vessel design. As illustrated by the schematic arrangement, Fig. 4, the following more advanced features were, however, incorporated:

(1) boiling D_2O as opposed to pressurized D_2O

(2) natural circulation

(3) direct cycle

(4) on load refuelling

(5) possibility for nuclear superheat

(6) pressure suppression containment.

Features (1), (2) and (3) together permitted the complete elimination of the coolant loops with its heat exchangers, pumps, electrical supplies, volume requirement within and outside the expansive pressure suppression space, etc., and it is expected that these features would together achieve important capital cost reductions when applied to large units. Major technical problems had to be solved if these aims were to be attained and accordingly a strong supporting development programme was mounted.

14. For the boiling channels this programme included, for instance, very extensive burn-out and instability tests which culminated with tests of full scale 36-rod assemblies in a 6 to 8 MW rig where natural circulation powers for an excess of the 'hot channel' power to the Marviken reactor was achieved, Fig. 5. In-pile tests were also performed in the Ågesta and Halden reactors, whilst the physics - including the vital void reactivity coefficients - were established by extensive tests in the critical R0 and hot exponential facilities at Studsvik.

15. Steam water separation was another important area, as Marviken will be the world's largest boiling water reactor with natural circulation. Experiments confirmed that the cluster fuel geometry of BHWRs allowed the use of favourable separation geometries which gave satisfactory performances at the channel powers of interest for Marviken and even much larger BHWRs.

16. The feature attracting perhaps most attention, however, was the use of the D_2O steam directly in the turbine. Here full scale tests were carried out on

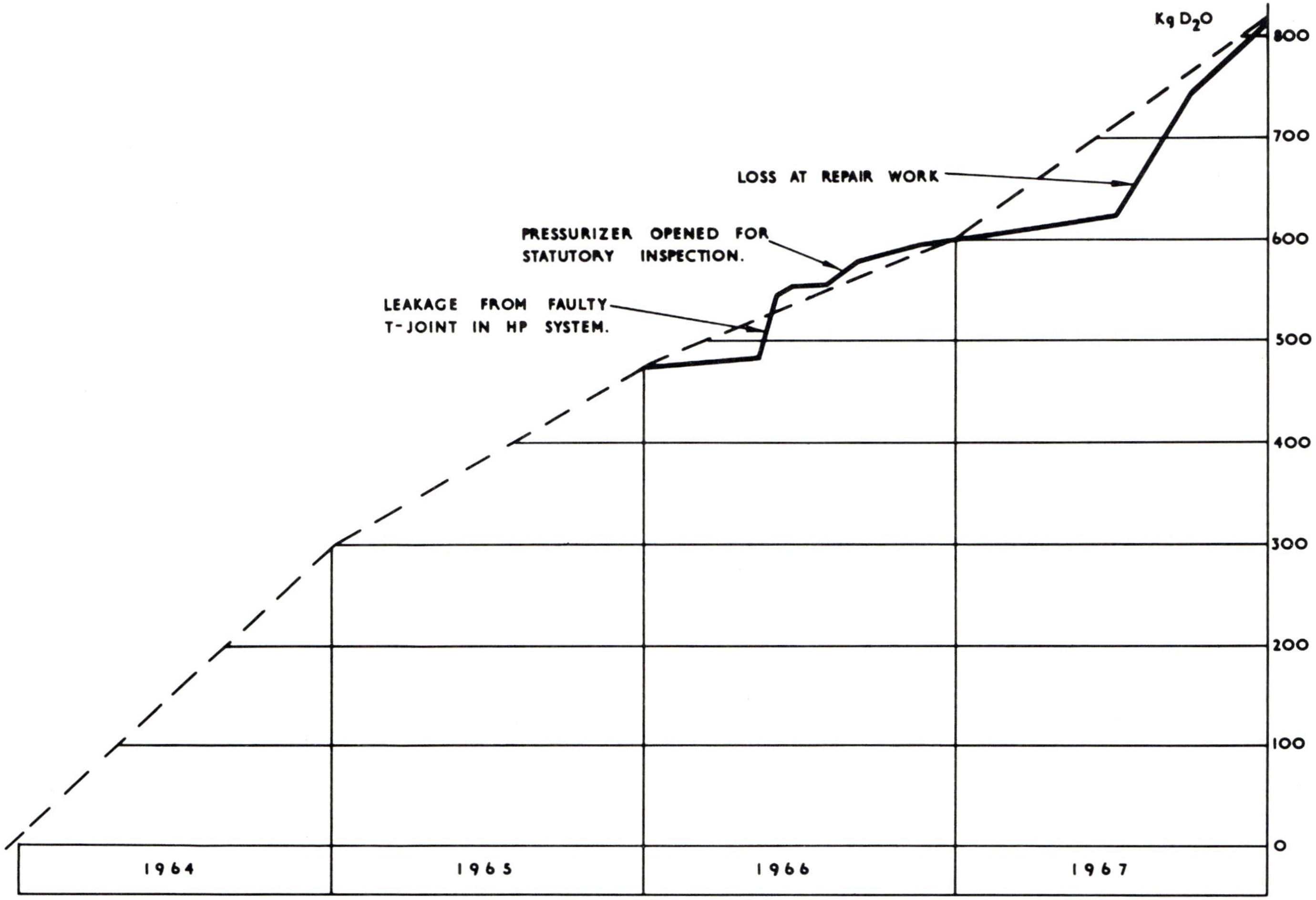
Kg D2O
800
700
600
500
400
300
200
100
0
LOSS AT REPAIR WORK
PRESSURIZER OPENED FOR
STATUTORY INSPECTION.
LEAKAGE FROM FAULTY
T-JOINT IN HP SYSTEM.
1964
1965
1966
1967

Fig. 3: Ågesta PHWR. Integrated D_2O leakage, 1964-1967

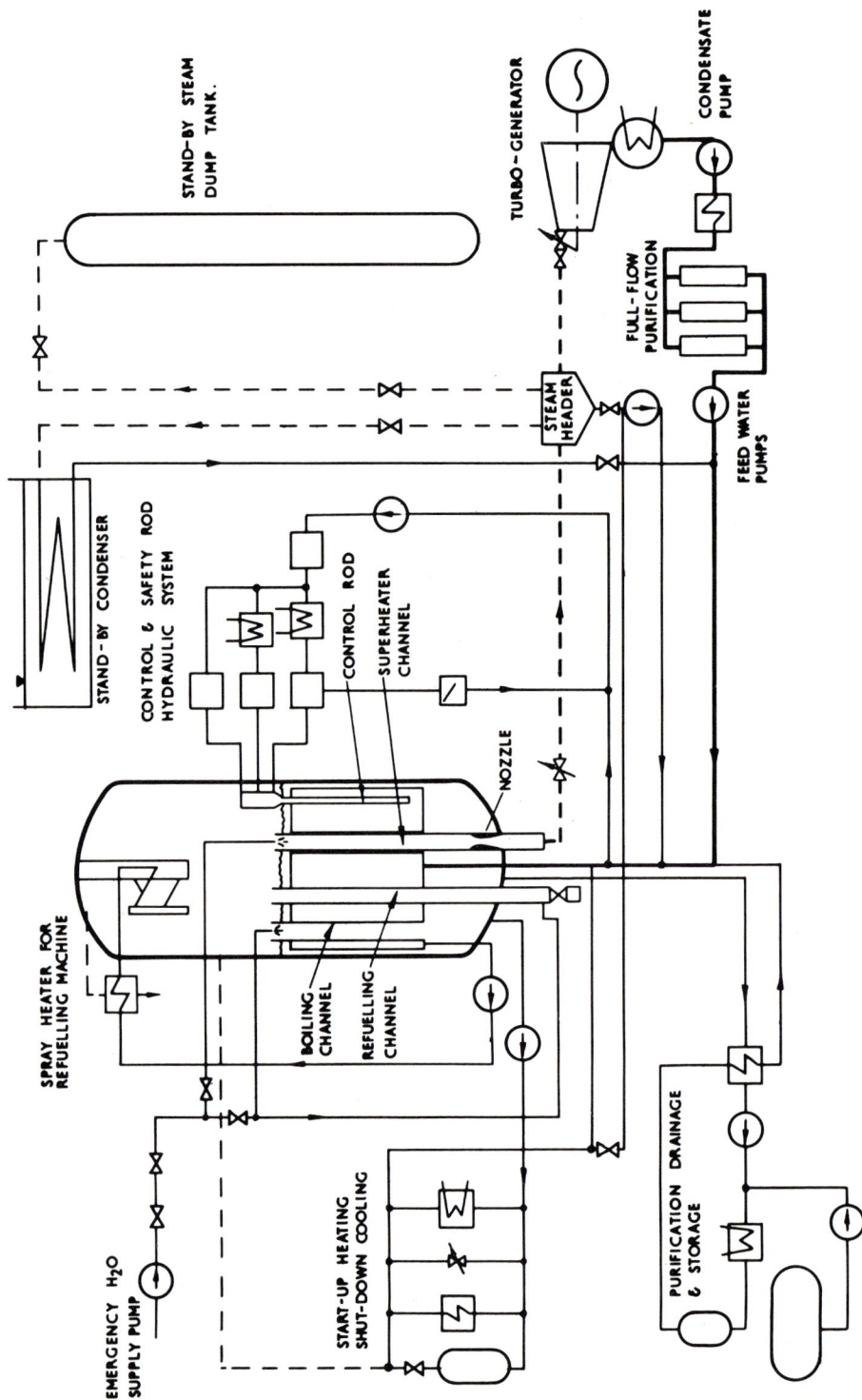

Fig. 4: Marviken BHWR. Simplified flow diagram

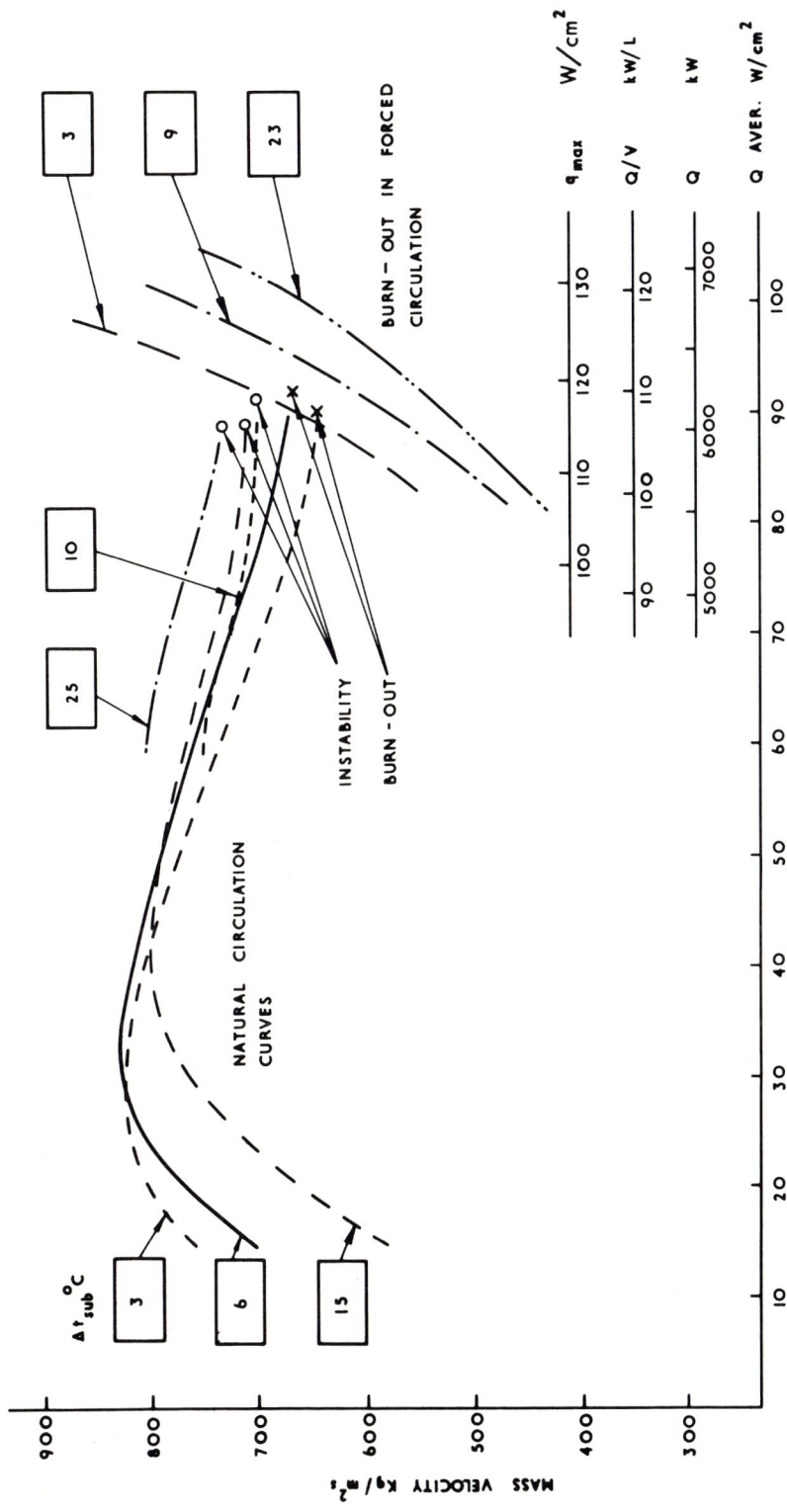

Fig. 5: 36-rod experiments in the FRIGG loop

213

turbine seals supplied with dried air to a shaft chamber between two labyrinths, and three power station condensers and one model condenser all with automatically rolled in joints and single tube plates were tested for inleakage of H_2O. The results indicated low D_2O loss and inleakage rates. Work of this type coupled with statistical analysis of condenser tube faults and development of rapid leak detection devices suggested that overall leakage rates in D_2O turbo-generators should be very low.

17. Feature 4, in the above list, on-load refuelling, has economic advantages particularly for natural uranium reactors where frequent or continuous refuelling reduces fuel cycle costs. In addition, it should reduce outage times for planned refuelling operations and the forced removal of faulty assemblies.

18. The Marviken refuelling scheme involves an internal manipulator which can be swivelled into position above any fuel channel, a mechanical grab on a cable and a refuelling shute with a double lock and intermediate drying station. Fuel assemblies can thus be removed without opening any joint between the reactor and atmosphere. The manipulator can be removed for an annual check and overhaul through a small flange in the top of the vessel. The manipulator represented a number of material development problems to find adequate bearing materials for steam atmospheres. Tests in autoclaves have given favourable results for the solution adopted. The machine was assembled at the maker's works and operating sequences were tested. It will shortly be reassembled at site for the final tests.

19. Feature 5, nuclear superheat, is regarded as a development feature which would not be adopted in currently offered BHWRs, the experience from operation of Marviken being awaited prior to any reassessment of this question. Shortened 5-rod prototypes of the fuel assemblies were irradiated in the superheated steam loop of the R2 reactor in Studsvik at maximum can temperatures and steam velocities and no failures occurred. A full scale 48-rod assembly was also submitted to out-of-pile endurance and vibration tests at full steam pressures and velocities.

20. The last feature, pressure suppression containment, follows basically the principle adopted in BWRs for taking care of the steam released due to pipe ruptures. Steam from the safety valves is, however, taken to a special tank which serves as a hot sink until the emergency condenser can cope with the residual heat release.

21. Progress on site is proceeding in accordance to plans with the building work complete, Fig. 6. The vessel is in position and most primary pipes are welded in place. Full power operation is due for Spring 1969.

22. On the customers' side, AE has the main responsibility, with the State Power Board acting as architect engineer. ASEA is the main contractor. Designs for the reactor were prepared jointly by AE and ASEA. The station is financed jointly by AE and the State Power Board.

OSKARSHAMN NUCLEAR POWER STATION AND THE POSITION OF LWRs (ref. 6)

23. Although this paper is concerned with the Swedish programme on HWRs, it is important to explain also the relation of this work to that being carried out on LWRs and the position of Swedish utilities on this work.

24. Whilst work on the Ågesta and Marviken HWRs proceeded, the private utilities in Sweden had been examining for some time the possibility of constructing independently a small (50 MW) BWR to gain experience. By 1964/65 the favourable cost data for LWRs in US had convinced them that a 400 MW BWR located at Oskarshamn would be competitive with conventional power. After collecting preliminary prices from various makers, a contract was awarded to ASEA in the middle of 1965 who submitted their own design, without license from any US firm. It was based on the experience gained by ASEA on the Ågesta and Marviken projects which have much technology in common with LWRs, published information on BWRs and ASEA's own specific BWR design work. In addition, an agreement was made with AE who agreed to do development work on important aspects such as physics, fuel testing and the development of steam separators. The 400 MWe BWR at Oskarshamn is scheduled for commissioning in 1970.

25. Thus, the decision to select water as coolant for the initial HWRs in Sweden to allow US technology to be used has now paid dividends in allowing Swedish industry to add, with a minimum of additional work, also LWRs to their 'product line'. This is illustrated by the schematic presentation of the Swedish programme, Fig. 7.

COMMERCIAL HWRs (ref. 7)

26. The work on Ågesta and Marviken was followed by designs being prepared for commercial HWR stations. The Johnson Company and AE prepared joint designs for a pressurized HWR (PHWR) with a uniform lattice which used a maximum of PWR technology. After making some offers to overseas customers, the Johnson Co., however, decided to leave the field of main contractors, and to concentrate on components.*

27. The ASEA Company selected instead BHWRs, using basically the design for

*It has recently joined ASEA in a consortium in which ASEA acts as technical co-ordinator.

Fig. 6: Marviken BHWR. Site photo, January 1968

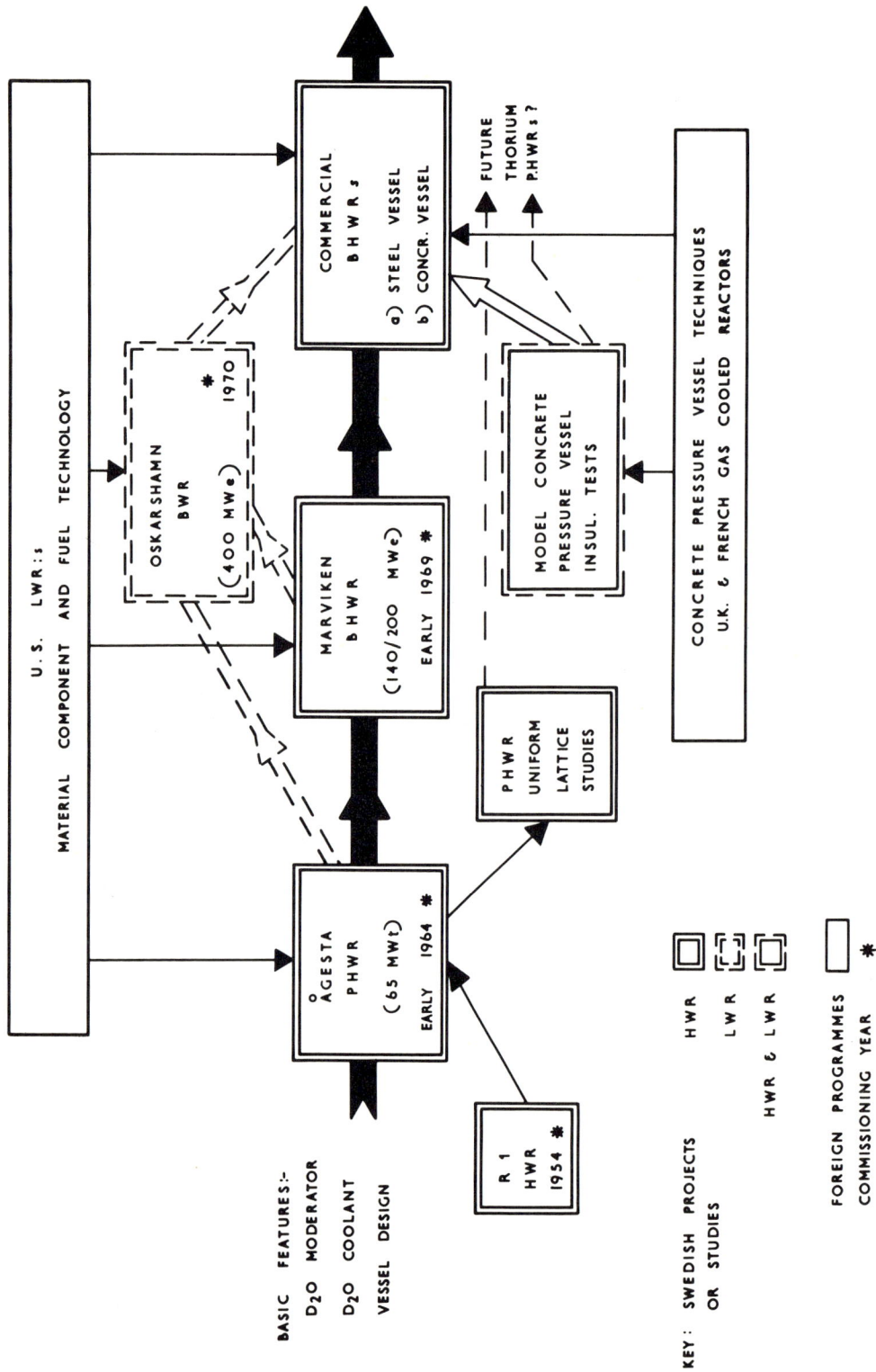

Fig. 7: Swedish HWR programme and relations to available technology

Marviken, but with the simplifications which the omission of nuclear superheat allowed. AE assisted with development work. Tenders for such reactors have been invited by and submitted to several overseas customers.

28. The circuit can be based on natural circulation, Fig. 8, or forced circulation, with the former giving better calculated economy for designs in which a positive void coefficient is not permitted, so that a fairly large coolant to fuel area ratio has to be chosen, which suits natural circulation. This gives the simplest system. When moderate positive void coefficients are permitted (which requires additional functions for the control system), a slight further improvement in economy can be obtained by using forced circulation. The axial pumps for these designs are located in the bottom of the reactor vessel with the motors below the vessel as shown on Fig. 8a. The pumps can be removed downwards. Columns 3 and 4 in Table 1 show typical data for BHWRs with natural and forced circulation respectively and direct cycles.

29. For BHWRs of large output, steel vessels welded on site or prestressed concrete pressure vessels have to be chosen and the latter give the lowest calculated cost. They are discussed in more detail in paras 31 to 36. For the steel vessel case, improved high strength steels with improved site welding and properties and reduced heat treatment requirements have been developed and are expected to be commercially available soon.

30. Whilst it is considered that the direct cycle gives somewhat (2 to 3%) lower costs than an indirect cycle, some potential customers may not accept a direct cycle until operating experience from Marviken has been obtained. Hence designs have also been prepared for indirect cycle BHWRs. In the case of concrete pressure vessels, the heat exchangers for these can be located within the vessel, as illustrated by Fig. 8. This is an approach which has also created increasing interest in Germany and France, and increasing co-operation between Sweden and these countries has occurred lately. For instance, a joint offer on a large BHWR is due to be made to Rumania by ASEA, Siemens and SOCIA representing the three countries.

CONCRETE PRESSURE VESSELS FOR HWRs
(refs 8, 9)

31. Concrete pressure vessels have a number of advantages for water reactors. They eliminate discussion on the possibility of crack propagation in steel vessels and, as the number of steel cables is large, they do not substitute a new corresponding subject for safety discussion. They avoid limitations concerning size regarding shop fabrication or transport - or the additional costs of

site fabrication of large steel vessels. They tend to save costs largely due to the fact that the concrete vessel serves three functions - that of pressure vessel, biological shield and merit of the containment.

32. Though experience on pre-stressed concrete pressure vessels is available from gas cooled reactors, application to water reactors involves new problems in all three above areas, namely

(a) the thermal insulation

(b) the design of a removable lid - which though not essential for BHWRs is an advantage - particularly for designs with integral heat exchangers

(c) the higher pressure.

33. Regarding the insulation, Swedish designs are based on the use of a metal foil insulation (e.g., the variants in use for British gas cooled reactors and proposed for some of the latest French ones) in an atmosphere of nitrogen, with a water lock separating the nitrogen from the steam, as illustrated in Fig. 9. Under pressure transients, the water surface in the lock acts as a piston compressing or expanding the gas in the insulation. A coolant system keeps the water surface normally below the temperature of the water cooled steel liner of the pressure vessel, avoiding condensation in the insulation. Tests in Studsvik have shown that the heat loss with an insulation of about 3 cm would be a fraction of a promille of the reactor power, and that the losses would be acceptable even under the worst accident condition, namely rupture of the bottom casing separating the gas space from the moderator space (a very unlikely event due to the absence of any significant pressure difference between these spaces). Duplicate coolant water systems are provided for the lining, either of which is sufficient for normal operation. In the case of the worst accident mentioned above, both are needed to keep the concrete below 70°C.

34. Due to the interest in removable vessel heads for concrete pressure vessels applied to LWRs and to a lesser extent, HWRs, many organizations abroad have started design work on this feature. Some of these use steel heads - which removes some of the safety advantages of the concrete vessels - others have joints subject to considerable movement, and again others require long times for lock removal and replacement. These pitfalls are avoided by the Swedish design illustrated in Fig. 8. It uses steel wedges pushed into position by hydraulic jacks to give contact between a collar on the vessel and a ring on top of the lid along the whole circumference of the lid but not used for pre-stressing the cables. They are used also to loosen the wedges prior to removal. The inner edge of the steel collar has separate teeth to prevent crack propagation affecting more than one tooth.

1. BOILING CHANNELS
2. REFUELLING SHUTE
3. FUEL MANIPULATOR
4. CONTROL RODS
5. MODERATOR INLET PIPES
6. STEAM GENERATORS
7. STEAM OUTLET PIPES (BEHIND THESE FEED WATER INLET PIPES)
8. WATER LOCK
9. REMOVABLE VESSEL LID

(a) DESIGN MODIFICATION FOR FORCED CIRCULATION

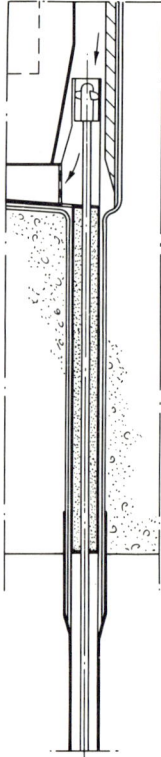

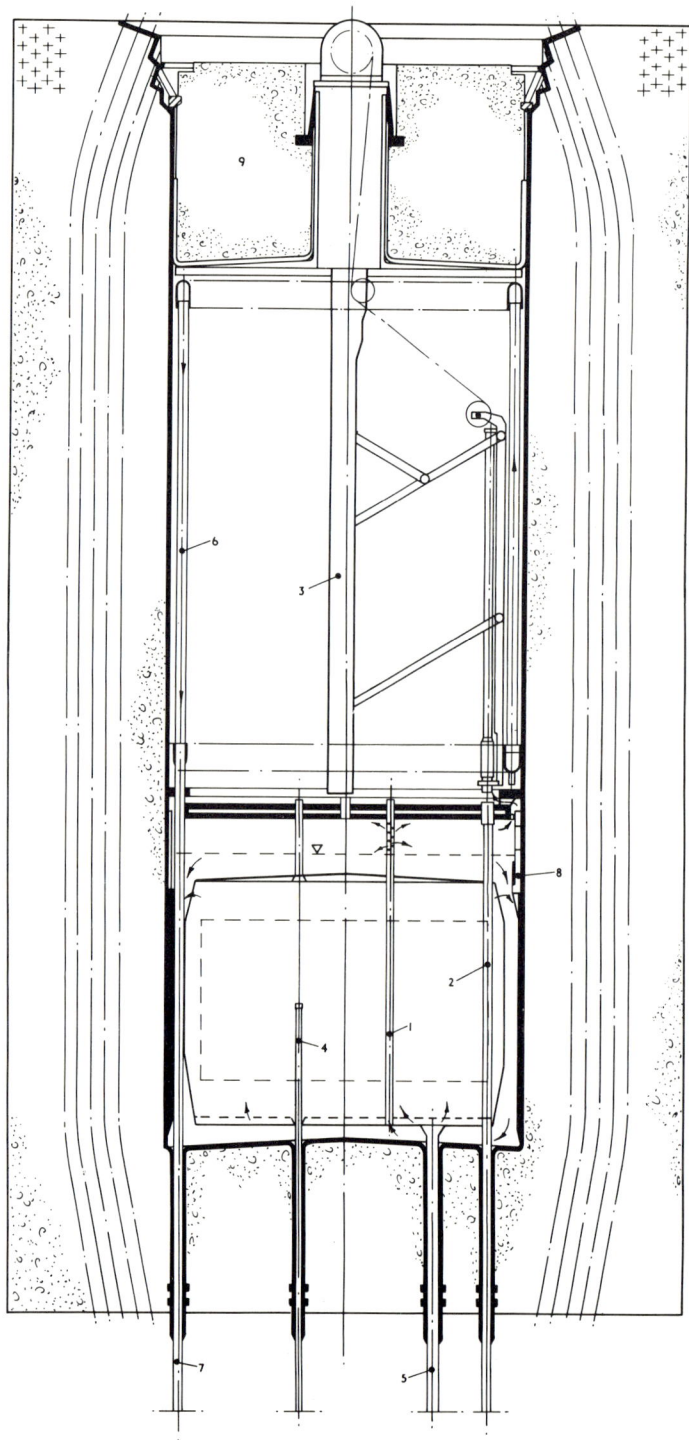

Fig. 8: 600 MWe BHWR with concrete pressure vessel, integral design and natural circulation

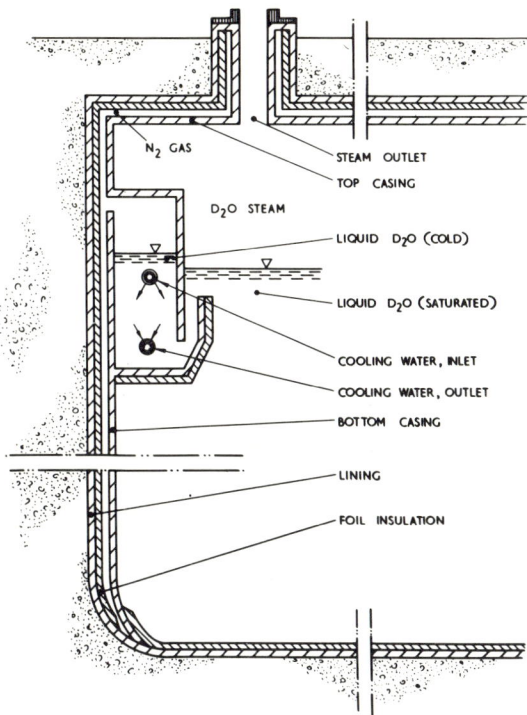

Fig. 9:   Thermal insulation for concrete
          pressure vessel

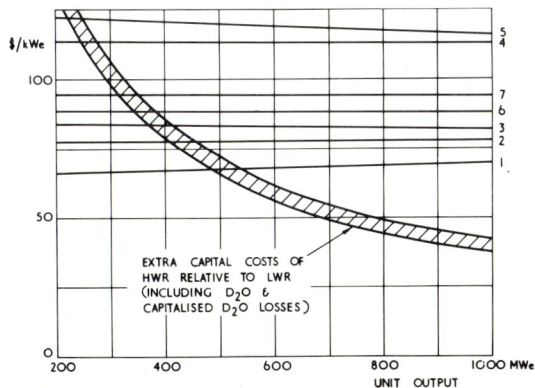

CURVE	NORMALISED FUEL FABRICATION COST $ / kg U	REFERENCE (HWR) REPROCESS. COST $ / kg U	URANIUM COST $/LB U_3O_8	Pu COST $/ g FISS. Pu	DEPRECIATION PERIOD YEARS
1	40	32	7	10	25
2	20	32	7	10	25
3	20	16	7	10	25
4	20	16	14	10	25
5	20	16	14	20	25
6	INITIAL $40/kg U HALVED IN 30 YRS.	INITIAL $32/kg U HALVED IN 30 YRS.	INITIAL $7/LB U_3O_8 DOUBLED IN 30 YRS.	INITIAL $10/g DOUBLED IN 30 YRS.	25
7					30

OTHER ASSUMPTIONS
LOAD FACTOR 80%
INTEREST RATE 7%

REPROCESSING COST INCLUDES
CONVERSION FROM NITRATES TO
OXIDES (NO U-CREDIT FOR HWR'S).
NORMALISED FUEL FABRICATION COST
REFERS TO 14 MM ROD DIAM. NAT U.
ACTUAL COSTS VARY AS 1/D IN
APPLICABLE RANGE.

NOTE :-
INFLUENCE OF FUEL THROUGHPUT
ON COSTS PER kg FOR FABRICATION
& REPROCESSING IGNORED; ALSO
INFLUENCE OF INTEGRATED
U-REQUIREMENT ON COST OF U
PER kg. ALLOWANCE FOR THESE FACTORS
WOULD IMPROVE HWR ECONOMICS.

Fig. 10:   Economic comparison between natural
           uranium BHWR and BWR

219

35. A model pressure vessel based on the designs shown in Figs 8 and 9 will shortly be built at Studsvik with funds provided by the National Development Organization's utilities and industrial companies of the four Scandinavian countries, with AE as the host organization. The model will have an internal diameter of 2 m and will be provided with the previously described thermal insulation and removable lid and with realistic penetrations. It will be tested cold and hot and may eventually be taken to destruction once all other desired information has been obtained. The objectives include more detailed tests on the insulation on a larger scale than hitherto performed with a realistic representation of all practical factors such as penetrations and breakable joints at the edges of the lid, testing of the behaviour of the lid, checks of calculation codes at high pressures, experience in construction and demonstration for safety authorities.

36. The novel feature of the higher pressure (about 70 bars working pressure equivalent to 85 bars design pressure would be used for direct cycle BHWRs, somewhat higher values for indirect cycle units) has been dealt with by the development of more refined calculation methods in several countries, including Sweden. The Swedish programmes include three dimensional stress calculation codes based on relaxation principles and temperature distribution codes which can be coupled to one another. Confirmation of the codes is sought in model tests and here also the previously mentioned model vessel programme will play its part.

ECONOMY (refs 7, 10)

37. HWRs with a good neutron economy (such as the Swedish BHWRs) have very low fuel cycle costs. Fig. 10 shows the capitalized cost advantages earning from the fuel cycle for BHWRs optimized for natural uranium compared to LWRs. It will be seen that this is substantially independent of reactor output, but quite strongly dependent on uranium price, normalized fabrication costs per kg and reprocessing costs per kg.

38. The same figure also shows the additional capital investment per kW in the plant and D_2O for the HWRs compared to LWRs. This falls strongly with increasing unit output, as certain plant components costing more in HWRs (e.g., refuelling plants) have a total cost almost independent of reactor output - the optimum fuel channel length being practically constant over a wide range. Hence an output is reached at which the five sets of curves cross. To the right of this point HWRs are more economic. For the accountancy conditions for which Fig. 10 is drawn and current costs of uranium and fabrication, this crossover point occurs at about 600 MW.

39. On the other hand, as discussed later, uranium prices and plutonium credits are expected to rise over the life of the plant whilst fabrication costs per kg and reprocessing costs per kg should fall as a result of technical progress and the increasing scale of plants. The latter feature affects the cost of natural uranium plants with their relatively low burn-up (9000-10,000 MWd/tU) more than enriched reactors such as LWRs. If account of all these factors is taken the minimum economic size of HWRs is substantially reduced and HWRs which have costs equal to those of LWRs at the beginning of their life reach substantially lower costs than LWRs at the end of their life (and integrated over the whole life) as illustrated in Fig. 11.

40. BHWRs optimized for slightly enriched uranium have still lower costs than natural BHWRs in the size ranges of current interest at present fuel fabrication and reprocessing costs but, due to their high burn-up, they do not benefit as much as natural uranium BHWRs from future reduction in these prices. Nor do they benefit as much from probable future increases in the value of plutonium. Thus, taken over a practical working life, large natural uranium units should achieve the better overall economy.

41. HWRs have an assured position for markets in which there is a distinct preference for natural uranium. The success of HWRs in markets lacking this preference will depend, to a large extent, on whether or not the promoters of this system succeed in persuading utilities to take account of the changes in fuel cycle costs to be expected over the life of stations ordered at present. If so, very substantial economic incentives can be shown to exist which should be sufficient to counteract the sales appeal by LWRs as a result of their prior development and recent vast sales successes in the USA.

LONG TERM ASPECTS (refs 11, 12, 13)

42. The promoters of national programmes have become increasingly aware in recent years that it is not sufficient to select reactor types now on the basis of present economics and to develop future reactors without regard to the types now being ordered. Certain present and future reactor types are complementary - for instance good plutonium producing converters fit well with fast, plutonium inventory demanding, breeders, whilst other reactor types are almost irreconcilable, e.g., bad plutonium producers or thorium reactors and fast breeders. Sweden has reached the conclusion that fast breeders are likely to be introduced on the world reactor market around 1980 due to vast effort put into this system in many countries and its potential merits, and thus initiated some effort in this field with a goal of co-operative effort with other nations. Such an interest in fast breeders should provide an added advantage

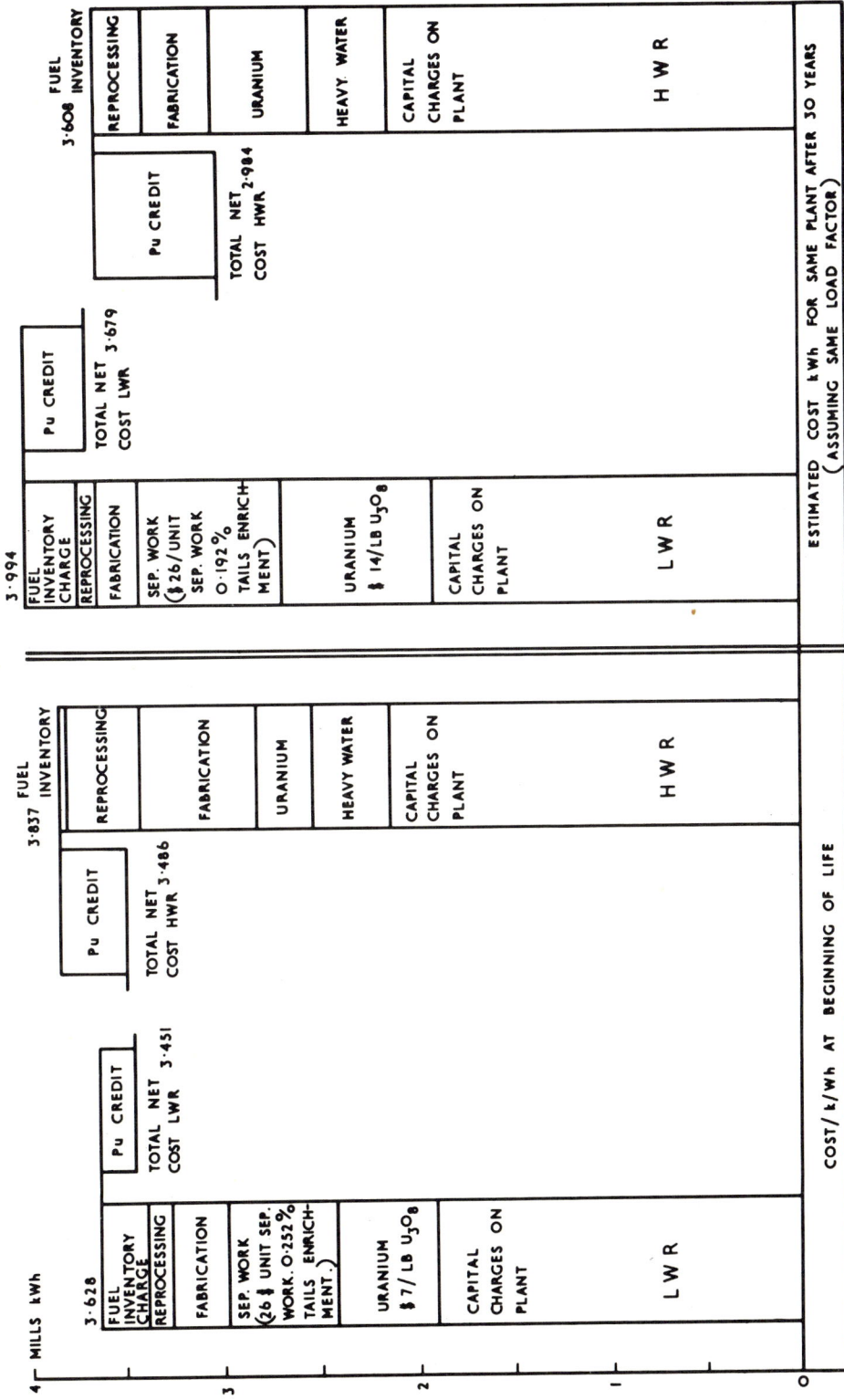

Fig. 11: Influence of possible future cost trends on economic comparison between LWRs and HWRs

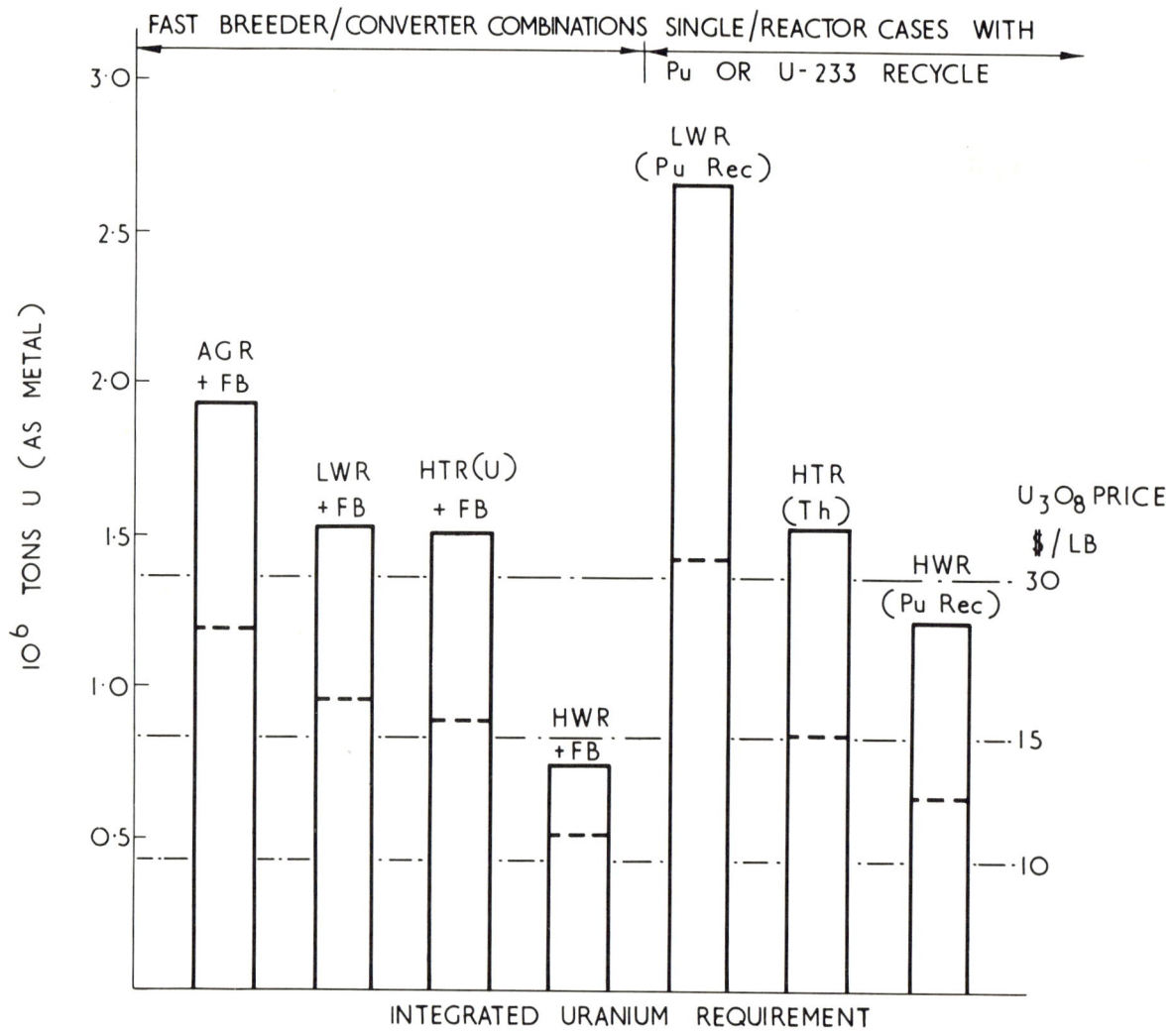

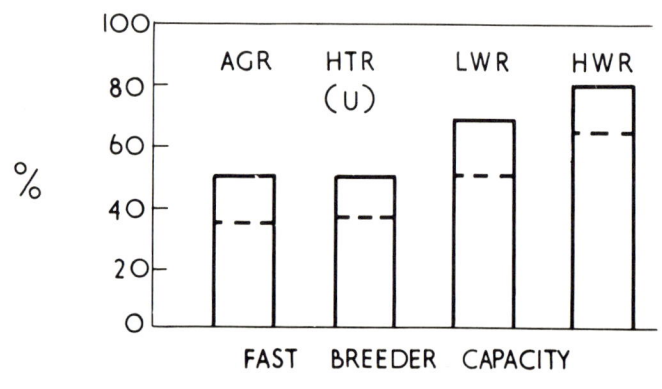

Fig. 12: Influence of reactor programme on estimated uranium requirements for Western Europe

to natural uranium HWRs which, apart from the now outdated magnox reactors are the best plutonium producers per unit energy.

43. Fig. 12 compares, for instance, natural uranium HWRs with LWRs, AGRs and HTRs operating on a uranium cycle as potential partners of fast breeder reactors assumed to become available in 1980. The top part of the diagram shows the integrated uranium requirements over the periods, 1970-2000 and 1970-2010 respectively, whilst the bottom staples show the fast breeder capacities which can be installed. The uranium requirement calculations are based on the latest data on power reactor characteristics recommended by an international team of ENEA experts, and the nuclear load predictions for Western Europe by the corresponding OECD experts. The last two staples on the diagram show HWRs operating without fast breeders on a plutonium recycle and thorium cycle respectively, and even these cases are seen to use less uranium over the period considered than all the converter/breeder combinations except that involving HWRs.

44. Uranium requirements of the magnitudes illustrated by Fig. 12 can have considerable economic significance. If, for instance, it is assumed that uranium resources will be found in the various price brackets in accordance with the 'reasonably assured plus probable additional resources' (for the regions in which some prospecting has been carried out) estimated in the ENEA report, then the influence of price increases in uranium above the estimated 1970 price of $7/lb U_3O_8 would affect the economic comparison of HWR + FB and AGR + FB strategies by a present worth amount (in 1970) of about $30x10^9 - if the whole Western World would choose between these alternatives (ref. 13). A 7% interest rate was used for this computation. But even in other respects, long time developments favour strategies involving HWRs, e.g., the increased rate of fast breeder installation made possible by the high plutonium production rates, the general trend of increasing unit sizes and the decreasing fuel fabrication and reprocessing costs.

CONCLUDING REMARKS

45. The paper has summarized the work which has been and is being done on vessel type BHWRs in Sweden and some of their technical and economic properties. At present, Swedish reactor industry offers both HWRs and LWRs of Swedish designs to customers with different preferences and environments. HWRs have, at present, a difficult task in balancing the appeal to the utilities in western industrial countries, which the prior start and current US sales boom has given LWRs. The paper has shown, however, that HWRs have compensating advantages including superior economy over the cost trends for various fuel cycle components predicted over the life of the plant, and these advantages

should increase as a function of time. Thus given continuity in the current development and construction programme - which requires the decision in the near future to order some commercial size plant - and adequate information to purchasers and planners, HWRs should conquer a significant share of the world's reactor markets. In this process, concrete pressure vessel BHWRs with their high burn-up with natural uranium, relatively simple circuit with few components, unlimited outputs, and relation to the technology of an established reactor system should play their part.

ACKNOWLEDGEMENT

46. The author is indebted to Mr. I. Haga for the calculations supporting Figs 10 and 11, and to many other colleagues for helpful comments.

REFERENCES

1. SWEDISH STATE POWER BOARD. Power supply in Sweden in the 1970s. December 1967.

2. AB ATOMENERGI. The Ågesta Nuclear Power Station. 1964.

3. ERICSSON E. et al. The Ågesta reactor plant - Operational experience 1963-1967. IAEA Symposium on Heavy Water Power Reactors, Vienna, September 1967.

4. MARGEN P.H. et al. The design of the Marviken Boiling Heavy Water Reactor with nuclear superheat. Geneva Conference, 1964.

5. NILSON R. Heavy water steam in direct cycle Marviken. Nuclear Engineering, June 1966.

6. LEINE L. and MOLIN A. Present status of construction of the 400 MWe Oskarshamn Nuclear Power Station with BWR Reactor. NUCLEX 66, September 1966.

7. MARGEN P.H. Swedish vessel BHWRs - Experience and prospects. Nuclear energy meetings, Milan, December 1966.

8. MARGEN P.H. et al. Prestressed concrete vessels - An application to boiling D_2O reactors. Nucleonics, September 1965.

9. RINGSTAD B. and SKINSTAD A. Performance of insulation for prestressed concrete pressure vessels for boiling heavy water reactors. Nuclear Engineering and Design 1, 1967.

10. HAGA I. Optimisation of BHWRs - Description of programmes and applications. IAEA Symposium on Heavy Water Power Reactors, Vienna, September 1967.

11. ENEA. Power Reactor Characteristics. 1966.

12. ENEA. Prospects for nuclear energy in Western Europe. Illustrative Power Reactor Programmes (due for publication).

13. ENEA. World uranium and thorium resources. February 1968.

The commercial SGHWR

H. CARTWRIGHT, MBE, MA, AMIMechE, MIEE
Director, Water Reactors, UKAEA, Risley

SYNOPSIS

Commercial factors can have a considerable impact on the actual costs of nuclear power stations. Also, as the proportion of electricity generated by nuclear plants becomes more significant, it is important that these plants are technically capable of operating to suit network requirements. The paper describes the particular features of the SGHWR which make it an attractive system for commercial use. The SGHWR can also be built to operate with natural uranium oxide fuel. The differences between the two versions of the system are briefly outlined.

INTRODUCTION

1. At a symposium organized by the IAEA on heavy water power reactors in Vienna during September, 1967, there were few people who did not believe that reactors of this type should play a large part in meeting future electricity needs (ref. 1). The majority, however, were concerned with reactors using natural uranium fuel and many of the arguments in their favour rested on assessments of future world trends. These included factors such as uranium availability, plutonium production and the dates for the introduction of fast reactors. The Steam Generating Heavy Water Reactor differs from the general pattern of reactors discussed at that symposium in that the plant as built at Winfrith uses enriched uranium oxide fuel. A natural uranium fuelled version is feasible and is being closely studied. Much of the nuclear and engineering experience gained in the development and construction of the enriched design is of direct application to the natural system. However, the immediate commercial future of the SGHWR system as a whole rests not so much on what it may have to offer in its various forms in the longer term but on its ability to meet what is wanted by electricity utilities today and in the next few years. It is with these aspects that this paper is largely concerned.

2. It is axiomatic that the SGHWR must at the very least be competitive economically with alternative power plants on whatever ground rules are adopted. All the work that has been done in the development, design and construction of Winfrith, and more recently to support commercial activities outside the United Kingdom, confirm that this is so. Earlier papers to

this conference also show why there is confidence in the nuclear and technical design of the SGHWR. The rapid way in which the Winfrith plant was raised to power, and the fact that its operational behaviour has matched prediction underline the basic capability of the system. But, for a successful nuclear reactor system even with attractive generation costs to be accepted as a truly commercial power plant, there must be confidence that it will satisfy other requirements as well. Among these are a demonstrable expectation that the plant can be built in a reasonable length of time and be brought to power without trouble by a planned date. Once in operation, it must have high availability and it must be capable of fitting into the pattern of load demand for the system to which it is connected. The design must also be such as to give confidence that throughout a life of twenty or more years the plant can be inspected and, if necessary, maintained without undue difficulty. These objectives were well to the fore in the design of the Winfrith SGHWR, and even more so when studying designs for commercial plants.

3. When considering the possible lines of development for any major commercial plant, it is important to look at all the cost factors involved; the ways in which these might be disturbed, or fail to materialize as expected, and how each one of them might be improved. Partly because of the way in which nuclear power grew up, with its strong emphasis on technical feasibility, there has tended always to be an emphasis on the scope a system may have for further development. Yet much of the money involved in the overall station cost is determined by commercial and financial factors, and it can be at least as important to design the system to

<u>Table 1</u>
Key construction dates

	Week Number	
	As scheduled in 1962	Achieved
Start on site	27	27
Complete primary containment concrete	105	107
Start installation shields and calandria	113	113
Start installation channel tubes	138	141
Complete installation channel tubes	153	156
Start installation of turbo-generator	156	156
Start installation rotating shields	180	180
Start hot tests	210	215
Commence loading heavy water	243	252
Reactor made critical	-	254
First power fed to National Grid	-	268
Reactor at full power	269	270

allow these costs to be reduced to a minimum as it is to seek the last ounce of technical performance, by extension of reactor parameters.

CONSTRUCTION TIMES

4. Of the direct capital costs which go to make up the price of a typical nuclear power station, approximately 25% is spent on the site in labour costs. If one examines labour graphs for the construction of plants which have been subject to delays, there seems to be one invariable rule. It is that the cumulative effect of delays in construction is to slow down the rate of run-down of the labour force. Instead of the latter building up to a peak, remaining there for a reasonable time and then falling off, it remains high giving a longer plateau to the curve. In other words, the additional site costs due to construction delays tend to be linked with the costs of the peak labour force. A delay of six months in a construction programme for a medium sized nuclear power station can in fact lead to additional costs of £1-2/kW in site work alone.

5. Quite apart from the additional construction costs, any delay in completion is going to lead to delay in bringing the station into operation and therefore to loss of revenue. If we assume that the capital charges in the total unit cost are 0.33 d, then the lost contribution to capital charges due to a month's delay is equivalent to £1/kW. Allowing for an expected load factor of 60-70%, this means that a six months' delay could eliminate a cost advantage of around £3-4/kW. If replacement units have to be provided from out-of-date plant with fuelling and operating costs in excess of the calculated total generation cost of the new station, there will be an additional penalty.

6. One way to avoid a station being late is to start construction earlier, in other words to allow a sizeable contingency in planning the on-power date. For this to be of maximum value, the extra time ought to be available at the end of the job and not spread evenly through it. This, however, ensures that there will be an increase in cost as money needs to be found earlier and the total interest charges during construction will be higher. The additional cost will depend on the rates of interest charged. With a rate of 8%, the additional cost for a six months' advance in the construction programme could be about £2/kW.

7. These sums of money are not small. If all, or some of them, have to be taken into account, they can offset part of the predicted reductions in costs obtained from advances in technology. However, the risks can be modified by the design of plant. At one extreme of the bracket, there is the possibility of constructing plants, each of which is in effect a development project and, at the other, the repetition of the same design with complete stagnation of development. Clearly neither is ideal and

the right course must lie somewhere in between. It is here that the SGHWR can establish its position as a thermal system which can give low costs within the realities of commercial practice, while at the same time allowing the technology to be extended without losing touch with engineering experience.

8. It is interesting to look at some of the construction dates that were actually achieved on the Winfrith SGHWR compared with the dates that were set in the original programme when financial sanction for the project was sought in 1962. These are set out in Table 1.

9. In any major construction schedule, some of the intermediate dates may have to be adjusted during construction to ensure the final time of completion. However, there are always key dates, for example when main contractors start work on site that, if not met, will throw considerable strain on later attempts to make up the programme. It is such key dates which are shown in the table.

10. The neutron shields and the calandria were the first parts of the reactor plant to arrive on site and marked the beginning of plant installation. Up to that point, the civil and building contractor had had a reasonably clear run and plant manufacture was being carried on off-site. Proving the manufacturing route for the channel tube assemblies took somewhat longer than had been expected but site installation took the scheduled fifteen weeks. Once the channel tubes were in position, work could continue on the primary circuit pipe welding and Week 156 saw the start on site by the turbo-generator contractor. The delay in loading heavy water reflects the set-back in completing the moderator circuit due to the calandria corrosion damage. Whereas it had originally been planned to have a period of months for testing the system, this in fact was not necessary.

11. In an earlier paper to this conference, N. Bradley et al. show how the reactor components for a commercial reactor design will still enable the logic of this type of programme schedule to be maintained (ref. 2). First, there is the emphasis on designing wherever possible for shop fabrication and for components to be shipped to site as complete units. As at Winfrith, this would then leave the building and civil contractor to get on with the containment and building construction, without conflict of activities, during the first period of construction. Secondly, there is the use of component designs firmly based on Winfrith experience, such as the channel tube assemblies, calandria and neutron shields but improved wherever possible to simplify erection procedures.

12. Although there was no doubt about the feasibility of designing an SGHWR when construction of the Winfrith reactor began, there were many detail features that had to

be proved before manufacture of some components could start, for example, the liquid shutdown valves, the channel tube assemblies and the seal plugs. Time for such development work would not be required on succeeding SGHWRs, even for stations of larger output. Hence some of the uncertainties that had to be allowed for in the Winfrith programme would not exist and, as a result, the programme could be tightened.

COMPONENT STANDARDIZATION

13. Even though a reactor system is technically capable of performing well, the plant performance as a whole is dependent on the successful operation of a large number of conventional or near-conventional engineering components. Failure of comparatively small items can lead to outage of more important components and even of the station. During the testing stages, plant commissioning and early operation at power, Winfrith did not escape a crop of such failures. However, a feature of the SGHWR is that the primary circuit and other plant are readily accessible when the reactor is shut down. As a result, component faults were traced quickly and rectification was carried out swiftly.

14. Examples of such faults were valves which failed to seat or were leaking. One valve had to be cut out because the body was found to be faulty. Couplings on several oil lines were unsatisfactory. A pump motor on one of the experimental facilities within the containment developed an earth fault. A number of stray earths on instrumentation lines had to be traced. Float switches had to be modified.

15. This type of experience is not confined to nuclear plant and is a problem with all complex process plants. The only way to ensure that minor component faults do not seriously interfere with the overall performance is to reduce unnecessary plant complication, to use as often as possible well-proven components and, wherever feasible, to provide good access to components for checking and maintenance.

16. The Winfrith SGHWR is more complicated than any commercial station would be. In addition to the provision of channels to test operation with superheat, the reactor has a number of experimental facilities each of which has its own additional controls and instrumentation. These facilities not only introduce a large number of additional components but they also add to the complications of circuit layout. It is likely therefore that the Winfrith plant will require more maintenance of components such as valves, transducers and instruments than commercial reactors of very much larger size. The arguments for standardization of such components is very strong and with the SGHWR there is no reason why a large number of components should not be common to reactors of different outputs.

PRESSURE TUBES

17. The most important single feature of the SGHWR is that it is a pressure tube reactor. It is this that makes possible designs for different outputs using substantially standard units. By using pressure tubes, the heavy water moderator is isolated from the light water coolant and this allows the former to be maintained at temperatures well below 100°C and at pressures no higher than are required to circulate the heavy water through the coolers and clean-up plant. Also with the pressure tube design, access to an individual fuel element requires only the removal of the plug which seals that particular channel. It therefore gives considerable freedom of choice as to the type of system to be adopted for fuel changing.

18. An earlier paper to this conference discusses the metallurgical behaviour of pressure tube materials under irradiation (ref. 3). It is, however, worth looking at some of the overall advantages of their use in an SGHWR designed for commercial operation. The use of standard units for modular construction of reactor cores having different outputs has already been mentioned and also the scope for works fabrication. Transport to a construction site is not a problem and the connections to be made at site require straightforward welding techniques. The quality of pressure tubes at the time they are installed can be ensured by the methods of manufacture and inspection adopted and there is no need for these to be any less good for a remote site in, say, a developing country than they were for Winfrith.

19. A pressure tube is a relatively simple form of engineering structure and the part of the tube subject to irradiation in the SGHWR core is well away from the ends. There are no discontinuities in this part, no changes of section or connections which might give rise to high strain concentrations. Not only can the tube be thoroughly inspected before the reactor goes into operation but periodic inspection of the tube during the life of the plant is also feasible. In finality, if it was found for any reason that a tube required replacement, this could be done.

20. The possible reason for wishing to change a pressure tube would be because of distortion and not because there need be fear of sudden rupture. Investigations have shown that under the worst stressed conditions that can be envisaged with the SGHWR design and with the metal heavily hydrided, a sharp-ended, full thickness crack several inches long will not propagate in a Zircaloy-2 SGHWR pressure tube. It is unreasonable to suppose that a crack of such dimensions could develop from the small type of defect that could pass inspection without detection, as significant leakage would occur from a crack of these proportions. The creep rate of zirconium alloys is, however, increased under irradiation and the effect is to

cause a slight belling of the tubes in the regions of highest flux. In-pile tests have shown that substantial creep strain can be produced without rupture and the time to failure under SGHWR conditions is likely to be over forty years. With the pressure and neutron flux conditions obtaining in a commercial SGHWR it is predicted that a creep strain of about 2% will be reached in about twenty years at 100% load factor. This distortion of the tube is insufficient to change significantly the reactor channel performance.

ACCESS TO REACTOR PLANT

21. The penalties for poor station availability as indicated earlier in this paper, are high, particularly in the early years of operation. For these to be kept down, there are two requirements; first the need to keep necessary planned shutdowns to the minimum and, secondly, the need to reduce the effects of unplanned outages. In each of these, one of the most important aids to keeping outage times short is access; both to plant and fuel. In these respects, the SGHWR offers scope to the reactor designer and the station operator.

22. Although the primary containment is closed up when the plant is in operation, access can be gained within a few hours of shutdown. Examination of circulators, valves and other remotely operated equipment is not then difficult. Also inspection of major pressure circuit components, such as the steam drums, does not require other plant to be disassembled. Though such operations will need to be done under health physics control, there is no reason why statutory and any other regular inspections should not be carried out comparatively swiftly and readily to a planned schedule.

23. As discussed in earlier papers to this conference, the reasons for using stainless steel for the pressure circuit of an SGHWR have been shown to be unfounded and water conditions that actually obtain do in fact permit the use of a mild steel circuit (refs 4, 5). With mild steel, decontamination to remove some of the residual activity on surfaces within the circuit is a much more practical proposition than with stainless steel, and this would have obvious advantages in increasing the accessibility to plant for close inspection and possible maintenance over the life span of the station.

24. With heavy water reactors, access to plant can be severely limited or made extremely difficult if there is leakage of irradiated heavy water with its associated release of tritium. This risk need not arise in the SGHWR because of the low temperature and pressure conditions in the moderator circuit. The calandria is not penetrated by moving mechanisms such as control rod drives and is in effect a sealed system.

ACCESS TO FUEL

25. To get at a fuel element requires only the removal of the seal plug in the appropriate channel. It is a practical proposition either to design for this to be done with the reactor normally in operation or alternatively with the reactor shut down. The former requires on-load refuelling equipment which under remote control will seal on to the channel in which fuel is to be changed and which will provide cooling for the irradiated fuel element. Such equipment has been provided at Winfrith to demonstrate this system. Off-load refuelling, however, needs much simpler and cheaper fuel handling equipment.

26. The arguments for and against the one or the other type of refuelling are basically economic though there are a number of factors which require the exercise of judgment. As the design of an on-load refuelling machine is essentially determined by the fuel element, the fuel channel and the operating conditions in the primary circuit, it is basically the same piece of equipment for a reactor of 250 MWe as for one of 600 MWe. The capital cost of the machine therefore acquires greater significance at smaller station outputs. However, the design of the SGHWR is such that with off-load refuelling equipment, moving fuel can be a reasonably quick operation and a rapid return to power is also possible with the type of control system used. Provided therefore that sufficient fuel handling time can be obtained with an off-load system to meet the requirements of the fuel management scheme without involving a significant availability penalty, then there is much to be said in favour of keeping the plant simple and not carrying out fuel changing operations with the plant in operation. It is because this can be done with the SGHWR that the off-load system is preferred for present commercial designs. However, the natural fuelled version of the SGHWR requires an on-load refuelling system and, looking to the future, it is always possible that some advanced design of SGHWR could use an on-load system to advantage.

GENERATION SYSTEM REQUIREMENTS

27. As small electricity networks plan to introduce nuclear power into their systems, and larger networks bring into operation more and more nuclear plant, the part that nuclear power stations must play in meeting variations in load demand and in maintaining the stability of the system becomes more significant. Insofar as this can lead to an overall reduction in actual load factor, the economic advantage will lie with reactors having low capital costs. However, this does not eliminate the necessity for low refuelling and operating costs, for it is these when taken on a system basis that will determine the load factor available to the nuclear plant. On this criterion, the SGHWR is well placed, being a low capital cost plant with the

advantage of having heavy water moderation to give low fuelling costs.

28. Quite apart, however, from the simple economic evaluation of the effect of different load factors, there is the question of technical suitability of the plant to accept load changes. Can the nuclear boiler and its associated generating plant follow the load requirements without reduction in plant or fuel element reliability? On the first of these points, the paper by Wray et al. discusses the control of SGHWRs and the factors involved (ref. 6). Because neutron moderation occurs both in the heavy water moderator and in the light water coolant, it is possible to adjust the reactor void coefficient by design, and hence to provide conditions favourable for control. As it is a boiling system, with the pressure controlled, the plant in general sees little variation in temperature when the power is cycled, and there is no reason to suppose that over the life of the plant such changes could be harmful.

29. Like the plant, the fuel element cladding is not exposed to coolant temperature variations when the reactor power is changed. Also Zircaloy at the temperatures involved, provides a strong can which does not creep down to match each dimensional change that occurs in the fuel pellets when the power and, therefore, the mean pellet temperature, is altered. Because of these factors, there is every indication that fuel elements for the SGHWR can be provided that will withstand any operating regime that varying load demands would impose, and at the same time have a satisfactory economic life.

STATION OUTPUT

30. Apart from differences already mentioned, the commercial SGHWR for the immediate future differs from the Winfrith plant in output and channel rating. Continuation of heat transfer tests with the same design of fuel cluster has shown that the maximum channel rating can be increased by as much as 50%. This gives considerable scope for design evolution without having to change the basic design of the fuel element. It also makes the fuel irradiation experience gained at Winfrith very relevant and, from the time the reactor went into operation, two channels have operated at 5 MWth, i.e., the up-rated condition of present advanced designs.

31. Designs of commercial reactors based on Winfrith experience were developed first at around 300 MWe and since then the range has been extended to include reactors of over 500 MWe. So far it has been possible to apply the same design principles. However, as core sizes become much larger, it may be desirable to introduce more sophisticated methods for power shaping than have been used to date.

CONTAINMENT

32. The Winfrith reactor is housed in a vented system of double containment. In the event of reactor circuit failure, the pressure which would otherwise build up in the primary containment, is released through water lutes to the turbine hall where it displaces an equivalent volume of air. The water lutes reseal the containment immediately the pressure falls and before a significant quantity of fission products have been released into the containment from the reactor circuit.

33. This form of containment has the great advantage that, in the unlikely event of a major circuit failure, there is a relief of the pressure within the primary containment and fission products can then be held at slightly below atmospheric pressure with any leakage being inward. However, it does require the whole of the reactor containment and the turbine building to be designed as a whole, the latter being an essential part of the containment. It therefore does not easily lend itself to some of the arrangements under which commercial nuclear plants are being built where the nuclear steam supply system, or the nuclear island, is provided separately from the rest of the station.

34. Alternative forms of containment have been examined and designed, including a form of double containment in which the reactor is housed in a structure which will accept the pressure generated as a result of reactor circuit rupture. All leakage from the inner or primary containment is trapped by the secondary or outer containment. This latter containment is maintained at a pressure slightly negative with respect to atmosphere and by this means all leaks are inward. The purge from this building is directed through a clean-up plant, comprising filters and activated carbon bed, which removes any particulate and volatile fission products. As a result of the double containment, a guaranteed high standard of leak-tightness is not a requirement for either the inner or outer structure.

35. The particular form of containment is not, however, a feature of the SGHWR itself which could be built in a number of different types of containment.

NATURAL URANIUM FUELLED SGHWR

36. In order to operate with natural uranium oxide fuel and to obtain an economic fuel burn-up, it is necessary to re-optimize the design of the reactor core. To improve neutron economy, the lattice pitch needs to be enlarged, the light water content reduced and the amount of heavy water increased. Because there is less light water in the channels, there is a reduction in the heat that can be transferred to the coolant. This leads to lower fuel ratings and the need for a larger fuel pin diameter. The channel length has also to be increased. A tighter restriction has

to be placed on the use of structural materials in the core, and this naturally leads to a greater interest in thinner pressure tubes and the use of alternative zirconium alloys. Also in order to obtain adequate fuel life, it is desirable to shuffle axially which cannot be done with the full length type of fuel element used in the enriched reactor. Shorter fuel elements are therefore necessary. Because of the number of fuel movements in the fuel management scheme due to the shorter fuel life, on-load refuelling is necessary.

37. The most important differences between the enriched and natural fuelled reactors stem from the fact that, with the natural system, one no longer has the freedom to choose the fuel/moderator ratios to give a void coefficient of reactivity which is near to zero. Instead, it is substantially positive. This, as a result, alters the control requirements and it is these aspects which are at present receiving intensive study. The problem is not one of searching for a method of control, but one of comparing various methods to identify a reasonably elegant and inexpensive solution.

38. The natural uranium fuelled SGHWR is a reactor which will inevitably have higher capital cost than the enriched one. The higher capital cost is offset to some extent by the lower fuelling costs arising from the use of natural fuel. Present design studies are planned to continue through this year and are directed towards obtaining data from commercial designs which can be directly compared with that from enriched SGHWRs.

39. There are clearly countries in the world where a natural system is to be preferred, always supposing that there is no really significant difference in generation cost when all factors, economic, strategic and long-term development are taken into account. The commercial development of the SGHWR could therefore follow two paths, one with enriched fuel and the other with natural, each providing the other with useful, and sometimes complementary, engineering, technical and operating experience.

ACKNOWLEDGEMENT

40. This paper is published by the kind permission of the Managing Director, the Reactor Group, UKAEA, Risley.

REFERENCES

1. Symposium on Heavy Water Power Reactors, Vienna, September 1967.

2. BRADLEY N., DAWSON D.J. and JOHNSON F.G. Engineering design of SGHWRs. Paper 2 of this conference.

3. NICHOLS R. W. and WATKINS B. Pressure tube materials for SGHWRs. Paper 8 of this conference.

4. TYZACK C., BERRY R. and CAMPBELL C.S. Some compatibility aspects of SGHWRs. Paper 9A of this conference.

5. DICKSON G.K., BURTON W.R. and RILEY J.A. Chemical control in SGHWR circuits. Paper 9B of this conference.

6. WRAY D., BUTTERFIELD M. and McMILLAN R.N.H. Control of SGHWRs. Paper 6 of this conference.

Session D: Discussion

PAPER 12

Mr L.M. Wyatt, Central Electricity
Generating Board

1.   I find it very difficult to believe in
the economic advantages to be gained by
designing 'standard fuel in comparatively
short bundles'. I can appreciate that this
can lead to production-line economies, but
I should have thought that these were far
outweighed by the increased number of
components, the waste space involved if
attempts are made to accommodate a plenum
for fission product gases inside a reactor
core, the flux peaking at the ends, and the
increased pressure drop that must result.
Could the Author give more detailed information?

Mr H.M. Carruthers, Central Electricity
Generating Board

2.   In Paper 12 it is implied that
irradiation creep may limit the life of
some of the Douglas Point pressure tubes to
about 15 years. Could the Author explain
whether this estimate is based on a
certain limiting creep strain, and if so
how has this been chosen?

3.   Has experimental work on pressure tube
failure led to a firm assessment of the
possibility of such failures propagating
to neighbouring tubes?

Mr A. Bahbout, Euratom, Ispra, Italy

4.   In para. 18, an invitation for international co-operation in the development
of cladding materials for nuclear superheat
in heavy water reactors is put forward.
However, Paper 1 states that no clear
economic or operational advantages of the
introduction of superheat which would
justify the necessary development work,
have so far been identified for the SGHWR.
Are any Canadian evaluations of the advantages to be gained from superheat available?
Along what lines is the Canadian development work proceeding?

5.   What is the present status of the
Douglas Point plant?

Dr D.G. Brown, Managing Director,
Atomic Power Constructions Ltd

6.   The Papers have shown that there is a
considerable choice of design for heavy
water reactors. Moreover, it is claimed
that natural uranium can be used as fuel,
albeit with some penalty in fuel burn-up
and in extra capital cost for the plant.
Isotopic enrichment of uranium is thus not
essential to a heavy water reactor
programme. Typically the inventory of
heavy water in these reactors is about
0.5-1 ton/MWe output for power plant of a
few hundred megawatts capacity, depending
upon the type of system selected.

7.   In the USA, the Savannah River plant is
currently operating at about 200 ton/year,
and the USAEC have said that the supply of
heavy water by the USA will now be matched
to current production, i.e., use of supplies
from stockpiles will be discontinued. The
two plants being constructed in Nova Scotia
will not be in full operating until 1969,
when they are expected to produce heavy
water at the rate of 800 ton/year. Already
Canada is reported to have commitments
amounting to 3000 ton of heavy water by
1971. The Canadian heavy water reactor
programme shown in Paper 12 anticipates
3000 MW of Canadian designed plant to be at
power by 1973. The heavy water requirements
are pretty well in accord with this.
Germany has recently contracted with
Argentina for a 300 MWe heavy water reactor,
and is understood to have guaranteed
250 ton of heavy water for the initial
charge.

8.   It looks very much as though any major
upsurge of orders for heavy water reactors
will need to be matched by expansion of D_2O
production. A considerable degree of international planning seems to be necessary.
The requirement for heavy water, once the
plant is operational, is small; on the
other hand utilities will require guaran-
tees of a replacement supply of the total
inventory of any one plant at short notice
in case of a major loss. Such a supply may
be held by a major D_2O supplier or by the

utility itself. In either case the capacity of D_2O plant will need to be sufficient not only to supply the initial inventories, but also this reserve, and to build it up in the very early years of operation of the reactor plant.

9. It would be of interest to have the views of the Author in particular on the plans for the Nova Scotia plants. It would be particularly interesting to know whether any expansion of the capacity of these plants is foreseen and how quickly this expansion could be achieved after the decision is made. It seems to me that the future cost of heavy water may become critically dependent on the capacity of plant which will have to be installed and the degree of utilization that such plant will achieve after the initial inventories of reactors has been met.

Author's reply: Paper 12*

10. Mr Wyatt queries the relative costs of short and long multi-element bundles. It is not likely that anyone can say with utter conviction that they 'know' which will be the most economic: there are points in favour of both. Certainly the short bundles cannot be assigned comparatively greater fabrication costs simply because of the larger number of end-plates. Examination of the long bundle reveals a grid arrangement every 9-12 in. and they are certainly not issued free! Among other aspects to be considered are:

    (a)   shop lifts ($\frac{1}{2}$ ton for the SGHWR bundle, and 36 lb for the Douglas Point bundle);

    (b)   differential reject level for long and short Zircaloy tubes;

    (c)   cost of a fuel failure, i.e., how much partially burned fuel is to be thrown away;

    (d)   fission product release in the event of failure of a single element;

    (e)   fuelling machine requirements.

11. On the possibility of standardization, the idea proposed in the Paper is that too much is being expended on repetitive development. If a 'standard' bundle for burning uranium in D_2O reactors is desired, the Canadian design might be considered. There is no doubt that standardization is economically advantageous.

12. In response to Mr Carruthers' question, the limit of pressure tube life of the Douglas Point pressure tubes is 15 years, when based on the assumption that this is the time required for Zr-2 operating at a stress of 14,000 lb/in^2 to reach 2% creep. This limit of 2% strain was selected early in the design stage as the possible strain limit for the onset of tertiary creep. Subsequent in-pile experiments have shown that a value in excess of 2% could now be tolerated before the onset

of tertiary creep. However, the tubes in the reactor can be replaced later in life, if necessary. Propagation of fractures in the pressure tubes is being studied experimentally and results should be available in the near future.

13. In reply to Mr Bahbout, for the Canadian plants which will be in operation in the decade 1984-1994, an increase in thermal efficiency from 30 to 40% would result in an economic benefit over that period alone of over 250 million dollars. Development will concentrate on high temperature materials.

14. Douglas Point enjoyed a capacity factor of about 88% during the winter of 1967-68 at the three-quarter full level to which it was limited until March, 1968. It is now operating at full power. Report AECL-3067 gives more detailed information.

15. Dr Brown's remarks on heavy water production capacity are of interest. Canada will have a D_2O production capacity of 400 ton/year late in 1968 or early in 1969, and a further 400 ton/year late in 1969. Further capacity of 400-800 ton/year will probably be committed in 1968. For the minimum expected Canadian installation, about 30,000 ton of D_2O will be required by 1988, and for that year alone the requirement will be about 4000 ton.

PAPER 13

Mr A. Bahbout, Euratom, Ispra, Italy

16. In para. 2 the Authors state that due to the positive void coefficients of natural uranium SGHWRs, control devices with high dynamic and mechanical performances are required. The usual noise of the reactor might result in almost permanent rod oscillations. Are these predictions based on some quantitative analysis or experimental data, and are they common to the Canadian, Italian and British developments of such reactor systems?

17. Are the burn-up calculations given in para. 28 related to a hexagonal or square pitch?

Authors' reply: Paper 13

18. It can easily be shown that if there is a positive feed-back it is necessary to have fast control, and if there is a fast control the system responds quickly to any variation, and in particular to the noise. No clear idea of the effect of noise in such a reactor seems to be available. It is one of the reasons which make it difficult to fix a practical limit to the positive void coefficient, but qualitatively it is possible that a problem exists.

---

*In the absence of Dr Lewis, the questions on his Paper were dealt with by Mr L.R. Haywood, Vice-President, Atomic Energy of Canada Ltd

PAPER 14

Mr J. Moore, UKAEA

19. I would appreciate further comments on
(a) the choice of 30 MW/t as the fuel
rating and experience with fuel at that
rating, and (b) the assumptions made in
estimating the capital costs quoted.

20. I should also like to ask about the
choice of 1% exit quality to avoid control
instability. An increase in exit quality
would tend to reduce the release of reactivity during a loss of coolant. In
choosing a low exit quality, was there some
difficulty in balancing the requirements
for control and safety?

Dr D. Hicks, UKAEA, Winfrith

21. Since Mr Stüger has criticised the
poor Pu production of the SGHWR, I would
like to point out that we were not obsessed
by the need to emphasize isolated parameters
when optimizing the system. Of course, a
reactor using a long burn-up, such as the
SGHWR, will not do as well as a low burn-up
natural uranium type; there is more time to
burn the Pu produced. Without introducing
design changes to the reactor or fuel, it
would be possible to increase fissile
plutonium production per MWe by 30-40%,
simply by reducing irradiation to 10,000-
12,000 MWd/t. However it will not pay to
do this unless or until plutonium credits
rise.

Mr A. Bahbout, Euratom, Ispra, Italy

22. I note that Siemens is virtually
abandoning boiling in its water-cooled D_2O
projects, because of the positive void
coefficient, while Sweden is submitting
commercial tenders for forced circulation
BHWRs. Is the controversy on the void
coefficient due to differing technical data
or divergent design philosophies?

Mr R.K. Haslam, UKAEA

23. The Siemens type of heavy water
reactor seems to combine features of the
PWR and CANDU systems. It has a large
steel pressure vessel, which may produce
problems in manufacture, transportation and
inspection whilst in service, and a high
pressure, high temperature, heavy water
coolant which may well have leakage problems and operational and maintenance
difficulties. The power density at 13 kW/l
is well below PWRs at 70 kW/l, and the
heavy water inventory is high at
0.75 kg/kWe. Mechanical control rods are
incorporated, and the fuel pins have a
small diameter. The irradiation is given
as 800 MWd/t, the station thermal
efficiency is 29%, and complex on-load
fuelling is needed.

24. Overall, therefore, the reactor
appears to be a large complex suggesting
difficult problems of construction and
operation. It would appear to encourage
high capital costs, and if this is so, it
is difficult to understand how it can

compete economically with PWRs. Since
Siemens are in the special position of
marketing both PWRs and HWRs, accepted
respectively by the German and Argentinian
utilities, it would be of interest to hear
on what basis these utilities came to their
respective decisions.

Mr N.G. Robertson, Central Electricity
Generating Board

25. The Authors state that a 49 m diameter
steel containment sphere surrounds the
Atucha plant, and that this sphere has been
designed to withstand 'the full pressure'.
I would like to ask the following questions:

    (a) what is the design full pressure?

    (b) what is the design leak rate to
        atmosphere at this pressure?

    (c) what provisions are there for
        containment pressure reduction
        and/or containment activity clean-
        up under accident conditions?

    (d) can this containment cope with the
        rupture of the reactor pressure
        vessel?

    (e) what is the form of fuel cluster
        cooling provided to guard against
        hydrogen evolution from the
        zirconium/water reaction?
        Alternatively, is the containment
        capable of withstanding a hydrogen
        explosion?

Mr G.K. Dickson, UKAEA

26. The MZFR prototype reactor has now been
operating for about two years. Could the
Authors please indicate (a) the observed
rate of loss of heavy water from the
circuit; (b) the resultant irrecoverable
loss of heavy water; (c) the amount of heavy
water which is isotopically diluted?

Authors' reply: Paper 14

27. In reply to Mr Moore, in considering
the specific power of 30 MW/t, one has to
take into account the fact that the fuel
rod diameter is considerably smaller than,
for example, that in the SGHWR design. For
the Atucha reactor we chose an outer rod
diameter of 11.9 mm, which is in the range
between that of the SGHWR design and that
for a PWR. For the present PWR fuel design
a specific fuel rating of 33 MW/t at a
burn-up of 33,000 MWd/t is envisaged. In a
natural uranium design the exposure is very
much less, 8000-9000 MWd/t on average. We
are therefore not unduly concerned about
the choice of a specific fuel rating at
29 MW/t.

28. The choice of 1% steam quality in the
first instance was due to the need to
achieve a stable control. In the case of a
pressure vessel system, safety considerations are of secondary importance because
it is most unlikely that a voiding of the
whole reactor would occur.

29. Mr Bahbout's statement that Siemens have abandoned boiling in the water cooled reactors requires some qualification. We have lowered the steam content because we could not convince ourselves that we would achieve a reactor system reliable enough to offer as a firm design on the basis of our current knowledge. This was due to a lack of experimental background information. We are interested in how the problems of positive void coefficient may be solved in the CIRENE project, and particularly in the Canadian BLW reactor experiments. If we gain confidence we would be able to go back to the higher exit steam quality at any time, and improve the economy of the reactor system. To the best of my knowledge, no reactor with a positive void coefficient has been offered to a client.

30. I do not challenge Mr Haslam's statement that the Siemens HWR has features which have certain similarities to other reactor systems. I believe this to be true of all reactor designs. I would, however, like to comment on some of his more specific points.

31. The power density of the design for Argentina is that appropriate to the use of natural uranium. Comparison with an enriched PWR on the basis of average power density is scarcely relevant. A better yardstick, if comparisons must be made, is the specific fuel volume rating, and in fact our 24 MWth/kg fuel compares favourably with some 32 MWth/kg fuel for light water designs, and in particular with the 17 MWth/kg fuel of the SGHWR. I agree with the comment on the D_2O inventory, but this should not be examined in isolation.

32. I do not follow the references to mechanical control rods. It is generally accepted that mechanical absorber rods which drop into the core form the simplest and most reliable shutdown system. They have advantages particularly in spatial control. Nevertheless I accept that an alternative solution must be engineered if this simple scheme of solid rods cannot be arranged or accommodated.

33. Fuel distribution in smaller pins leads to a higher power density and savings in cost. In relation to such costs, I would refer to Mr Margen's remarks earlier on the attractive possibility of future substantial reductions in the manufacturing costs of such fuel.

34. The fuel burn-up at 8000 MWd/t is not unattractive for a natural uranium reactor. The quoted thermal efficiency of the station is the minimum guaranteed. I cannot accept that the on-load refuelling system is complex.

35. I would agree that the Atucha project is large, but not that construction, operation and maintenance will be difficult. On Mr Haslam's final question relating to the comparative costs of STADE and Atucha, I regret that this is a matter of commercial consideration on which I do not have the liberty to speak.

36. The points raised by Mr Robertson may be answered as follows.

37. The full design pressure of the Atucha steel containment vessel is 4.5 atm; the leak rate to the atmosphere will be that usual in Germany, i.e., below 1% per day.

38. For normal decay cooling we use the moderator circuit. This system can also be used in cases of emergency. The moderator circuit can be run as two independent heat sinks and can thus fulfil safety requirements.

39. As is current practice on other pressurized water reactors, the containment is not designed specifically to deal with the fast failure of the main pressure vessel. There is a safety injection system provided, which uses light water. At present there is no need to take into account the extra heat which may arise from a possible zirconium/water reaction.

40. In reply to Mr Dickson, I regret that I do not have any specific data available on recoverable and non-recoverable D_2O losses. I may state that we had two accidental leaks which resulted in D_2O losses, but most of this was recovered. One leak was caused by an inadvertent jacking of the fuelling machine amounting to about 2-3 mm, caused by a design fault in the hydraulic lift system. The fault was minor and lasted less than 1 s, but it did allow D_2O to escape. The second leak was due to a lifting of a safety valve following a discharge into the container. There is no blow-down tank provided at the MZFR. However, one will be included on the Argentinian station.

PAPER 15

Mr R.N.H. McMillan, UKAEA, Risley

41. I would be glad if Dr Villani could provide the following information on the two-phase control tubes.

(a) Is there any problem of unstable two-phase flow patterns in the control tubes at low liquid flow rates? Does this set a lower limit to the liquid flow rate?

(b) What is the range of liquid flow velocity in the control tubes, and what is the time constant between a change in control valve position and a change in reactivity at the lowest fluid flow rate?

Mr D.R. Ebeling, Australian Atomic Energy Commission

42. In paras 39-40, Dr Villani mentions the use of fly-wheels to ensure a 1.5-2 s supply of water to avoid a fast voiding accident. Since the double circulator, non-return valve and outlet choke system covers most circuit burst and individual pump failures, I presume that the fly-wheels

cover a loss of power supply. Would
Dr Villani comment on the reliability of
the power supply and shutdown system in
relation to this?

43. In the case of the SGHWR fuelled with
natural uranium and with two segment fuel
assemblies, we require shutdowns of only
36 h every six weeks with the off-load
system, but we still find that the outage
penalties (approximately £200,000/day per
year for a 500 MWe unit) are sufficiently
severe to make the on-load system more
economic. Could Dr Villani expand on this,
particularly on the assumed outage penalties?

Mr J. Moore, UKAEA

44. During the design study for the
natural fuelled SGHWR we have been examining a number of different types of control
system. Methods suitable for fast control
require detailed examination. Could the
Author comment further on the choice of
helium with boron? Was the possibility of
using flow control for fast control
examined fully?

45. In relation to reactor safety under
fault conditions, could the Author comment
on the methods used for safety analysis?
Have probability methods been used?

Author's reply: Paper 15

46. In reply to Mr McMillan, the geometry
adopted for the control tubes in the
present design consists of a U tube,
1.5 cm ID. With this diameter it was
found possible to operate in the complete
density range from 'all gas' to 'all
liquid' without flow instabilities. The
operating density range is from 0.8 to
0.05 g/cm^3. The lower limit of the flow
rate (0.05 g/cm^3) is determined by dynamic
response considerations. The design
specification for the control system
refers to an equivalent time constant not
in excess of 2 s. The range of liquid and
gas flow velocities in the control tubes
is selected to comply with these requirements.

47. Circulating pump fly-wheels are
proposed for the CIRENE primary circuit
mainly to guard against a complete loss of
power, as envisaged by Mr Ebeling. I am
sorry that I have no statistics relating
to the reliability of power supply but it
should be noted that no guaranteed
emergency supply is envisaged for the
circulating pumps. The fly-wheels extend
the run-down time of the pumps enough to
prevent the overheating of fuel following
a reactor trip. We shall use pumps with
mechanical seals and with this arrangement
there is no economic penalty involved.

48. As regards on- and off-load fuelling,
it is true that the former does impose an
economic penalty. The difference in the
loss of burn-up and outage has been
estimated to be £160,000/day per year,
compared with the figure mentioned by
Mr Ebeling. This penalty is, however,
partially offset by the higher capital and

operating costs of the on-load system,
which we have found to be about 1 million
dollars for a 500 MWe plant. In any case,
a lack of experience with and confidence in
the performance of on-load fuelling in
boiling channels favour the adoption of the
off-load system at the moment.

49. The possibility of using a fast
control of recirculating flow rate, as
suggested by Mr Moore, was examined, and
although the method was found attractive it
was considered that operating experience
should first be acquired on slow flow rate
performance control as reactivity compensation for load variation.

50. On his second question, we have not as
yet analysed safety on a probability method
but are intending to do so. The results
will no doubt be interesting.

PAPER 16

Mr R.J. Haslam, UKAEA

51. Mr Margen's Paper was extremely
interesting, but I am afraid that I do not
share his enthusiasm for the pressure
vessel heavy water system he describes, nor
his confidence in the future prospects of
this kind of plant. In seeking with such
fervour a design which uses natural
uranium Mr Margen has accepted the problems
of operating and maintaining a large steam
turbine plant supplied with tritiated
heavy water vapour. Could he say what the
reactions have been to his proposal from
power engineers?

52. In Fig. 11 comparative costs for light
water reactors and boiling heavy water
reactors are given, and these show that at
the onset the LWR has an advantage of about
5% in generating cost and 20% in capital
cost. The BHWR is shown to have lower
costs only 30 years later, on the assumption that the price of U-238 will double.
On these figures it is not surprising that
a Swedish electric power company chose a
light water reactor instead of a BHWR. I
wonder how it will be possible for the BHWR
to break into the market once the light
water type of reactor is established? In
my opinion the enriched SGHW reactor is the
only hope for heavy water reactors.

Mr F.G. Johnson, UKAEA, Risley

53. I would like to ask why superheat has
been dropped in the future designs based on
the Marviken reactor. What is the Author's
view on the economic and technical position
of superheat?

54. Could Mr Margen give the Swedish views
on containment for future reactors. What
are the economics and the technical pros
and cons of rock cavern containment, closed
pressure, and complete containment?

Author's reply: Paper 16

55. In reply to Mr Haslam, we have no
absolute commitment to natural uranium in
Sweden. We are quite prepared to offer

each client what he wants - slightly enriched BHWRs for those who wish them and natural uranium types for those who, for various reasons prefer this solution. We find that quite a number of clients are in the second category.

56. On the comparative economics of the system, we find that on the basis of present day prices for uranium, fuel fabrication and reprocessing, for the smaller size of reactor the slightly enriched system gives greater economy. On longer-term predictions the natural uranium system can compete. The differences are never very great.

57. Regarding the D_2O turbine for Marviken, I would like to emphasize that the supporting work has been very thorough. Full-scale tests on shaft, seals and condenser show very low leakage. Not only is the turbine maker confident, but so is the customer, the State Power Board, and this confidence is supported by the favourable operating experience with the Agesta reactor.

58. The designs which we are offering are by no means restricted to direct cycle reactors. As it happens, the reactor itself looks exactly the same whether on direct or indirect cycle. It is quite possible that some clients will prefer the indirect cycle until the Marviken turbine has been in operation and confirmed the earlier test results. The difference in cost is about 2.5% of cost per unit generated and for the first units this is not very important.

59. Mr Haslam seems to have misinterpreted Fig. 11. For the conditions shown, the difference in kWh prices is negligible in the initial years. Thereafter the fuel cycle costs for the LWR will probably rise slightly as reductions in fabrication costs and reprocessing costs are insufficient to balance probable increases in uranium prices, whereas the fuel cycle costs for the natural uranium HWR should fall strongly due to the pronounced influence of reductions in fabrication and reprocessing costs on kWh costs at the lower burn-up values. Thus HWRs should, during their life, achieve progressively greater savings. The figure is drawn on the assumption that several units of each type are built so that common design and verification costs can be shared.

60. Mr Johnson raised a question on superheat. Nuclear superheat has never been a feature of Swedish commercial designs, but it is incorporated in the Marviken reactor as an experimental feature to permit the possibilities to be investigated. The main purpose of Marviken is to demonstrate the most important features of the BHWR, such as direct cycle, natural circulation and on-load refuelling, to the stage at which commercial offers can be based on these features. The nuclear superheat facility could be incorporated into the reactor at a relatively low additional cost, and our calculations have

shown that using Cr Ni-25:20, or Incoloy-35:20, the break-even point corresponds to a can thickness of about 0.45 mm. Below this figure a profit is produced. Experience with nuclear superheat in the USA and our own bundle tests in the superheat loop of the R2 reactor have been encouraging. Longer-term irradiation testing to give statistical evidence will produce greater confidence.

61. I do not think that it is possible to discuss the type of containment without considering the type of reactor. We have found, for instance, that for BWRs the pressure suppression containment is the most suitable because the volume of the primary circuit is small, and this applies particularly in the natural circulation plants. For a PWR, pressure suppression is not very economical. Rock excavation is unlikely to produce direct economies in containment cost, especially when compared with pressure suppression designs. Rock caverns also force the designer to 'freeze' his design at a very early stage. This can be a disadvantage, though there can be some safety advantages for sites close to large centres of population, which is why rock excavation is being considered for the district heating reactor proposed for the northern part of Stockholm.

PAPER 17

62. In his verbal presentation, Mr Cartwright mentioned that there had been comment that the SGHWR had yet to prove itself. Any system new to the commercial field had to establish itself against such criticism, but Winfrith had demonstrated that the SGHWR could be built to programme and the system was well proven. There was, however, the question of how any plant would behave during its lifetime. It was all important for this that the component parts of the plant should be well proved and that there should be access to as much plant as possible so that inspection and repair, if required, could be properly and swiftly carried out. The first ensured a high probability that the unforeseen would not occur, and the second that, if anything did, it need not be unexpected and action could be taken as on any non-nuclear plant. The rapid commissioning and raising to power had also demonstrated that the over-all system behaved as expected, and the close correspondence of theoretical predictions and measurements made on the reactor showed that the methods of calculation developed for the SGHWR were satisfactory. As the design of the larger units used the same channel size, the same fuel cluster, the same lattice pitch and the same type of control, the step from 100 MWe to, say, 500 or 600 MWe units probably involved less uncertainty than some of the steps being made with other reactor systems.

63. With regard to the fuel element there was no reason to be less confident of the endurance of a fuel element for the SGHWR than for any other reactor using UO_2 and Zircaloy-2 as the cladding. Fuel elements

at a rating of 5 MW were already in two channels of the Winfrith reactor. Heat transfer and thermal performance data were also very firmly based on the work already done and continuing in the 9 MW heat transfer loop at Winfrith. The effects of using natural uranium as the fuel were referred to in paras 36 and 37 of the Paper. The substantially positive void coefficient had to be taken into account in control and safety. The effect on control was now being closely examined in a joint design study with Australian and New Zealand colleagues, and a system utilizing flow control was being evaluated. Fig. D1 showed the arrangement of such a control system. A multiport valve which would have ports enabling pre-set adjustment of relative flow between a number of channels supplied by one valve was being examined. With such an arrangement, it was practical to achieve zero control and some degree of core flattening in addition to control of total reactor power. For start-up with such a system, voidage would be generated in the core by injection of steam with low water flow down to about 10% of normal flow.

64. The safety aspect which had received most attention in the design study was the evaluation of the effect of loss of coolant, in particular that due to a pressure circuit failure. To deal with such a fault, it was necessary to have a high integrity shutdown system and to ensure that it operated on the required time-scale. One way of increasing the time available for shutdown was by connecting a volume of water directly to channel inlets through the multiport valve so that if a failure occurred in the most critical parts of the circuit, in the core inlet and circulator headers, water could be supplied for a short period (a few seconds) to enable insertion of the emergency shutdown system. This category of fault had, of course, a low probability of occurrence.

Mr P.J. Cameron, TNPG

65. With reference to the containment of a 400-600 MW SGHWR could the Author say, (a) how many circuits are considered to fail simultaneously, and (b) whether propagation of failure in the pressure tubes can be ruled out?

66. How is the serviceability of the re-fuelling machine guaranteed with full con-tainment, when (as shown in Fig. 13 of Paper 2) the machine is always inside the containment?

66. Is rapid removal of the pond bottom plug possible if the charge machine is kept out of the containment by making the pond bottom part of the containment boundary?

67. Finally, could the Author say what condensation efficiency he would underwrite with a fully contained, pressure suppres-sion form of containment?

Mr K.P. Gibbs, Central Electricity Generating Board

68. I would like to make a general comment about the different heavy water reactor designs which have been presented. As the cost of the nuclear parts of the power stations becomes smaller, the opportunity to make substantial further savings becomes less, and I have gained the impression that the differentials between the generating costs of the different reactors presented are marginal.

69. In this situation, the utilities buying nuclear power stations are able to pay more attention to aspects other than the purely economic. Mr Booth mentioned two of these, flexibility and freedom of siting, in his opening address. A further important aspect is the availability that the reactors are likely to attain in service. The economic effects of attaining, say, only 60% instead of a hoped for 80%, greatly outweigh any differential in initial capital or running costs.

70. Until we know more about the analysis of the reliability of complex mechanisms than we do at present, the best way to obtain a high reliability is to select simple designs, in which the number of components which can cause outages is as few as possible, and in which as much maintenance as possible can be carried out with the reactor on load, or during short outages. I have been disappointed in the lack of emphasis on these points in the Papers.

Author's reply: Paper 17

71. To take Mr Cameron's points in turn, only one circuit is expected to fail at any one time, but we have examined the conse-quences of the second failing. Our experi-mental work being carried out at Foulness shows that failure of one pressure tube (based on the Winfrith design) will not propagate to adjacent tubes. Clearly the answer to his second question is simplicity. The mechanisms must be kept simple so that extensive maintenance is not required. We believe that rapid removal of the pond bottom plug is possible and have considered some designs of this kind. Much more detailed work is, however, still required. On his final point, without doing some large-scale experimental work or having access to results from elsewhere covering the appropriate conditions, I would not care to underwrite any figure for condensation efficiency for a fully contained pressure suppression system.

72. I agree fully with Mr Gibbs on the need to concentrate on achieving high reliability, and therefore good station availability. I would emphasize the impor-tance of timely completion in keeping capital costs down, and also the way in which the use of proved components coupled with access to plant is a key factor in ensuring that plant continues to operate satisfactorily during its lifetime. In the design of commercial SGHWRs emphasis has

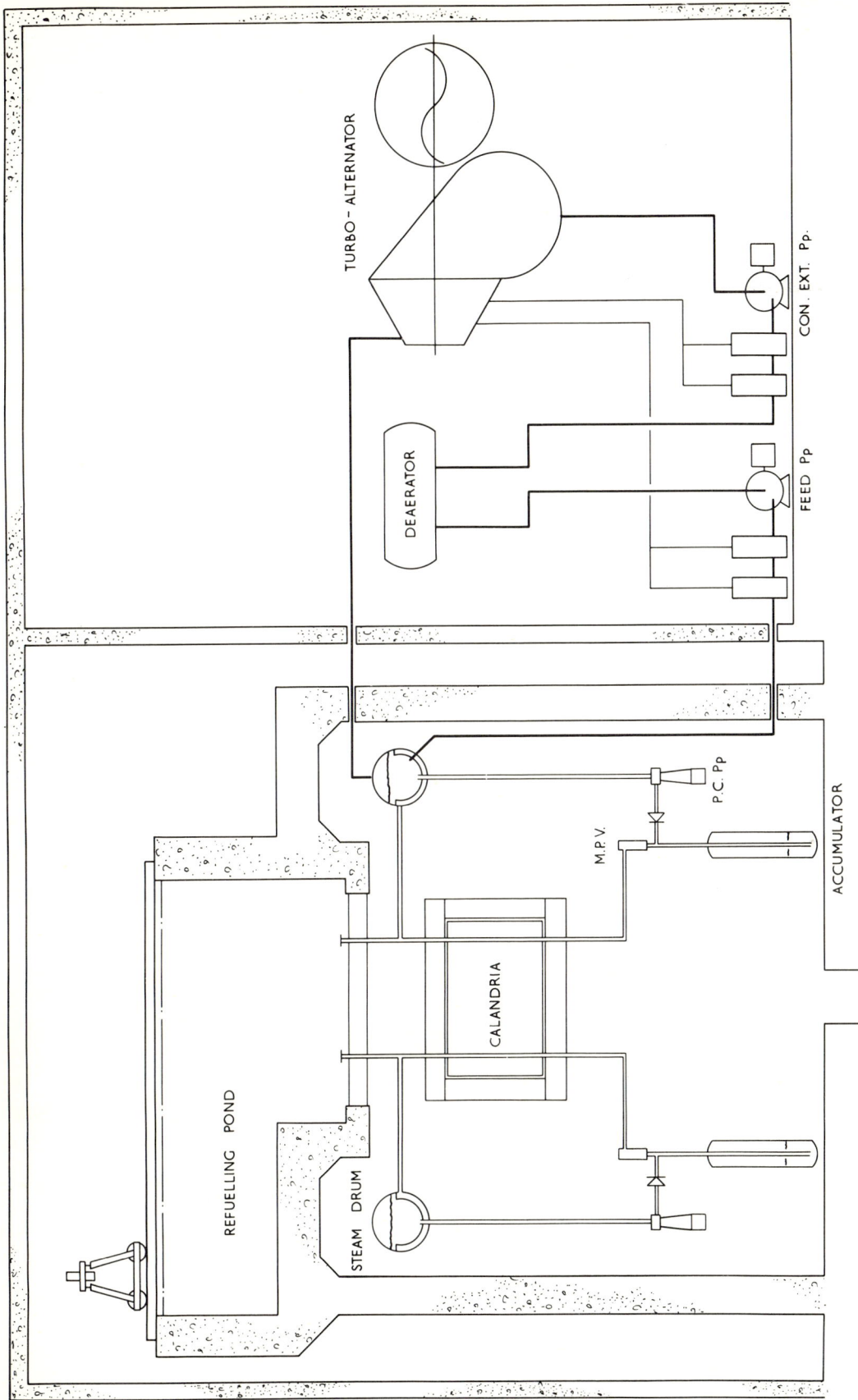

No. OF CIRCUITS 6
No. OF PUMPS / CIRCUITS 4
No. OF MULTI PORT VALVES / CIRCUIT 6
No. OF ACCUMULATORS / CIRCUIT 6
No. OF CHANNELS / CIRCUIT 72
TOTAL No. OF CHANNELS 432
NETT ELECTRICAL OUTPUT .... 500 MW

Fig. D1. Simplified flow diagram: 500 MW(e) NSGHWR

239

been given to these very factors.

73.   Reliability is becoming a national
problem, not only for nuclear plants but
also for refineries and chemical works,
etc. Where the capital cost of plant is
very high, the penalty for adverse reliability is also very high. The problem
needs to be attacked at two major points:
first, in the design office to ensure that
every endeavour is made to simplify at the
design stage, and secondly in the manufacturing shops, to make certain that they
are aware of the modern requirements of
good quality control. Every effort must be
made to improve this situation, but it is
appreciated that the problem could be
difficult.

Closing address

J. C. C. STEWART, CBE, BSc, FInstP, MIChemE
Board Member for Reactors, UKAEA

1.   I would first like to express my appreciation to the British Nuclear Energy Society for organising this conference on heavy water reactors and to the Institution of Civil Engineers for allowing us to use their magnificent hall and rooms for this occasion.

2.   The amount of effort required to produce an international conference of this magnitude is considerable, and I am sure I speak for everybody when I express our thanks to all who have had a share in this activity. I should particularly like to thank those authors and speakers from abroad whose contributions have made this conference truly international. I hope you feel that this has been a successful conference and has provided a good forum for discussing the technical and economic features of heavy water moderated reactors.

3.   The extent of the support for this meeting, and the lively discussions that have followed the presentations of the papers have demonstrated that there is a very considerable interest in heavy water reactors both in this country and around the world.

4.   The origin of heavy water reactors is obscured somewhat by events during the war years. If I remember rightly, the French bought up the stocks of heavy water in 1939. This was brought to the Cavendish laboratories in England in 1940 and then transported to Montreal in 1943. A joint Anglo-French and Canadian team started work on heavy water reactors. The cause of the heavy water reactor has been well championed by Ben Lewis of Canada who unfortunately is unable to be with us today. It has received much support in the UK and there are now many organizations around the world who are pursuing this system.

5.   We have heard papers describing the British Steam Generating Heavy Water Reactors in some detail and have had the benefit of having a series of review papers from organizations in other countries engaged on the construction of heavy water reactors for power generation. These papers have described the present position and the prospects for the future.

6.   'Heavy water reactors' is a description which covers a wide range of differing types of reactor having the common feature that heavy water is used in the core for neutron moderation. They have considerable flexibility in the fuel cycle which can be used. This versatility is of itself attractive, in that a design can be tailored to a particular requirement. There is, however, a draw-back in that it represents fragmentation of development effort among many organizations. A potential customer expressing an interest in a heavy water system is today presented with an array of designs all differing to some degree and at different stages of development.

7.   This is a world where uranium is already not only competitive with other forms of fuel, but clearly beating them. The fact that various nuclear reactors are in intense competition with one another is not surprising. Establishing a thermal neutron class of reactor is therefore a tough task.

8.   It will be clear to all that heavy water systems fall into two main classes, according to the form adopted for the pressure parts of the primary circuit. Thus, we have pressure vessel designs and pressure tube designs, both of which are now available for commercial construction. However, some of the developments we have heard about today lie further in the future.

9.   Judging by what has been said, the future could see the emergence of two basic types of heavy water reactor: pressure vessel reactors with boiling heavy water and pressure tube reactors with boiling water coolant. Our Canadian friends, I believe, have open minds as to whether the boiling coolant will be heavy water or light water. We, in the UK, believe it should be boiling light water in the pressure tubes.

10. The use of either enriched or natural fuel has been the subject of lively debate here and this is likely to continue for some time to come. I feel it is clear from the work being done in the UK and from the comments of our friends from overseas that the adoption of natural uranium fuel brings with it a greater technical challenge. Much of what has been said in the discussion depends on the influence of dif-

fering ground rules, such as amortization period, interest rates and load factors on the choice of design. Personally, I am not yet clear that these differences, combined as they are in some countries which have indigenous natural uranium deposits but not necessarily the fuel manufacturing and re-processing capability, will be enough to withstand the greater simplicity of enriched systems. However, I do not expect that such views will dissuade my fellow nuclear engineers and physicists who are pursuing natural uranium designs.

11. Heavy water reactors are, as a class, capable of being designed to be efficient producers of plutonium. While they have the possibility of recycling this plutonium or utilizing thorium as a fertile material, perhaps the most significant use which could be made from this potentiality is to provide feed material for fuelling fast breeder reactors on a scale which would not be possible with certain other types of reactor.

12. From what you have heard, it will be clear that we in the UK presently consider that a pressure tube design with slightly enriched fuel holds the most promise for early commercial application at home and in the export market.

13. Heavy water moderated power reactors are today operating in Canada, France, Sweden, Norway, Germany, Belgium with VULCAIN, the USA with PRTR and Britain.

14. I believe that heavy water reactors will provide a significant proportion of the nuclear power stations to be installed in the future. The extent of this instal-lation will, I am sure, largely depend on strictly commercial considerations of capital and generating cost, reliability and flexibility of operation, and accep-tability for urban siting on safety grounds. I would remind you that these requirements were identified by Mr Booth in his opening address as the requirements of a reactor system to be incorporated in the CEGB network.

15. In conclusion, I hope you have found this Conference both profitable and enjoyable: renewing old friendships and making new ones. I believe everyone will go away with much food for thought, even though we have not agreed that one particular form on heavy water reactor is superior to all others. This we must leave for the future.

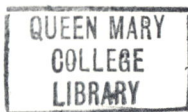